Mr. Thomas

57/6.

GEOGRAPHIES FOR ADVANCED STUDY

EDITED BY PROFESSOR S. H. BEAVER, M.A.

THE POLAR WORLD

GEOGRAPHIES FOR ADVANCED STUDY

Edited by Professor S. H. Beaver, M.A.

The British Isles: A Geographic and Economic Survey
The Tropical World
The Soviet Union
Malaya, Indonesia, Borneo and the Philippines
West Africa
The Scandinavian World
A Regional Geography of Western Europe
Central Europe
Geomorphology
Statistical Methods and the Geographer
Land, People and Economy in Malaya
An Historical Geography of South Africa
The Polar World
North America: Its Countries and Regions
The Western Mediterranean World

THE POLAR WORLD

BY

PATRICK D. BAIRD, M.A.
McGill University, Montreal

LONGMANS

LONGMANS, GREEN AND CO LTD
48 Grosvenor Street, London, W.1

Associated companies, branches and representatives
throughout the world

© Patrick D. Baird 1964
First published 1964

Printed in Great Britain by
The Camelot Press Ltd., London and Southampton

PREFACE

AT the time when the author was a student Rudmose-Brown had recently written his *The Polar Regions*, and the American Geographical Society had published its two volumes *Geography of the Polar Regions* by Nordenskiöld and Mecking and *Problems of Polar Research* by a variety of authors including the greatest name in Polar science and exploration, Fridtjof Nansen.

These textbooks have served us for many years but progress in Polar knowledge has accelerated, particularly in the Antarctic, during the last decade.

In 1955 *Geography of the Northlands*, edited by Kimble and Good, did much to bring Arctic Geography more up to date within the covers of one text. In fact, when I was approached by the publishers to prepare this volume I was hesitant because of *Geography of the Northlands* and more so because the International Geophysical Year was causing the geography of the Antarctic to be unfolded at an unprecedented rate with which it was difficult to keep abreast.

My dilatoriness in completing this book has served to amend certain facts about the South Polar continent as they became known but it will be years before much of the recent data is satisfactorily sifted by a single author.

I wish to thank the many people who helped me especially Professor A. C. O'Dell of Aberdeen University for the initial shoves. Mrs. Muriel Barnett kindly prepared many of the original diagrams, and latterly Paul Laurendeau of Montreal assisted in this way Mr. H. R. Harvey who re-drew some of the final maps from my very rough approximations. Finally I should like to pay tribute to the late Sir James Wordie who was responsible for first setting my feet, as he did with so many, on the fascinating path of Polar Exploration.

P.D.B.

McGill University, 1963

CONTENTS

PREFACE   *page*   v

1. INTRODUCTION   1

2. HISTORY OF ARCTIC EXPLORATION   12

3. THE METEOROLOGY AND CLIMATE OF THE ARCTIC   48

4. LANDFORMS OF THE ARCTIC   66

5. THE ARCTIC SEAS   89

6. ARCTIC FLORA AND FAUNA   111

7. NATIVE PEOPLES   130

8. TRANSPORTATION   146

9. POLITICAL GEOGRAPHY OF THE ARCTIC   169

10. REGIONAL DESCRIPTION OF THE CANADIAN ARCTIC   182

11. ALASKA   201

12. THE SOVIET ARCTIC   211

13. SVALBARD   229

14. GREENLAND   239

15. THE HISTORY OF ANTARCTIC EXPLORATION   255

16. THE ANTARCTIC CONTINENT   271

17. METEOROLOGY AND CLIMATE OF THE ANTARCTIC   296

18. THE ANTARCTIC SEAS   300

19. THE SUB-ANTARCTIC ISLANDS   312

INDEX   326

MAPS AND DIAGRAMS

1.	Low Sun Refraction	2
2.	Tree Growth and July Temperature	6
3.	Climatic Hazard	7
4.	The Tree Line	8
5.	Arctic Limits	9
6.	Scandinavian and Eskimo Penetrations	13
7.	The North-East Passage to 1630	15
8.	Canadian Arctic to 1640	18
9.	Exploration of Siberia	21
10.	North America, 1640–1840	24
11.	Canadian Arctic, 1840–70	28
12.	Greenland Ice-cap Traverses before the Mechanical Age	32
13.	Polar Basin, 1870–1905	35
14.	Polar Basin, 1905–30	37
15.	Polar Basin, 1930–58	40
16.	Arctic Exploration Diagram	46
17.	Principal Frontal Zones in Winter	52
18.	Principal Frontal Zones in Summer	52
19.	Mean Surface Pressure in January	54
20.	Mean Surface Pressure in July	54
21.	Mean Air Temperature, January	55
22.	Mean Air Temperature, July	56
23.	Precipitation in Canada	58
24.	Wind-chill Nomogram	62
25.	Mean Wind-chill Factor, January	63
26.	Ice-shelf Areas off Northern Ellesmere Island	70
27.	The Permafrost Zone	74

28. Ground Profile to illustrate Permafrost Terms   75
29. Seasonal Temperature Variation in the Ground   76
30. Thermal Régime of Ground at Skovorodino, Siberia,
      1928–30   76
31. Formation of Frost Boil and Naled   78
32. Permafrost in the Northern Hemisphere   79
33. Tundra Polygons   82
34. Tundra Phenomena   83
35. A Cross-section of Pingo in the Mackenzie Delta, North-   84
      West Canada
36. Pingo Formation   85
37. Protection of Hillside Roadway   88
38. The Arctic Ocean and its Constituent Seas   90
39. Block Diagram of North Polar Basin   92
40. Water Masses in the North Polar Sea   93
41. Relation between Freezing-point and Maximum Density
      for Water of Different Salinites   94
42. Hinging of Fast Ice   97
43. Arctic Currents   101
44. Pack Ice Cover   103
45. Polar Food Chain   119
46. Calanus   123
47. Relative Importance of Reindeer and Dogs from Western
      Eurasia to North America   131
48. Native Inhabitants of Northern Eurasia   133
49. Stages in the Construction of an Igloo   135
50. Sled Hitches   149
51. Types of Sled   150
52. Types of Oversnow Vehicles   154
53. Insurance Premiums: Hudson Bay Route   160
54. Russian Aircraft Landings, 1948–57   162
55. Transpolar Air Routes, 1958   164
56. Locations of North Magnetic-Dip Pole   166

57. Potential Southern Great-Circle Air Routes   168
58. Arctic Sovereignty, 1960   171
59. Canadian Arctic Physiographic Regions   186
60. Alaska   202
61. Northern Territories of the U.S.S.R.   212
62. Ice Clusters and Shipping Routes   225
63. Svalbard   231
64. Greenland: the Ice-cap and Ice Free Zones   241
65. Mean Annual Accumulation on Greenland Ice-cap   244
66. Limits of Antarctic Continent   272
67. Map of Antarctica   276, 277
68. Byrd Station Traverse   279
69. Ice Surface Elevation   280
70. Rock Surface Elevation   281
71. Antarctic Ice   300
72. Antarctic Waters   302
73. *Euphausia superba*   303
74. Main Types of Whale   304
75. Whale Concentrations, Migration Routes and Inter-
     national Whaling Sectors   306
76. Latitudinal Comparison, Southern Isles and British Isles   313

PLATES

between pages
72 and 73

1. Captain Roald Amundsen (1872–1928)
2. Amundsen at South Pole, 14 December 1911
3. Swiss Bay, Sam Ford Fiord, Baffin Island
4. Stages in lake-ice melting
5. Ice-shore boulder beach
6. An esker
7. Parallel drumlins in northern Canada
8. Patterned ground—unsorted polygons
9. Patterned ground—unsorted stripes

facing pages

10. Frozen strait, Franklin, N.W.T.   112
11. Boulder block raised by frost action   112
12. Ice-foot   112
13. Pancake ice; in distance, Erebus, volcano, Antarctica   113
14. Pancake ice, off Cape Evans, Antarctica   113
15. King penguins, South Georgia   128
16. Husky dog   128
17. Caribou bull, chewing piece of discarded antler to get lime   128
18. (i) *Cassippe tetragona*   129
18. (ii) *Salix arctica*   129
18. (iii) *Campanula uniflora*   129
18. (iv) *Rhododendron lapponicum*   129
18. (v) *Ranunculus glasialis*   129
18. (vi) *Saxifraga aizoides*   129
19. Woman, aged about 70, from Mackenzie delta   160
20. 'Copper' Eskimo woman from Victoria Island   160

xii

21. Half-breed 'Copper' Eskimo with wife and adopted daughter, Victoria Island 160

22. Eskimo women cutting up slabs of whale blubber 161

23. 'Square flipper' seal being cut up to make skin line, Southampton Island, N.W.T. 161

24. Indian trapper with pack-dogs in the Yukon 176

25. Sled dogs in Antarctica 176

26. Sno-cats and sleds of Fuch's Trans-Antarctic Expedition at South Pole 177

27. U.S. icebreaker *Glacier* forcing a passage through pack ice in Ross Sea 177

28. Russian icebreaker *Moskva* 272

29. The Danish Arctic station at Godhavn, Greenland 272

30. Reconstruction of interior of Scott's hut 273

31. Admiral Byrd taking observations from aircraft 273

32. McMurdo Sound, Ross Sea, Antarctica 288

33. Mawson station, Australian sector of Antarctica 288

34. Antarctica vegetation—*Mastodia* and *Caloplaca elegans* on ice-smoothed rocks, Goudier Islet 289

35. Antarctic vegetation—lichens 289

36. Whale factory ship, showing stern ramp up which whales are hauled 289

ACKNOWLEDGMENTS

MAPS AND DIAGRAMS

For permission to include maps and diagrams based on copyright sources we are indebted to the following:

Figs. 17 and 18 from Petterssen: *Weather Analysis and Forecasting* (Mcgraw-Hill Book Company, Inc.); Figs. 19 and 20 from Dorsey: *Compendium of Meteorology*, 1951 (American Meteorological Society through contractural support of the Air Force Cambridge Research Laboratories); Figs. 21 and 22 from Hare: *Climate of the American Northlands;* Fig. 23 from material prepared jointly by the Division of Building Research, National Research Council and the Meteorological Division, Department of Transport, Canada, reproduced in *Climatological Atlas of Canada*, Ottawa, 1953; Figs. 24 and 25 from Thomas and Boyd: *Canadian Geographer, 10*, 1957, with permission of the Director, Meteorological Branch, Department of Transport, Canada; Fig. 32 from Müller: 'Beobachtungen über Pingos', *Meddelelser om Grønland*, Figs. 33 and 34 from Fitzpatrick: *Scottish Geographical Magazine;* Fig. 62 from *Journal of Glaciology, 3*, p. 107; Fig. 65 from Diamond: *Journal of Glaciology, 3*, No. 27, p. 565; Fig. 67 based on a map prepared by Prof. Herfried Hoinkes for *The Mountain World*, 1960/61; Figs. 68, 69 and 70 from Bentley and Ostenso: *Journal of Glaciology, 3*, 1961, pp. 886, 892, 893.

PHOTOGRAPHS

For permission to reproduce photographs we are indebted to the following:

Paul Popper for Plates 1, 2, 13, 14, 16, 17, 19, 20, 21, 22, 27, and 31; M. H. W. Ritchie for Plate 3; Royal Canadian Air Force for Plate 4; A. L. Washburn and the Geological Society of America for Plates 5, 8 and 9; Canadian Department of National Defence for Plates 6 and 7; Royal Geographical Society for Plate 10; P. D.

Baird for Plate 11; *Polar Record* for Plate 12; J. P. Morley for Plates 15 and 28; Dr. F. H. Schwartzenbach for Plate 18; Dr. A. W. Mansfield for Plate 23; Polar Photos for Plates 24, 32 and 36; British Antarctic Survey for Plates 25, 34 and 35; Dr. Ulrik Røen for Plate 29; L. B. Quartermain for Plate 30. Plate 26 is an Official U.S. Navy Photo and Plate 33 is an Anare Photograph by G. Newton.

Chapter 1

INTRODUCTION

THE polar regions of the world form a distinct and recognizable environment, one with which the average temperate latitude dweller is quite unfamiliar. He can often get as it were a peep into the polar environment by visiting mountain regions above tree line. Here at first there seems to be a remarkable similarity: the cold, the ice, the poverty of the vegetation are equivalent to those polar characteristics. But the analogy must be treated with care. The chief contrast is the great and continuous area of the polar world, the Arctic a semi-frozen sea surrounded by tundra lands several million square miles in extent, the Antarctic a continent between Europe and North America in size. It is the environment least altered by man, one in which the stage of pure physical discovery has been prolonged up to the present day. But despite the rarity of human habitation man must understand his entire world and cannot neglect any part however difficult its penetration may be. The map of the Arctic is nearly fully unrolled, that of the Antarctic has still many blank areas, though the activities of the International Geophysical Year have resulted in a tremendous amount of new knowledge in recent years.

Distinct as this environment is, its boundaries are not too simple to define, nor are its divisions. Let us examine some of the characteristics of nature which can be considered truly polar. First comes high latitude. The so-called Arctic Circle (66° 33′ 03″ N.) and its equivalent in the south are arbitrary mathematical lines on the earth's surface, that are supposed to govern the presence or absence of the midnight sun. The facts that the sun has an appreciable diameter and that its light rays are refracted (especially when on the horizon) in a rather unpredictable manner, destroy the mathematical exactitude of this line. I can recall a midnight walk on 23 June 1937 near the mouth of Repulse Bay in latitude 66° 15′. The sun was just visible rolling along the northern horizon and the full moon appeared above the horizon to the south distorted by refraction into a kidney shape.

As we shall see the 'Arctic' area includes parts of the Hudson Bay coast as far south as 55° N., and at sea-level northern Norway in 71° N. is certainly not Arctic in character. One can therefore reject this latitude line as a satisfactory boundary for the polar regions. However, high latitude, with long summer days and winter nights, the great fluctuation of solar insolation from almost nil in winter to an amount as high as anywhere

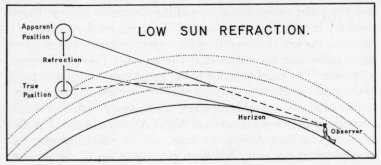

Fig. 1. The sun's rays are bent by successive atmospheric layers.

in the world in mid-summer, is a characteristic which we cannot entirely neglect.

The climatic characteristics we expect of the polar regions are a long, cold winter with reliable continuous frost, passing suddenly, if at all, to a brief cool summer and that in turn equally rapidly back into winter—the old traditional saying of the Arctic is, 'It's always winter up there, but July is bad sledging.' Another feature to be considered characteristically polar is the frequent but not essential occurrence of winds, and the varying types of drifting snow conditions with which we are familiar in the term of *blizzard*. High *wind-chill*, a combination of cold and wind which whips the warm air around the human body rapidly away into barren space is a polar characteristic contrasted to the still cold of the northern forests. Often the polar regions are termed 'cold deserts'. Indeed they are dry when total precipitation figures are given prominence, but in addition evaporation is very slight and the hard-frozen sub-soil preserves surface moisture. It is difficult to agree to a desert description for a land which is covered by swamps and even some flowers in summer and with water in its solid form to the depth of feet for the major part of the year—man is seldom thirsty in the polar desert. Total precipitation is in fact at best a guess in the polar regions where it is extremely difficult to differentiate between snow newly falling or blowing from an adjacent area, but undoubtedly it does count as a polar characteristic and it may be considered necessary to rule out those regions where more humid conditions bring them into a different climatic province.

Permanently frozen ground again is a characteristic of the polar regions. The explorer who succumbs to the severity of the climate must be buried above ground or with the benefit of dynamite. Investigations into the geographical limits of frozen ground are still very incomplete, but areas where it does not exist must be thought of as rejectable for inclusion in the polar realm. Also one would hesitate to call polar any area where the lakes and smaller rivers and the sheltered portions of the sea fail to freeze in winter. The characteristic which seems most important of all is the absence of trees of any height excluding dwarfed or horizontal birches or willows. The tundra lands beyond the tree limit may be well vegetated but this vegetation is of a very distinctive type.

The list of polar characteristics therefore is as follows:

1. High latitude.
2. Long winter, short cool summer.
3. Low precipitation.
4. Permafrost.
5. Frozen lakes and sea.
6. Absence of trees.

After detailing these approved criteria for a truly polar region, let us now examine some of the climatic factors that could be used to define it. To carry out the conditions of a short, cool summer a warmest month isotherm could be selected as a polar boundary. The convenience of 10° C., a round number on both temperature scales (plus 50° F.), is immediately apparent. A temperature of plus 43° F. or plus 6° C. is generally accepted as the onset of photosynthesis in vegetation. A polar factor could well be a maximum number of days or hours during the summer when the temperature stood above this level, but here we are confronted with the difficulty of knowing the temperature actually within the vegetation cover. For example, taking only the mean daily air temperatures above 6° C.—Chesterfield Inlet, N.W.T., has about 63 days (definitely polar) Churchill, Manitoba has 90 days (borderline case) Yakutsk has 111 days (definitely non-polar).

The winter temperatures of the polar regions must be low, but not necessarily so extreme as the continental sub-Arctic of western North America or of Siberia. Also polar homes must be fuelled to a degree unexampled in the remainder of the world, and the degree-days of heating required per year would indicate well the prolonged cold of the Arctic winter. For example, assuming 65° F. as the optimum that requires no heat (a temperature which many Arctic dwellers would consider insufferably warm) the following results obtain: northern Ellesmere Island 24,000 degree-days; Fort Chimo (borderline case) 16,000; Winnipeg 11,000; Vancouver 6,000.

To obtain the high wind-chill cited as a requisite of polar regions mean annual values could be chosen to delimit the boundary. The acceptance of a formula for arriving at a wind-chill value is still delayed, and this method suffers again, from a complication of computing and plotting that mitigate against its use in a simple but scientific polar definition.

The definitions which have been advanced are several: first Köppen has given as the fifth of his world divisions 'polar climates—no warm season, mean temperature of warmest month less than 10° C.' This formula which has been widely accepted to date is simple but perhaps insufficient. The long, cold winter is omitted altogether—surprisingly, for in dividing his next two world groups Köppen sets in addition to a warm month isotherm, a coldest month boundary of -3° C. Such omission allows certain stations where the annual range is very small to become polar in climate—e.g. Evangelistas, a lowland station in southern Chile, in the midst of a rainbelt where precipitation totals 120 inches, the mean annual temperature of +43° F. rivals that of Montreal, and considerable forests are present.

Vahl modified Köppen's definition by a formula combining

warmest and coldest month temperatures. This formula was adapted by O. Nordenskiöld and now reads $W = 9 - 0\cdot1$ C. where W is the mean temperature of the warmest month and C. of the coldest in degrees Centigrade. This formula satisfactorily excludes the forested southern tip of South America from the polar regions, and when plotted in the Arctic along with the 10-degree warmest month isotherm it is noteworthy how in maritime regions Nordenskiöld's line lies to poleward of Köppen's and is further from the Poles in the continental areas of America and Eurasia; the points where the two lines cut being roughly on the coast of these land masses.

Thornthwaite in a new classification of climate based his divisions on 'Potential Evapotranspiration' a figure derived from the temperatures of each month of the year and given as an annual evaporation figure in centimetres or inches. His boundary of the tundra climate (28·5 cm.) lies again far to the north of the tree line on the continents.

Blair in his recent classification of climate has drawn for us a picture of the polar characteristics discussed above: 'Tundra climate. Average temperature of warmest month below 50° F. but above 32° F. (distinguishing it from ice-cap climate), extremely long and cold winters, short raw and chilly summers with the possibility of frost at any time, sub-soil permanently frozen with summer thawing resulting in bogs and swamps, although annual rainfall is mostly less than 10 inches: extends from poleward limit of trees . . . vegetation consists of low bushes, mosses, sedges, lichens.' Köppen claimed a close parallel between the tree line and the warmest month plus 10° C. isotherm. We have already noted that there are some discrepancies here and that the definitions of Nordenskiöld and Thornthwaite placed the polar climatic boundary closer in some places to the tree line. It seems to be necessary to reject, however tempting they may seem, any actual climatic mathematical definitions and accept in fact the 'tree line' as the boundary of the polar region. This also is by no means easy to define but then no simpler is a climatic solution in view of the great distances between reporting stations. The tree line itself, however, must be treated with some caution. There are, for instance, many treeless areas in Iceland, the Aleutians, and even the northern and western parts of Scotland, which we cannot accept by any of the other definitions as polar and where the warmest month isotherms of 10° C. is a long way off. In Alaska, for example, Griggs states that at Kodiak the forest is advancing steadily three miles a century against the prevailing wind, but it is not catching up with the more rapidly advancing climatic amelioration in the area. Many factors besides temperature contribute to the limitation of tree growth, but recent work does show that mid-summer temperature is extremely important. In addition, however, strong winds with the danger of uprooting in shallow soil together with the great increase in transpiration that wind causes, the growth of peat moss in a cool climate causing a deep acid poorly drained soil layer inhospitable to

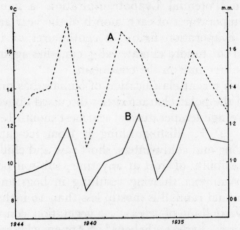

Fig. 2. Tree Growth and July Temperature.
The July mean temperature at Inari (line *A*)
compared for thirteen successive summers with
the radial growth in millimetres of Scots Pine
at Utsjoki (line *B*) (after Hustich).

seedlings, are some of these factors. Tanner has said 'the tree line is hardly a limit only climatically conditioned in the real sense of the word. . . . In Labrador it is evidently a resultant of many different coinciding effects. It is conceivable that the conditions of the site play an important part, especially slope declivity, exposure to winds, duration of the snow cover, and the humidity and temperature of the sub-stratum. Moreover, historical and competitive biological circumstances must also affect the boundary.'

The most prominent worker on the tree line in recent years has been Professor Ilmari Hustich of Helsinki. He points out the correlation in northern Finland between the July temperature and the growth in thickness of the Scots Pine (*Pinus sylvestris*). There is poor correlation between growth and rainfall chiefly because the water available to the tree roots is not liable to fluctuation between seasons, being held fairly constant by melting snow and/or the permafrost table.

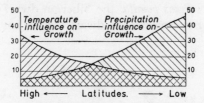

Fig. 3. Climatic Hazard: in high latitudes temperature control is all important.

Another most important factor curtailing the growth of trees at their extreme limits is the interval between successful seed years. At a conference in the U.S.S.R. in 1955 on tree growth in the Arctic it was pointed out that the treelessness of the polar region is caused particularly by low seed production (fruiting only every ten years or so) poor quality seeds, inhibition of the sapling's growth by moss cover and their destruction by animals.

Hustich produces the following definitions:

Biological Forest Limit—the limit of continuous forest.
Tree Line—Absolute limit (poleward, seaward, or upward) of a given species as a tree—i.e. with a trunk projecting above the maximum winter snow cover.
Limit of Species—The line of advanced outposts of a species whatever form the growth may take, even prostrate.

The transitional zone between the biological forest limit and the limit of species is the Russian 'lyesotundra'. Somewhere within lyesotundra therefore comes the tree line of Hustich—the boundary of the polar regions.

Hustich has drawn maps of the north polar limit of certain species.

Picea	glauca	(American)	Spruces	P. abies	(Eurasian)
	Mariana			obovata	
	sitchensis			ajanesis	
Abies	lasiocarpa	(American)	Firs	A. sibirica	(Eurasian)
	balsamea				
Pinus	contorta	(American)	Pines	P. Silvestris	(Eurasian)
	banksiana			sibirica	
				pumila	
Larix	laricina	(American)	Larches	L. sukatschevi	(Eurasian)
				sibirica	
				dahurica	
Juniperus communis					

He then rejects *Pinus pumila*, the Siberian dwarf pine, and the juniper, *Juniperus communis*, as dwarf shrubs not qualifying as

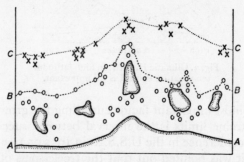

A. Biological Limit of Forest. B. Tree Line. C. Limit of Species.

Fig. 4. The Tree Line: idealized sketch showing the
various limits suggested.

trees above the snow cover. His resultant map shows the polar 'limit of species' of tree-like conifers as a whole. Hustich points out that if non-coniferous trees were included, birch, alder, willow, etc., of *tree* proportion the line would be extended to include Iceland and southernmost Greenland and more of Alaska and the extreme eastern parts of Siberia.

This would be in closer agreement still with Nordenskiöld's line. It would be in closer agreement also with our five other polar characteristics. The inner part of the Julianehaab fiord region, where conifers have been planted recently and sheep graze as they did when it was the Osterbygd of the eleventh century, fails to qualify on all counts: its latitude is only 61° N., its precipitation is considerable, there is no permafrost in the neighbouring mine and the sea remains open enough to allow boat travel and prevent dog team travel all winter.

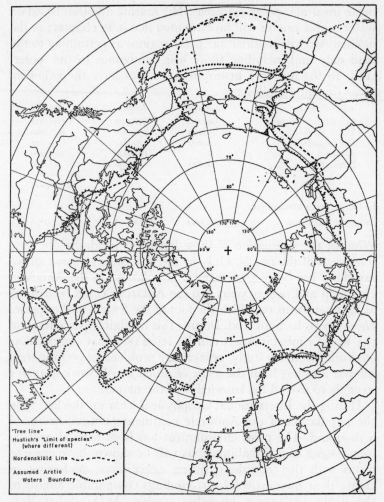

Fig. 5. Arctic Limits.

Yet for convenience in this geography of the polar regions we must include all Greenland noting its 'maritime sub-Arctic' corner. Similarly we will exclude Iceland, the Norwegian treeless coast to open Murmansk, Labrador south of latitude 55° and the Aleutians.

As M. J. Dunbar has pointed out, the northern limit of trees or a given climatological definition are of no use in delineating polar from non-polar sea areas. His marine divisions based on water source origins will be examined in a later chapter; at the moment we will consider our polar regions as pertaining to the land only and including those seas contiguous to the 'polar' land. In the northern hemisphere we thus have the following areas (in square miles):

	Ice-covered	Ice-free	Total
Canadian territory	60,000	970,000	1,030,000
U.S.S.R. territory	25,000	870,000	895,000
Greenland	720,000	120,000	840,000
Alaska	—	161,000	161,000
Svalbard	20,000	4,000	24,000
			2,950,000

In the southern hemisphere:

Antarctic continent	5,420,000	—	5,420,000

What of the population of these lands? It is admittedly tiny, some tens of thousands. Only in the last twenty years can we say there has been a permanent population on the Antarctic continent and twenty years ago the Antarctic could be defined as that continent on which the foot of the female of the species *Homo sapiens* had not trod. Despite this negligible percentage of the world's inhabitants it can be reiterated that the peculiar environment needs study, poses many problems of geographical interest and has been the scene of much heroic work in man's struggle to extend his knowledge of the planet.

During the International Geophysical Year for the first time the population of the Antarctic continent at times exceeded a thousand. The polar environment has been little altered by man—some of its inhabitants, as will be shown, have come to terms with the conditions; others never have, preferring to create their own artificial surroundings comparable almost to the likely settlements on other worlds. At Frobisher Bay, Baffin Island in 1953, I was pointed out a man—a cook in a U.S. Air Force detachment, who had not been out of doors for a year—he went out the first day, did not like it, and remained housebound thereafter.

FURTHER READING

The two useful periodical publications in English are:
The Polar Record, Cambridge, England, from 1931.
Arctic, Montreal, Canada, from 1948.

For Arctic Geology:
Geology of the Arctic (Ed. G. O. Raasch), 2 vols., Toronto, 1961.

Other references for Chapter I:
Tanner, V., *Geography of Newfoundland Labrador*, Acta Geographica, Helsinki, 1944.
Hare, F. K., 'Climate and Zonal Divisions of the Boreal Forest in Canada', *Geogr. Rev.*, 40, 1950, p. 615.
Thronthwaite, C. W., 'An Approach Toward a Rational Classification of Climate', *Geogr. Rev*, Jan., 1948.
Blair, T. A., *Climatology*, New York, 1942.
Hustich, I., *The Scots Pine in Northernmost Finland*, Helsinki, 1948.

Chapter 2

HISTORY OF ARCTIC EXPLORATION

'There is no land unhabitable nor sea unnavigable.'—R. THORNE

THERE have been 'Arctic explorers' for much of the time that man has existed as man. We as a species have been coexistent with the age of ice, and our forbears were wanderers in the tundra for thousands of years. We must remember that ten thousand years ago Britain and Germany were tundra lands, part of Scandinavia was still glacier covered, and as the ice melted back from its coast the Fosna and Komsa peoples of the Stone Age were colonizing Arctic Norway and Finland. Along the northern fringe of Asia the hunters of reindeer and musk-ox must have moved steadily north and east until they spread over into Arctic America. This wave of old Asian peoples had reached Greenland from the west before history began. But primitive man had not been able to cross the wider open waters to Iceland or to Svalbard.

For the historical record of Arctic discovery we must turn to the literate civilizations. Some of these have taken no part in polar journeys, their roots were too southern, or their encompassing world too large. Such were the Greek, the Roman, the Arab, and the Chinese realms. It is true that Pytheas the Greek from Marseilles upset the current notion of the frozen northern wastes, but the account of his journey (was it to Scotland and beyond or to Norway?) was not generally believed and has not itself survived. The French-Canadian explorer Bernier proudly lists him as the first polar voyager—nationality, French! It is European civilization that has unrolled the northern map to latitude ninety and the preponderant part has been played by those countries with northern roots—Scandinavia, Britain, Russia and (later) the United States. It is easy to understand the attraction the polar regions held for the Scandinavians and Russians; they are accustomed to cold winters and to movement

over the snow. It is less easy to grasp why British explorers
have achieved so much. Probably the appalling discomfort of
his housing has ensured that life in an igloo or on the Antarctic
plateau is quite tolerable to the Briton.

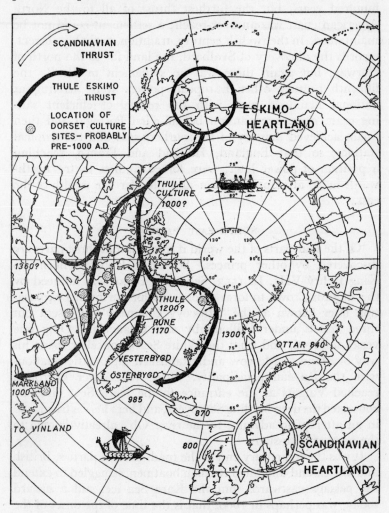

Fig. 6. Scandinavian and Eskimo Penetrations.

It was the Scandinavians who, reaching the peak of their
expansive urge first, drove through Europe and across the

North Atlantic. Iceland was occupied from 874 and in 'sixty winters' was to all intents fully settled. About the same date Norwegians under Ottar had reached the White Sea. The Greenland colony began in 985 and lived on for at least four hundred years, but the furthest thrust of all to the North American coast was an over-reach; a settlement could not be maintained. In the twelfth century, tradition, probably correct, records the discovery of Svalbard, the land far to the north of Norway, but again there was no settlement made. By the fifteenth century other European powers were arriving at national manhood and, with the revival of efficient sailing craft, oversea expansion began. First Portugal and then Spain achieved mastery of the southern seas and the tropical stations, so that England, Holland and France, reaching a position of power later, were forced at first to try northwards in an attempt to attain and plunder the wealth of the east.

NORTH-EAST PASSAGE

'Of the four parts of the world it seemeth that three parts are discovered by other princes.' So wrote Robert Thorne to King Henry VIII. In 1553, Sebastian Cabot was induced by the English Crown to form a company for northward exploration later known as the 'Muscovy Company', and sent out three vessels under Willoughby and Chancellor. Only one vessel survived, and from the White Sea Chancellor made his way overland to Moscow and established diplomatic relations with the Russian principality. Three years later Burrough reached Vaigats at the entrance to the Kara Sea. Here he contacted the deer-herding Samoyeds, and here he was frustrated in an attempt to advance to the river Ob', already known to the northern Russians.

It was the temporary end of the road. Several parties, British and Dutch and unnamed Russian boatmen, struggled to extend the passage eastwards, but the Kara Sea ice, still a hazard today, was perhaps in 1600, that is the time of the onset of the alpine glacier advance, an even greater bar to navigation. In 1580 Pet and Jackman tried again, the latter had already been in Arctic regions with Frobisher in the north-west. But they got no further into the Kara Sea, it remained for unknown servants of the Muscovy Company to reach the mouth of the Ob'. This had already been attained by a Netherlander O. Brunel overland from Russia, but in a seaborne trip in 1584 he was again unsuccessful. Dutch interests were now aroused and three expeditions in successive years were organized. The name of Barents, who actually commanded none of them, is associated with all three. Willem Barents was the rediscoverer of Svalbard and was one of the first party of west Europeans to winter in the Arctic. This was on his last voyage of 1596 when after

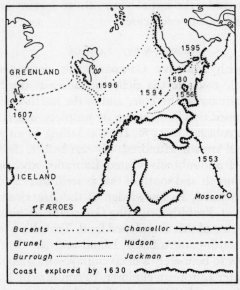

Fig. 7. The North-East Passage to 1630.

rounding the northern end of Novaya Zemlya his ship had to take refuge on the east coast. Driftwood served them for fuel and to build a house which survived to be found intact in 1871. Bears were a continual menace, the musket of those days was not a sure defence, but some were killed and the fat and skins were used but surprisingly little of the meat. They did eat foxes, though, and were only partly affected by scurvy. But Barents himself was a dying man when they escaped in the ship's boats next summer.

Barents had only touched at Svalbard; Hudson followed him in 1607 in what was actually an attempt to cross the north polar basin in a direct route, and he traced the whole of the western shore of Spitsbergen reporting quantities of whales. In the next decades the efforts of England and Holland (later joined by Denmark) were directed to exploitation of this valuable resource, the thirst for the North-East Passage was quenched for all these nations, especially for the Dutch who were now rounding Africa and challenging Portugal in the Indies. We shall see immediately how the North-West Passage search was similarly diverted by commercial exploitation, this time the fur trade, the initial sixteenth- to seventeenth-century drive petering out in each case.

NORTH-WEST PASSAGE

The English Muscovy Company was determined to try every possible route to the riches of the east: the North-East Passage, north across the Pole, and to the north-west also. The westward expedition sent under its auspices was commanded by Martin Frobisher in 1576. He was sailing to an area which had been well known. Hundreds of years before, the Greenland colonists had undoubtedly visited Labrador and possibly the lands to the north and south of this as well, but the colony had been overwhelmed, its knowledge of the American continent completely lost. Frobisher sighting Greenland on his voyage was the rediscoverer of this abandoned land. Travelling further west he reached south-eastern Baffin Island and his 'Straits', which we now know to be merely a deep embayment. Here he was the first of the later European explorers to contact the Eskimo, and his relations were disastrous, both in this first expedition and subsequent ones in the succeeding two summers. These two penetrated no further. Unfortunately rumour of gold had arisen from specimens he brought back in 1576, and his efforts were directed entirely to the recovery of what proved to be worthless ore. His third expedition contained a great quantity of supplies for a permanent settlement and the mining of this ore, including the first prefabricated house for an Arctic station which we hear of in history. His fleet of fifteen ships scattered by a gale, he was forced to return and, the ore proving worthless, his voyages were considered a total failure. His 'Straits' in fact became transferred on the map to cut off the southern part of Greenland instead of their true location, and it was several

years before another company was founded to press once more
for the North-West Passage. John Davis was in charge of the
next three expeditions under its auspices. He penetrated deeper
into the strait, now named after him, between Greenland and
Baffin Island, explored Cumberland Sound and noted the
opening which subsequently proved to be Hudson's Strait. Into
this strait Captain George Weymouth sailed in 1602 in the
small vessel *Discovery* of fifty-five tons, which was to be used
on many subsequent North-West Passage searches.

First was the famous last voyage of Hudson in 1610. He was
sponsored by three private individuals to search for a North-
West Passage 'through any of those inlets which Davis saw'.
The story of his wintering in Hudson Bay, and the subsequent
mutiny when he, his son, and several of his party were set
adrift is well known. He had discovered the great bay, named
after him, and he pushed the limits of knowledge several
hundred miles further to the west. Within a year the same
sponsors had sent forth another expedition led by Thomas
Button, which was remarkable in that it carried two of the
mutineers of Hudson's expedition, apparently reinstated, and
for an extraordinary lack of interest in the fate of Hudson, who
could still conceivably have been surviving on the shore of
Hudson Bay. This is in sharp contrast to the modern interest in
a vanished expedition when human life seems more valuable.
Button's party wintered successfully at Port Nelson, and reached
latitude 65° in Roe's Welcome. Shortly after Bylot, one of
Hudson's mates, who had been with Button, was back again
this time with, as pilot, William Baffin, a man who proved to
be the outstanding voyager in the North-West Passage search
of this century. Bylot and Baffin went north-west from the end
of Hudson Strait up the coast of Southampton Island, but were
stopped by ice and returned in the same summer. A year later
these two sailed on the fifth North-West Passage voyage of the
little *Discovery*, and this was the longest and most successful of
the seventeenth-century attempts on the Passage. Coasting up
west Greenland, they passed the furthest latitude of Davis,
reached Smith Sound on 5 July (old style) examined Jones
Sound and Lancaster Sound and then coasted down Baffin
Island off which still lay the fast ice of the previous winter. This
tremendous voyage, which established the northernmost record

in North American longitudes for over two centuries to come, delineated with considerable accuracy the great bay now named after Baffin. But Baffin's map was not published and the knowledge of this bay gradually fell into disuse till two centuries later when his voyage was repeated by John Ross. It was marked on the maps, if at all, as 'the coast as laid down by Baffin but not now generally believed'.

Frobisher –·–·–·–·–·–	Button ....
Davis ●●●●●●●●●●●●●●●●●●●●	Bylot – – – – – – – – –
Weymouth	Baffin —·–·—·–·—·–·—·–·—
Hudson – ·· – ·· – ·· – ·· –	James +–+–+–+–+–+–+–+
	Foxe – – – – – – – –

Coast explored by 1631 〜〜〜〜〜〜

Fig. 8. Canadian Arctic to 1640.

In 1619 the Danes entered the area, Captain Jens Munck in two small vessels being dispatched by the Danish king to search for the North-West Passage. He also reached the west coast of Hudson Bay, turned south and, caught by a very early winter, harboured in the Churchill River. Here practically all his crew died of scurvy, leaving Munck and two others to

sail one of the ships home. In 1631 two British expeditions sailed
for Hudson Bay, one sponsored by London merchants under
Captain Luke Foxe, the other by rivals from Bristol under
Captain Thomas James. Between them they finished off the
delineation of the western coast-line of the Bay. Foxe pushed
northward on the coast of Baffin Island but, mistaking the latitude, placed his Cape Dorchester a hundred miles too far to the
north. Captain James was trapped at the head of the bay now
named after him and was forced to spend a particularly miserable
winter, the account of which when published on his return did
much to discourage further English efforts in the exploration of
the bay. But it did more than this: it discouraged also the Court
at Paris when in the 1660s the French-Canadian explorers
Radisson and Groseillers who had reached Hudson Bay overland, returned to the French Court with the story of the wealth
of furs to be obtained on the shores of the bay. King Louis had
read James' account and was unsympathetic. The Frenchmen
took their story to London where a different reception awaited
them. Prince Rupert was interested, a company of adventurers
was formed and an expedition dispatched in the *Nonsuch* under
Captain Gillam to establish a fur trade post on Hudson Bay.
This was the beginnings of the great Hudson's Bay Company
chartered in 1670 under Royal patronage, and at this point,
as with the North-East Passage, commercial exploitation put
a temporary stop to further attempts at the discovery of a passage
to the Orient. Hudson Bay now became a theatre of the struggle
between Britain and France for control of North America.
Naval battles were fought in the bay—trading posts changed
hands, were returned at peace treaties, changed hands again.
Some further attempts to push to the north-west were made
during this period. Some were by the Hudson's Bay Company
itself under one of their longest-lived servants, James Knight.
Others were sponsored by critics of the Company's trade
monopoly who maintained that for financial reasons the Company was impeding further discovery to the north-west. The
result of these eighteenth century exploration trips was the complete mapping of the western shore of the bay including its inlets
as far as Repulse Bay, but in effect this was no advance on the
voyage of Bylot and Baffin in 1615 which had reached much
the same position. For the further story we must now turn to

overland exploration, east across Siberia and west across the North American continent.

SIBERIA OVERLAND

The rapid spread of the Russian Empire overland across the enormous length of Siberia is one of the most astounding stories of human tenacity. We can call it a Cossack penetration. The Cossacks were armed communities of freemen living on the eastern bounds of Russia as she existed at the end of the sixteenth century, and started their movement north-eastwards with the conquest of the Tartar kingdom of Sibir in 1584. Thence there was a steady penetration of the unorganized tribes living in Siberia—the conquest followed by settlement and by trade chiefly in the pursuit of the Siberian sable (marten)—a wealth of furs being collected. This penetration took place chiefly to the south of the Arctic regions of Asia making use of the closely linked waterways and comparatively short overland hauls between them. But the rivers were pursued to their mouths: the delta of the Lena was reached in 1617, next year the Yana, by 1644 both the Indigirka and the Kolyma, by 1638 the Sea of Okhotsk. In 1648 the Cossack Dezhnev sailed from the Kolyma River round the extreme eastern part of Asia, a journey the record of which was lost for a long time. The list below shows the amazing speed of this penetration from the foundation of the various Siberian towns.

Tobolsk	1587
Tomsk	1604
Yeniseisk	1619
Yakutsk	1632

By the end of the seventeenth century, the furthest point of the Kamchatka Peninsula had been reached. Only in the south-east had the Russian settlers and conquerors met with a check on the bounds of the Chinese Empire. So in effect Siberia was Russian in its totality. In the eighteenth century Peter the Great, having secured the western frontiers of his empire by military success, determined to consolidate Siberia by 'winning glory along the lines of Arts and Science'. He set in motion the Great Northern Expedition of 1725 to 1742, which among other

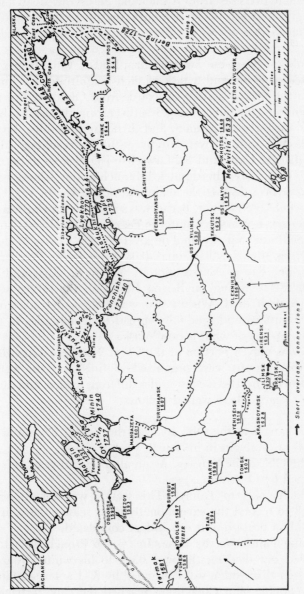

Fig. 9. Exploration of Siberia, including dates of foundation of Russian towns.

things was to press east from Kamchatka across the ocean and fill
in the gaps between the river mouths on the Arctic coast so that
a full knowledge of this northern edge of his empire would be
obtained. This expedition was organized on enormous and
semi-military lines, but lacked a firm leader. Vitus Bering was
not fitted to command a task of such magnitude. He himself
took on the task of sailing eastwards from Okhotsk. But after
a tremendous effort in crossing Siberia carrying heavy hardware
such as anchors and cannon, and then building ships, his first
two seasons' sailings were unsuccessful in reaching Alaska
although East Cape and St. Lawrence Island were discovered.
In 1730 one of his subordinates did touch at the 'Island' which
must have been in fact the mainland of Alaska. In 1733 after
a return to St. Petersburg, Bering was sent east again but was not
ready for seven years to sail in the *Peter* and *Paul*. It was on this
last expedition that the final discovery of Alaska was made, by
both vessels after they had separated. Bering in the *Peter* landed
for only one day in Alaska opposite Mount St. Elias and they
were forced to winter on Bering Island on the return where
Bering himself died. Within two years Russian traders were
in the Aleutians and gradually spread their activities to most
of the coast-line of what is now Alaska.

This was only a portion of the Great Northern Expedition.
Five other groups were organized to finish off the various
sections of the northern coast under different leaders and during
different years. These were as follows:

1. Archangel to the Ob'. In 1737 the Yamal Peninsula was
rounded by Malygin in his fourth year of trying.

2. The Ob' to the Yenisey. Again after several years this was
completed by Ovtzin in 1737.

3. The Yenisey to Taimyr. This section was not attempted
till 1738 so missed the exceptionally good season the year before. Only a portion of it was in fact completed.

4. Cape Taimyr to the Lena. In 1735–6 Pronchishef almost
succeeded but died on the way back to his winter quarters.
In 1739–41 this section was continued by K. Laptev, and in the
latter years his pilot Chelyuskin reached the cape bearing his
name which is the northernmost point of Asia. It seems possible
now that Russian traders in the period 1610–20 had rounded

this cape from the west, since a boat hut, skeletons and coins were found there in 1940–1.

5. The Lena to the east. Between 1735 and 1740 much of this coast-line was surveyed as far as a point well to the east of the River Kolyma, but the complete task was not achieved. So ended the Great Northern Expedition lasting fifteen or more years on which hundreds of men had died, but a large amount of useful work had been achieved. A pause followed, but in 1770 we see some new discoveries. Lyakhov, following a deer trail northward over the ice from the mainland, discovered the New Siberian Islands. Within a few years others had followed to exploit the extraordinary deposits of ivory, fossil mammoth tusks, which these islands yielded. Finally in this period of history we come to the figure of Baron Wrangel, who in the 1820s after many trips out over the Arctic Ocean by dog team, reached North Cape on the Chukchi Peninsula tying up with Cook's furthest west in 1778. On this last stretch of the journey he covered 1,530 miles in the amazing time of seventy-eight days.

NORTH AMERICA OVERLAND

In this same eighteenth century the North American continent was being explored overland, but at a far slower pace and with less energy and results than in Siberia. In 1769 Samuel Hearne was sent out by the Hudson's Bay Company to seek a river that Indian rumour said was rich in copper. He went as a lone white man with Indian guides, an Indian tribe in fact with wives and children along, travelling necessarily therefore at their speed and completely in their hands. His first two starts were unsuccessful, but on the third one in 1770 he trekked for seven months to the mouth of the Coppermine River along the edge of the timber line that lies between here and Churchill. Here one of the reasons for the Indian's patient guiding was revealed. A massacre of the Eskimo living at the mouth of the Coppermine ensued to Hearne's horror. Though his error in the published latitude of the river mouth was considerable, he had accomplished something else. He had begun a tradition of living off the country, living as did his native guides and this was to be followed by other Hudson's Bay Company overland travellers in succeeding years.

Meanwhile on the Plains of Abraham the struggle for control of North America between France and Britain had come to an end. With Canada all British a new westward overland expansion began. Fur traders based on Montreal began pushing up the inland waterway via the Great Lakes, Manitoba, and the rivers to the north and west from there, challenging the

Fig. 10.

long established Hudson's Bay Company. This was still at first confined to its posts on the shore of the bay but was rapidly forced by competition to move inland to continue to get its share of the Indians' fur. So the great days of the *voyageurs* began. The heavily laden huge trading canoes paddled up and down the waterways, were hauled over the portages between rivers, until the river was reached which flows into the Arctic

Ocean—the Mackenzie River. Soon the rival traders reached Great Slave Lake, the eastern end of which had been passed by Hearne on his journey of 1770–1. It was from here that Alexander Mackenzie set off to complete the course of his great river and reach the North Polar Sea, establishing thus a second known point on its shore. This is the only river in North America which can compare with the great rivers of Siberia down which the traders had pushed and fanned out eastward and westward along the Arctic coast. It was left to Franklin in the 1820s to attempt such coastwise journeys from these two established river mouths. His first of 1821 ran from the Coppermine River eastward for a few hundred miles and then came a disastrous retreat overland to his base on Great Slave Lake during which ten of his men died from cold and starvation. On his second journey of 1825–7 he travelled down the Mackenzie, establishing winter quarters at Fort Franklin on Great Bear Lake. During the subsequent summer with two separate parties, the coast was explored eastward to link with the mouth of the Coppermine and westward to a point only fifty miles short of Point Barrow. A few years later, in 1834, another river mouth was reached, Captain Back travelling down the river now named after him from the Great Slave Lake area. Meanwhile, however, the attempt by sea on the North-West Passage had been renewed and it is to this that we must now turn.

NORTH-WEST PASSAGE BY SEA

With the end of the Napoleonic wars what might be termed the Golden Age of Exploration of this region began, sparked by the British Admiralty and particularly by its Secretary, Sir John Barrow. We now knew the whole coast of northern Siberia as delineated by the Great Northern Expedition, but on the coast-line of North America only the two river mouths laid down by Hearne and Mackenzie and to the east Hudson Bay and Strait and Baffin Bay 'now not generally believed'. A war-swollen Navy manned by experienced officers and men was at hand to continue this tremendous project during forty years of peace. Four ships were dispatched in 1818, two northwards via Spitsbergen to attempt the polar route (once again credited as possible) and two others the north-western passage through Baffin Bay. These under Captain John Ross with Lieutenant

Parry as second-in-command followed a course almost identical with that of Baffin two centuries before, failing once again to penetrate into any of Baffin's sounds—particularly Lancaster Sound which was to be the real passage. Ross saw imaginary mountains extending around the head of this Sound and returned declaring no passage would be found this way. His main achievement seems to have been contact with the northernmost tribe of Eskimo on Greenland, a tribe he termed the Arctic Highlanders who then believed themselves the only people of the world. It was only a year before Parry was back again to investigate, properly this time, Lancaster Sound which he, along with many other officers, had been convinced was not a cul-de-sac. Parry was one of the great Arctic commanders. He had determined in advance on wintering his ships in the ice, continuing if need be a second or third season, and careful plans had been drawn up for the health and entertainment of his sailors during their enforced wintering. In his first summer he sailed west from Lancaster Sound to Melville Island thus passing the 110th degree of longitude and winning for himself and his crew the Parliamentary prize of £5,000 which had stood for many years, but next season he was unable to penetrate any more than a few miles further to the west, and years elapsed before this final section of the northern North-West Passage was achieved. In 1821 he entered Hudson Bay and pushed north along the continental coast from Repulse Bay. Here again progress was stopped. The strait of *Fury* and *Hecla* (Parry's two ships) was impossible to penetrate and remained so in fact till modern postwar ice-breakers achieved the passage only a few years ago. Parry tried a third time, this time down Prince Regent Inlet between Somerset Island and Baffin Island, another possible channel of advance. But here he was unfortunate enough to lose one of his two vessels in a storm and had to return with both crews on *Hecla*. Back again to this route came Sir John Ross—this time in a privately sponsored expedition, on the first steam-engined vessel to attempt the Arctic, but the engine was a pretty sorry affair and was in fact removed during the first winter—the first of four that this expedition suffered on the barren coast of Prince Regent Inlet. Ross's nephew, later Sir James Clark Ross, was his most energetic second-in-command, who travelled by sledge across Boothia to discover and chart the location of the north magnetic Pole. This expedition had missed the narrow opening now known as Bellot Strait which divides the mainland of Canada from Somerset Island. It was missed not only in the voyage southward but in the retreat in small boats to which Ross was forced after all attempts to extricate the *Victory* had failed. He was lucky to obtain stores from the wreck of Parry's *Fury* further up the coast and to be picked up by a whaling vessel in Lancaster Sound. It was to search for Ross, so long missing, that Back had descended his river in 1834 although news came to him before he left his winter quarters that Ross had safely returned to Britain. Five years later another section of the coast was filled in between Franklin's furthest east and the mouth of Back's river. This was by the youthful Hudson's Bay Company servant Thomas Simpson who travelled south of King William Island and past the mouth of Back River to a point from which he saw sea extending without limit to the east, connecting therefore, it would seem, with Prince Regent Inlet. This was believed by Sir John Barrow in preference to Ross who stated that the land of Boothia Peninsula was continuous with the continent. Both of course were wrong, Ross much less so, however, as he had only missed Bellot Strait between Boothia Peninsula and Somerset Island. Simpson two years before had completed the small section of the coast of the continent between Franklin's furthest west and Point Barrow. One more expedition was to follow, again led by a servant of the Hudson's Bay Company, John Rae, who after wintering at Repulse Bay completed in 1847 the section between Ross's Lord Mayor's Bay and Fury and Hecla Strait.

The stage was now set for the last voyage which was finally to discover the North-West Passage, the continental coast being now reasonably well known, but some confusion still existing about the islands to the north. This was the famous expedition of Sir John Franklin which started in 1845, and with more than a hundred men vanished from sight. Only one brief written record of this expedition has ever been found from which one knows that after wintering at Beechey Island the ships were beset in Victoria Strait for two winters. After Franklin's death the sick crews abandoned ship in April 1848 and all perished on the hopeless march southward via the

mouth of Back River. The next few years are distinguished by
the multitudinous Franklin search expeditions. Large naval
groups attacked the Passage from west and from east, overland
trips were made from the Canadian mainland, independently
sponsored voyages by several nations also took part, but despite

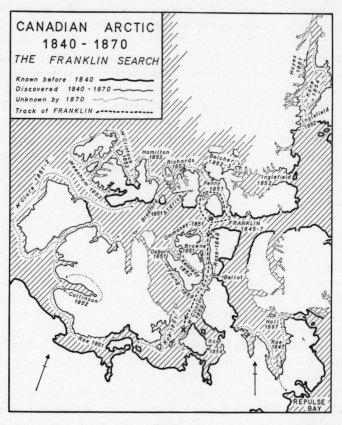

Fig. 11.

the delineation of a tremendous amount of new ground, the
Canadian northern islands, it remained for only two of these
parties to bring back authentic traces of Franklin, John Rae
in 1853–4 and M'Clintock in the last of the Franklin search
expeditions in 1857–9. The Passage itself was actually accomplished partly on foot by M'Clure and some of his crew who
had been frozen in on the coast of Banks Island and escaped to

wintering vessels coming from the east. Now a great deal of the effort north of North America was devoted to pushing towards the Pole. It was many years before the Passage was attempted again, and this time it was to be crowned with success. Roald Amundsen, sailing from Norway in 1903, reached King William Island and after spending two winters there making magnetic observations, sailed west again, and although he was forced to spend another winter on the Alaskan coast came out into the Pacific in August 1906, thus completing the first North-West Passage by sea. In the 1920s came Rasmussen's overland journey from Hudson Bay to Alaska and Siberia, and then in the 1940s a further chapter in the history of the Passage when the Royal Canadian Mounted Police vessel *St. Roch* first traversed from west to east, spending two winters on the way, and in the summer of 1944 returned via Melville Island and Prince of Wales Strait to achieve the first Passage in a single season. This was repeated as recently as 1954 by the new Canadian naval ice-breaker H.M.C.S. *Labrador*. There is no question that a modern ice-breaker could achieve the Passage in any summer season, but it is still rare for the possibility to occur for any ordinary vessel to do so. This is in sharp contrast to the comparative ease of the North-East Passage as we know it today, and we will now turn to the final story of this route across the northern stretch of Siberia.

THE NORTH-EAST PASSAGE BY SEA

As we have seen, practically the entire coast of Siberia had been mapped by the 1740s, yet it was a century and a quarter before new efforts were made to attempt the Passage by sea. Then a few vessels began using the western section as far as the Yenisey, and soon further attempts were made to press eastwards. Meanwhile a few more details had been filled in on the land mass of Siberia—chief among these was the expedition of Middenorf in 1843 who examined the interior of the Taimyr Peninsula. Most Russian efforts, however, during this period were directed further south to an expansion towards China and Central Asia. It remained for foreigners to attempt the Russian passage, and the first of these came from a new nation, new that is to Arctic exploration, the Empire of Austria-Hungary. But Lieutenant Payer was beset in his ship the *Tegethoff* off

Novaya Zemlya and, drifting away to the northward, accidentally discovered Franz Josef Land, an entirely new group of islands, the furthest north land in the Old World. This group was surveyed again by Leigh Smith in 1880 and by Jackson in the 1890s. It was Jackson as we shall see who relieved Nansen after his famous trans-polar drift. The final achievement of the North-East Passage fell to a Swedish explorer, A. E. Nordenskiöld, who in his third voyage in the *Vega* almost achieved the passage in 1878, wintering only a hundred miles short of his objective and reaching the Pacific in July of 1879. During the next successful passage (that of Vilkitski in 1913–15) a new group of islands was discovered lying to the north of Cape Chelyuskin. This group named Nikolas the Second Land is now known as North Land (Severnaya Zemlya.) Amundsen in the *Maud* achieved the Passage in 1918–20, but it remained for the *Sibiriakov* to be the first vessel to make the traverse in one season in 1932. Now as we shall see in a later chapter the North-East Passage has been frequently traversed by even ordinary commercial vessels in a single season, and it has proved, in this century anyway, to be an easier waterway than the North-West Passage.

THE EXPLORATION OF GREENLAND

The Scandinavian colony in Greenland established in 985 lasted between four and five hundred years, for as long it must be remembered as the Europeans have been settled in North America. Norsemen had certainly travelled up the west coast to latitude 73° as a runic stone has been discovered there dating from the twelfth century, but for various reasons the colony eventually failed. Ships began to go there less and less frequently and sometime in the fourteenth or fifteenth century the last colonist must have disappeared, perhaps absorbed in the oncoming Eskimo peoples. These were the only inhabitants to be discovered when the country was revisited by Davis in 1585. At other times in that century Greenland had been sighted, and was referred to as 'Friesland' a mythical land which had appeared on the medieval charts. Davis renamed it the Land of Desolation and put in at what is now the capital of the country Godthaab. In 1587 he explored the western coast as far as Sanderson's Hope in latitude 72°. Baffin as we saw earlier, completed the coasting of his bay as far north as latitude 76°. Meanwhile two expeditions led by James Hall had revisited the south-western coast in 1605 and 1612, sent out by the Danish king in an attempt to find the lost colonies that his country had so long neglected. It was another century before Denmark once again renewed interest in the country when Hans Egede the missionary established his colony in 1721. From this settlement Danish colonies went ahead steadily missionizing and trading with the Eskimo peoples, but for nearly two hundred years their posts were confined to the western coast as far north as Upernavik. The eastern coast, always more difficult of access, remained neglected for a long time. Hudson had seen it in 1607 and a few other sightings had been made in subsequent years. The nineteenth century arrived before any serious exploration began to take place here. The first was the scientifically-interested whaler, William Scoresby who in the early 1820s surveyed in part some ten degrees of latitude (65° to 75°) of the east coast. In 1823 Clavering saw the last survivors of the Eskimo inhabitants of this north-east coast who shortly afterwards became extinct. In 1829–30 Graah surveyed much of the south-eastern coast up to the latitudes where Scoresby had been active. In 1869 an Austrian-German expedition under Koldewey and Payer explored much of the east coast including the great inlet known as Franz Josef Fjord. Then in 1884 came the Danish expedition of Gustav Holm who, finding Eskimo inhabitants on the south-eastern coast, succeeded in interesting his government enough to establish at last a colony on this side of the island; it was 1894 before this took place and the settlement was at Angmagssalik. Meanwhile another area outside Danish control had been discovered. John Ross in 1818 had found the tribe he named the Arctic Highlanders, living in a latitude of 76° to 77° in the extreme north-west. It was from this area and with these people that the explorations of Peary towards the Pole were based. These are dealt with in the ensuing section, but as far as Greenland itself was concerned, Peary reached the northernmost point of land (in the world) in 1900 and passing this travelled a short way down the eastern coast. Only a small section of the north-east therefore remained to be filled in, the section which no ship has yet reached. The completion of the map here was the result of exploration by Mylius-Erichsen in

1906–8. Erichsen himself perished on the return journey and
it remained for another great Danish explorer Einar Mikkelsen
to search for and discover the records of his expedition.

Thus the coasts of Greenland became known, but what of the

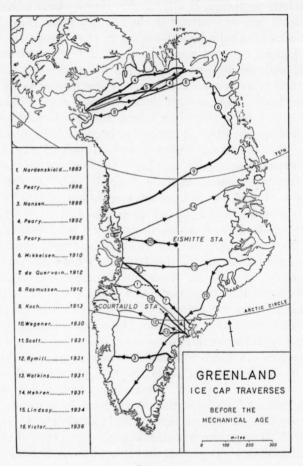

1. Nordenskiold....1883

2. Peary...............1886

3. Nansen...........1888

4. Peary...............1892

5. Peary...............1895

6. Mikkelsen.........1910

7. de Quervain...1912

8. Rasmussen.....1912

9. Koch................1913

10. Wegener...........1930

11. Scott................1931

12. Rymill.............1931

13. Watkins...........1931

14. Mehren............1931

15. Lindsay...........1934

16. Victor.............1936

EISMITTE STA

COURTAULD STA

ARCTIC CIRCLE

GREENLAND
ICE CAP TRAVERSES

BEFORE THE
MECHANICAL AGE

miles
0   100   200   300

Fig. 12.

interior of this near-continent? For many years this had intrigued
some of the Danish colonists on the west coast. What kind
of country could lie inland beyond the ice-covered mountains?
Various short journeys had been made by Danes from the southern settlements. In 1870 A. E. Nordenskiöld made an attempt

to cross Greenland from the latitude of Disko Island and again in 1883, after his successful North-East Passage, he returned and reached a point in the interior about seventy-five miles inland dispatching his Lapp skiers even further to the east on a non-stop thirty-hour journey. It was in 1888 that the first crossing occurred—that of Fridtjof Nansen in about latitude 64°. It was this journey that revealed for certain the nature of the interior of Greenland, a tremendous ice-cap rising to over eight thousand feet altitude, featureless from coast to coast. There have now been many subsequent crossings of this ice-cap. Chief among these are the journeys of Peary in the 1890s from Thule to the far north-east, journeys subsequently repeated in the 1910–20 period by Rasmussen, who had established his own trading colony in the Thule district. Other famous crossings were those of de Quervain in 1912 and Koch in 1913. In 1930 two ice-cap stations were established; one, Eismitte, belonged to Wegener's last Arctic expedition; further south occurred the lonely vigil of Courtauld, a member of Watkin's British Arctic Air Route Expedition. Finally, after the Second World War has come the age of the mechanical vehicle, particularly exploited by Paul-Emile Victor in the French Greenland expeditions where journeys in all directions across the centre of the island have been achieved with detailed scientific work, including the sounding of the ice-cap, being carried out. Further north the Americans based on Thule and the British expedition of 1950–2 have also made major mechanical vehicle traverses of the northern ice-cap.

THE NORTH POLAR SEA

To the northward of the two Passages and of Greenland lies the immense polar basin, an area in which a continent could be lost, and still completely unknown at the beginning of the nineteenth century. The earliest beliefs of the seventeenth century were that it might be possible to sail right across this sea and avoid the landward passages. This could conceivably have been possible a few hundred, and almost certainly was a few thousand, years before, but we now know that in modern centuries it has been too choked with pack ice to permit anything except the most powerful of ice-breakers to travel across its surface. But the belief was still current in 1818, and as

D

an adjunct to John Ross's North-West Expedition, the British Admiralty dispatched two vessels under Buchan and Franklin to sail northwards from Spitsbergen. They achieved little further northing than had many of the much earlier whalers and sailing ships in Spitsbergen waters, but in 1827 a new definite attempt was made by W. E. Parry after his North-West Passage voyages to reach the Pole over the ice to the northward of Spitsbergen. Even if Parry's equipment had been more efficient, and he was attempting to haul heavy wooden boats over the rough pack ice, this attack was doomed to failure. He was the first to discover the strong southward flowing current, the East Greenland current between Spitsbergen and Greenland; every move forward was nearly cancelled out by a drift backwards when the parties were resting. They did, however, achieve the highest latitude to date 82° 45', and from now on we see a new concept creeping into exploration, the attempt on the great geographical prize, the Pole itself.

Now a new route came into use for this attempt to reach the North Pole. We may call it the American route since most of its users came from the United States. Dr. Kane, who had been on a private United States expedition to search for the missing Franklin, in 1853 attempted Smith's Sound, the route which we now know extends through to the polar basin itself. Dr. Hayes (who was with Kane) was a firm believer in the open polar sea theory—that once he could push northward past confining lands he would meet open water. He attempted this channel in 1860 but was unable to penetrate appreciably further than Kane. Eleven years later, C. F. Hall on his third and last expedition to the Arctic with the vessel *Polaris* passed Kane's winter quarters and reached the high latitude of 82° 11' in his ship, but the leader died during the winter and the retreat of the expedition is memorable for the drift of eighteen of the party on an ice floe which eventually took them to open water off Labrador to be picked up in April 1873. The next thrust in this area came from a highly organized British expedition with two large vessels, both of which wintered on the Ellesmere Island coast, that of Commander G. F. Nares in the *Alert* in the neighbourhood of Cape Sheridan. Exploration to the north and west was carried out, but the expedition suffered severely from scurvy and was forced to retreat after only one winter season.

Next came another American expedition under Lieutenant
Greely, this time part of the International Polar Year that had
been organized by Lieutenant Weyprecht of Austria. Further
journeys along the Ellesmere and Greenland coasts and out
into the polar basin were made, but the relief of this expedition

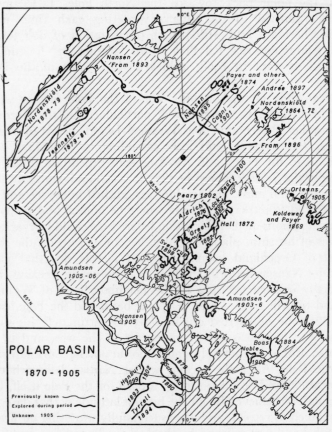

Fig. 13.

was bungled and Greely was forced to make a disastrous
retreat, losing most of his men by starvation in emergency
winter quarters. In 1898 two important expeditions reached
the area, both with objectives of trying to sail around the north
coast of Greenland, and that of Peary to attempt the Pole itself.
Each of them spent three winters in the Arctic; the expedition

of Sverdrup, encountering exceptionally bad ice, was diverted towards the west and carried out important exploration of new islands in the Canadian archipelago. Peary, as we saw before, reached the northern tip of Greenland and established a new high latitude record for the American side in an attempt to cross the polar pack towards the North Pole. Twice more Peary returned to the attack, wintering each time near Cape Sheridan, and with superb organization of dog teams and equipment reached first of all latitude 87° 6′ and in his last attempt in 1908, achieved the region of the Pole itself.

Meanwhile on the opposite side of the Pole further work had been done. It was believed, particularly by the German geographer Petermann, that Wrangel Island, heard of in the 1820s, was a great land mass extending to Greenland and perhaps to the Pole itself. An American expedition under de Long in the *Jeanette* set out in 1879 to reach and winter on this supposed land mass, but his ship was crushed in the ice and he was forced to retreat to Siberia where he himself and many of his companions died of starvation before help could be reached. Relics of his ship, plainly identifiable, turned up on the west coast of Greenland years later, and it was this that gave Fridtjof Nansen his brilliant idea of deliberately freezing in a specially constructed ship in the neighbourhood of Wrangel Island to drift right across the polar basin and the Pole itself. This scheme he carried out in 1893. Unfortunately his stout vessel the *Fram* was frozen in too far to the west and in its erratic drift was obviously going too far to the Eurasian side of the Pole. After the second winter Nansen left with one companion and dog team to try a dash for the Pole itself, but although he achieved by far the highest latitude of that date, he was forced to retreat, and after successfully wintering on Franz Joseph Land was relieved by the Jackson Expedition in 1896. Within days of his triumphant return to Norway, the *Fram* under Sverdrup, who later was to take it to the Canadian archipelago, was also released from the ice near Spitsbergen and returned to Norway. Nansen's record did not remain for long, for that world-wide traveller the Duke of Abruzzi organized an expedition based on Franz Josef Land where successful detailed exploration was carried out, and one of his men, Captain

Cagni, by dog team over the ice, came twenty miles closer to the Pole than had Nansen six years before.

Back on the Canadian side of the Pole another explorer had a courageous new idea; this was V. Stefansson, who after two earlier expeditions believed that it was possible for skilled

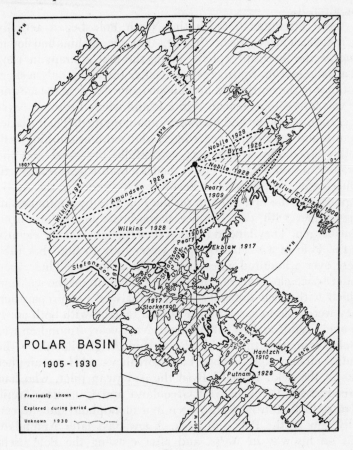

Fig. 14.

hunting white men to survive out on the floating ice of the polar basin and travel long distances completely non-supported. He put this idea into practice on the Canadian Arctic Expedition of 1913-18, travelling for many months on the ice of the Beaufort Sea and in the Canadian archipelago beyond, filling in the last of the few remaining gaps that had been unvisited by Sverdrup. All that could be achieved now by unreinforced vessels, dog teams, and courageous athletic men had been achieved, the next chapter in the story of the exploration of this basin is dependent on the coming of a new technique, that of the aircraft.

Aerial attempts to reach the North Pole began actually several years before the first heavier-than-air machine had flown. Andrée the Swedish explorer made the first attempt in 1897 in a balloon from Spitsbergen, but after travelling only a short distance to the northward his balloon came down on the ice and he was forced to retreat to White Island where for some as yet uncertain reason he and his two companions died. Their diaries were found over thirty years later, and more astonishing still, undeveloped film which was successfully processed and the photographs subsequently published. In both Russia and North America in the 1920s pilots began flying aircraft in the Arctic regions, but the first attempt on the Pole was by Amundsen in 1925 when with two Dornier flying-boats he set out from Spitsbergen. They landed in what they thought was the vicinity of the Pole in a stretch of open water only to find that they were over a hundred miles short of the objective. Their open water space closed in rapidly, forcing them up on the ice from which with great difficulty and several weeks of preparation they were able to carve a runway and take off with both crews in one aircraft and fly safely home. Next year, Amundsen was back again, this time with the airship *Norge* piloted by the Italian airship expert Nobile, but before they could leave another was in the field. Richard Byrd the American pilot, who had already been flying in west Greenland and Canadian Arctic islands, took off from Spitsbergen in a monoplane and successfully flew to the Pole and back. A few days later Amundsen was on his way in *Norge*, and after crossing the Pole itself, flew on with the airship all the way across to the Alaskan coast and finally descended at Teller. Two years later another very important flight, this time not to the Pole itself, was carried out by Wilkins, who flew from Alaska via the tip of the Canadian archipelago and Greenland and again landed at Spitsbergen with scarcely a cupful of fuel remaining in the aircraft's tanks. So by 1928 a map of the polar basin could be prepared which showed yet a large amount of territory, unseen either from the ground or from the air, as blank but cut through by the swathes of the known. There was still a slim hope that land might exist in these blank areas, but in the last few years this has been disproved. The newest era of polar basin exploration began in 1937 when the Russians succeeded in landing no less than four four-engined aircraft equipped with skis in the immediate vicinity of the Pole itself. There they set down equipment for a year for Papanin with three companions. His station drifted on the ice floe for a matter of some seven months, at first close to the Pole itself, and then with gradually increasing speed in the east Greenland current till they were gyrating wildly off the east coast of Greenland in the winter's night and were fortunate to be picked up by a Soviet ice-breaker when they had come as far south as latitude 70°. The Second World War now intervened to curtail such activities, but subsequently both the United States and the Soviet Union have put down several of these drifting stations on the north polar pack. United States ones have usually manned the so-called ice islands, large floating masses of land origin perhaps scores of feet thick, whereas the Soviet scientists have usually relied, as did Papanin, on merely very thick salt-water ice floes. It is from these drifting stations that the soundings of the polar basin have been made, which will be discussed in more detail in a later chapter, but they, together with aircraft flights supporting them and accessory to them, have effectively eliminated those blank areas that still remained on the 1928 map.

HISTORY OF TECHNIQUE

Before leaving the history of Arctic exploration, we must examine what is perhaps the most important aspect, the improvement of technique. This improvement was as uneven as were the steps forward in geographical discovery. It is true that sometimes poorly equipped expeditions have accomplished an amazing amount of work, but on the whole the traveller who has efficient transport, who is comfortable, healthy, unextended, secure in his belief of a safe return will achieve very much more. We will leave discussion of the techniques of transport to a later chapter; here it is only necessary to point out the major changes—from sail through steam to modern ice-breakers—

from man-hauled sleds to dogs to vehicles—and finally the great revolution of air travel, which eliminates the difficulties of the ground flown over but produces new difficulties of its own in landing and taking off. Under the heading of comfort can be included housing, clothing and food. The first obstacle

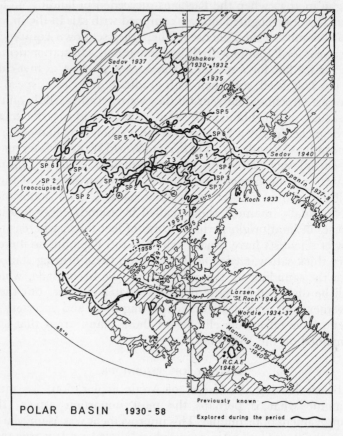

Fig. 15.

to be overcome was the fear of wintering, of being caught in the Arctic regions after the summer season of sea navigation was over. Once the belief in the possibility of wintering was established, the winter quarters tended to be either the ship itself or, say on the shores of Hudson Bay where timber was available, a hut built on the land. It was Parry who advanced the technique of converting the sailing ships of his day into comfortable winter quarters, with elaborate heating arrangements and covering over of various ships' spaces. The advantage of a ship for winter quarters was the availability of considerable stores of fuel, weight being comparatively unimportant. But where fuel is limited, insulation against the winter cold becomes vital, and when extensive journeys began to be made in spring and then in late winter, camping equipment had to be greatly improved. From the single-walled tent we move gradually through to double-walled tents and eventually to the complicated shelter which is almost a hut and to expedition hut bases themselves. But for winter travelling in small parties there is no shelter equivalent in comfort to the Eskimo igloo, and this technique was one which it took white explorers a long time to learn. Hall the American explorer, began using them by wintering with the Eskimo on Baffin Island, but they were used much more by Peary and Rasmussen the greatest exploiters of Eskimo techniques in overland and over pack ice travel. For the less severe temperatures of an ice-cap in summer the modern double tent is extremely convenient, is quicker to erect than an igloo, has the disadvantage of slightly more weight to carry, and is certainly colder when conditions are very severe. The last word in tents came with the shelter provided for Papanin on his north polar drift in 1937. This was in effect a base hut, but one that had to be light enough to be moved if the ice floe on which they were camped began to break. The shelter for four men was made of layers of eiderdown, reindeer skin, tarpaulin, and air-filled rubber cushions, weighed some 350 pounds, and was painted black on the outside to absorb extra heat from the sun. In the Canadian Arctic Dr. John Rae established a base at Repulse Bay in 1846 and constructed there a stone house, the walls of which can still be seen. In this house the ink froze on the table six feet from a blazing fire and continual condensation plagued them during their winter sojourn in it. On returning to the same locality seven years later he wintered his party in igloos. Today wintering parties have tended to reject the ship as winter quarters and establish well-insulated huts or houses on shore. Great advances have been made in recent years in design of these prefabricated huts, easy to erect, well insulated against the cold, able to withstand the blizzards and extreme low temperatures even at the South Pole itself. We have examples of ordinary buildings as erected by the Hudson's Bay Company in Arctic Canada where a comfortable modern house for a family with children can be heated adequately throughout the intense cold of the Arctic winter on only four or five tons of fuel per year.

In clothing, too, immense strides have been made since the early days when garbed in thick wool, underwear and outer garments alike, the polar explorers of the nineteenth century sweated and froze alternately. Now after many trials and tribulations we can use three different types of clothing. The windproof outer garment, a closely woven cotton fabric able to withstand wind and yet breathe moisture. The fur clothing, developed again from the Eskimo and used particularly by Peary and many North American and Russian exploration parties, the warmest of all perhaps for its weight, but needing skill in design and use, particularly for repair. The Eskimo woman is almost irreplaceable for this purpose. And finally the quilted eiderdown clothing as used on most recent Antarctic expeditions and for high altitude mountaineering, a surprisingly modern application when one considers that this has been the Chinese winter clothing system for centuries.

Cooking equipment has also improved over the years. The early travellers were forced to use 'spirits of wine' but the advent of paraffin pressure-cookers, the familiar Primus and other makes, has enormously advanced efficiency in the weight of fuel carried for the number of hot meals produced, and at base huts oil-fired cooking furnaces have replaced Rae's fireplace burning heather.

The provision of suitable rations for an exploration party is a technique which again has improved considerably. Here we have to distinguish between long sled journeys over country where game is completely absent—such as on an ice-cap—and a party based at a shore station or drifting over the ocean where food is available if we have the techniques of finding and obtaining it. In the latter case the ability of living off the land is one which was only slowly developed among white explorers. Once again they had to learn the technique of hunting from their Eskimo teachers. Rae and others in Arctic Canada began by deliberately limiting the supplies they took with them to only a third of what they would require. Other expeditions took native hunters to amend their food supply, but it remained for explorers of the present century to prove that the skilled white man could hunt as successfully as, or perhaps even better than, the Eskimo. The chief exponent of this art was Stefansson who showed that even on the allegedly lifeless polar sea a man as skilled as himself could with his rifle provide the necessary food for existence. Again in Greenland in 1930 the young explorer Watkins proved himself a master of the skill of killing seals from a kayak, and was able in fact to make a boat journey around the southern tip of Greenland carrying fuel almost alone, and relying on his rifle to supply the party with food. But hunting can be a full-time occupation, or certainly full time for certain members of the party; the need for living off the country detracts from the time available for proper scientific work and in fact is scarcely permissible with the present Game Laws in many parts of the Arctic regions.

For sled journeys the scientific development of concentrated rations has now been brought to a fine pitch. In 1827 Parry attempted his boat haul towards the North Pole with a ration of twenty ounces of solids and a gill of rum per day. M'Clintock thirty years later had developed an excellent sledding ration of about two and a quarter pounds per man per day and this has been further reduced during this century to a sledding ration worked out by V. E. (now Sir Vivian) Fuchs, for the Falkland Islands Dependencies Survey, where twenty-seven and a half ounces of food per man/day provides a caloric value of over four thousand. This is perhaps on the low side for maintaining weight indefinitely under conditions of considerable energy output and cold, but it suffices for the types of journey undertaken. An example of an unnecessary rich ration was that taken by Papanin to the Pole, where over six thousand calories were provided, and after a short time the explorers became satiated with caviare.

It is essential to include in rations not only sufficient energy but also some of the trace elements and vitamins to maintain health. Scurvy has been the scourge of polar exploration from its earliest time until a few decades ago. We now know that this is a deficiency disease caused by a lack of ascorbic acid (Vitamin C) in the food, and today we have ascorbic acid pills which can be taken regularly and absence in the diet neglected. Man cannot synthesize Vitamin C chemically as can rats and most other animals including dogs, nor can he store much. He has to have it daily—about ten milligrammes of it. It is present in large quantities in certain fruits and vegetables and in lesser quantities in meat, particularly in the liver and internal organs, but it is destroyed in part or completely by heating, so the undercooking of meat is a vital factor.

Because scurvy occurred in besieged towns or on long sea voyages and in the polar regions, for many years it was believed to be infectious and to be due to starvation or poverty, lack of sunlight, exercise or warmth (and this despite the fact that it had been rampant on long tropical voyages). The discovery of the anti-scorbutic powers of fresh lemon juice was made by a Royal Navy surgeon in 1753, and fifty years later its use was made compulsory in the British Navy. Most of the Admiralty North-West Passage expeditions were free of the scourge and on their longer sledge-hauling trips a fair amount of game was killed and eaten. One still notes, though, the belief in the importance of fresh air and exercise together with such habits as those of Parry in growing cress in his cabin. But in 1860 West Indian limes were substituted for lemons in the Navy, fruits which were much less potent in their Vitamin C content (the lemons had also been known as limes, hence the mistake and also the Americans' opprobrious name for the British sailor—limey). The official daily dose now became far too little for maintenance of Vitamin C level, and in many expeditions the ration of other fruits and vegetables failed to bring the total up to the necessary value. The outstanding failure was Nares' Royal Navy Expedition of 1875–6, which was curtailed and wrecked by scurvy. Yet all along, Vitamin C was available in fresh meat, this is the Eskimo source of it, though his diet is sometimes deficient but the level frequently enough renewed. The Eskimo met with by travellers of the nineteenth century had never eaten fruit or vegetables except the occasional berries in summer or undigested material from a caribou's stomach, but the white man tended to reject the more obscure 'delicacies' in meat that are the richest anti-scorbutic source. So the sorry history runs with the evidence plain now to see. In 1630 a shipwrecked party of English sailors in Spitsbergen cheerfully survived a year on their single resource—ammunition to kill game. In 1633 a Dutch party well supplied with what seemed all the necessary provisions for a planned winter on Jan Mayen Island were all dead by May. Often we hear of the best financed and equipped groups suffering from scurvy, the poorer ones who had to supplement their rations with a rifle escaping. Scott's first Antarctic party suffered from the disease (by this time lime juice had fallen into disfavour and the whole subject was chaotic). Shackleton's 1907–9 expedition, relying far more on seal meat and dried milk, escaped. Those who deliberately accepted Eskimo methods were free—those who require quantities of meat for dogs will always get by themselves, and as it is believed that Vitamin C is lost from the body by sweat, so once again the easier traveller will score.

As far as security goes the great advance has been the invention of the radio, by means of which an expedition in trouble can request aid and by which various groups on the same expedition can maintain contact and discover changes of plan. One can imagine what might have happened to the Franklin expedition had they been able to reveal their position and the fact that they were inextricably beset. Again one compares the radio communications between Fuchs and Hillary across the South Pole with the impossibility of Shackleton doing likewise when he, having planned a similar transantarctic journey, was unable to acquaint his Ross Sea support party with the fact that his vessel had been crushed and he was unable to start. The first recorded rescue attributable to a radio distress signal was that of Nobile in 1928 when his airship force-landed on the polar pack and his faint distress signals were picked up by a Russian amateur in Archangel who directed the search to the right locality. But radio, despite its great advantages, can at times be an irritation to an expedition leader. When Courtauld was alone on the Greenland ice-cap and the news reached Europe that the first attempt to relieve him had failed, frantic air preparations were made to do the job that was eventually, and could have always been, done on the spot by the expedition itself.

Scientific advance, or more particularly the advance in the amount of scientific work achieved on expeditions, has continued to progress uniformly. In particular, the technique of mapping and surveying has taken considerable strides forward. In early days many of the surveys were done from the decks of exploring ships by simple sextant means, and traverses of coast-lines by sled-wheels and compass direction made during spring sledding journeys. Such improvements to a map were still possible as recently as the thirties of this century in places like the Canadian Arctic, but the new technique of aerial photography has so revolutionized map-making that the

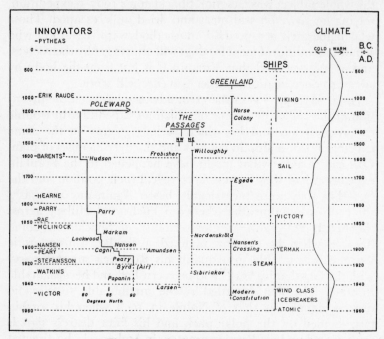

Fig. 16. Arctic Exploration Diagram.

primitive surveys of earlier times can no longer make any valid contribution. Ground control, however, is still required to tie in aerial photography correctly with the latitude and longitude. An example where the results have not been achieved was on the American 'High Jump' Expedition of 1946–7 in the Antarctic, where a great deal of aerial photography cannot yet be used owing to the absence of proper ground controls.

With the improvement of technique, the ever-growing complication of machines, aircraft, vehicles, scientific research using expensive apparatus, has enormously increased the cost of polar exploration. This has caused a change in the character of expedition organization. It is still possible for groups of eager young men, not too well financed, to do a limited amount of useful work, but the major achievements of today must almost certainly be backed by government funds or at any rate the monies from great industrial concerns. The amateur patron has almost ceased to exist and in fact the amateur attitude in exploration so well developed by British parties in the past, is rapidly becoming an outmoded possibility. The supreme example of the amateur explorer is perhaps the Duke of Abruzzi who was in the fortunate position of being able to finance large-scale parties, and to visit any place in the world which he felt inclined.

So have techniques advanced and certain great names have stood out through the record as the originators of the forward steps. Among these are Parry for his wintering techniques and the beginnings of spring sled journeys; M'Clintock for the development to its maximum possibility of man-hauling spring sled parties; Peary for his introduction of Eskimo methods, those of dog driving and igloo building; Rae and Stefansson for the further Eskimo skills of living off the land; Nansen and Papanin for the new idea of drifting in or on the polar ice to explore the frozen ocean; Byrd and Amundsen for the development of flying, and Byrd again and Victor for the use of vehicles in both Arctic and Antarctic ice-cap travel. If one was to select one man who epitomizes most if not all of these advances in techniques it would be Norwegian explorer Amundsen, who single-mindedly devoted his entire life and training to polar exploration. His supreme achievements were his dog team journey to the South Pole, his navigation of the North-West Passage, his drifting expedition north of Siberia, and the pioneering of flight by flying-boat and airship. His brief active life-span of some thirty years ended on the way to rescue his former companion and he was mourned by Norway and the world.

FURTHER READING

Bertram, G. C. L., *Arctic and Antarctic: the Technique of Polar Travel*, Cambridge, 1939.
Croft, Andrew, *Polar Exploration*, London, 1947.
Kirwan, L. P., *The White Road*, London, 1959.
Mirsky, Jeannette, *To the North*, New York, 1934.
Sverdrup, H. U., 'Roald Amundsen', *Arctic*, 12, 1959, pp. 221–35.

Chapter 3

THE METEOROLOGY AND CLIMATE OF THE ARCTIC

In the first chapter of this book there was some discussion on the limits which may be put to the Arctic regions. Climate entered very considerably into this discussion because, of all the factors in the polar region, it is the climate that most directly affects man's activities. The meteorological processes are the same as those in temperate latitudes, the difference is merely one of degree. Compared to air of other latitudes Arctic air is, of course, colder, contains more ozone and probably slightly less carbon dioxide. It is extremely dry on the absolute scale and very noticeably free from impurities. The low absolute humidity of the air is a direct function of the low temperature, since at the January mean temperature in the vicinity of the North Pole the saturation vapour pressure is only about a tenth of a millibar. The freedom from impurities, such as desert dust, industrial soot and forest fire smoke, results in extreme clarity of the Arctic air where visibilities extend over enormous distances and the judgement of distance becomes extremely difficult to those accustomed to more hazy temperate latitude air. It is only in recent decades that soundings have been made far up into the atmosphere in the high latitudes, and from these results it has become known that the tropopause, the boundary between the troposphere in which temperature decreases with elevation and the stratosphere where the temperature is relatively constant, is much lower in the polar regions than in equatorial latitudes—eight to nine kilometres as opposed to approximately double this height. Thus, whereas the lowest surface temperatures on the earth are in the polar regions, the lowest mean atmospheric temperature is at the height of seventeen kilometres above sea-level near the equator, where the mean temperature is around $-100°$ F. A temperature inversion where there is a rise in temperature with altitude is in fact a general rule in the Arctic regions, particularly so in the winter. Then the radiating snow surface loses heat rapidly and the air in contact with it cools much faster than air aloft. In summer the cold source is due to the melting of snow and ice while air aloft is heated by solar radiation. In studies by Belmont on two years' soundings at ice island T3, the inversion began directly at the surface on 84 per cent. of occasions in winter (late September–April). On 81 per cent. of occasions in summer a lower normal layer 450–600 metres thick (1,500–2,000 feet) was succeeded aloft by a 200–300-metre thick inversion (650–1,000 feet). The Arctic temperature inversion is normally present when clear and calm conditions prevail, which are frequent in winter time, but is destroyed by strong winds and by cloudy skies when there is a reverse radiation from the cloud cover. The inversion layer also acts as a reflector of sound waves as does the surface of hard snow or ice and therefore under clear calm conditions in the Arctic regions audibility is vastly increased as well as visibility. The temperature inversion also results in an optical phenomenon often seen in the Arctic particularly in summer—the mirage—when intense refraction raises objects above the observer's natural horizon and often distorts them vertically so that low lying coasts appear to be steeply cliffed. In the history of polar exploration several mistakes in identification have perhaps been due to the mirage, such as Sir John Ross's mountains blocking Lancaster Sound and Peary's twice-sighted Crockerland which turned out to be mythical and was probably exceptional refraction of an ice island.

AIR MASSES

Hare has described the polar regions as the world's energy sinks, or heat deficit areas, and defines the Arctic atmosphere as 'the hemispheric cap of low energy, sluggish circulation, lying north of the main course of the planetary westerlies'. The boundary of this atmosphere is, of course, a variable one depending on the vigour of the westerlies. Sometimes the Arctic atmosphere extends far south to cover eastern Canada or Siberia. An air mass, as defined meteorologically is 'a large body of air whose physical properties, temperature, humidity, etc., are more or less uniform in a horizontal direction'. In the

E

polar regions air masses tend to be larger, more stable and slower moving than in temperate or tropical latitudes. Hence despite the comparative lack of stations or the large distances between them, forecasting is made relatively simple and can, in fact, be considerably more accurate than where air mass movements and interplays are frequent. In the North Polar regions the typical air masses have been grouped into: (1) Arctic; (2) polar-continental; (3) polar-maritime. The Arctic air mass is developed over the central portion of the region and in winter is characterized by extreme low temperatures and low absolute humidity. At altitude the absolute humidity is extremely low, and as a result high clouds are practically absent over the central Arctic in winter. In winter, polar-continental air, developed over the snow-covered northern large land masses, is almost indistinguishable from the Arctic air developed over the frozen sea. In summer there is more excuse for separating Arctic air from polar-continental. Over the Arctic pack the temperature is controlled by the thawing of snow and ice to between 32° and 35° F. The atmosphere in contact with it, therefore, is cold and damp with sea fog, stratus cloud and drizzle. Inland, however, over the warm continent quite vigorous convection develops, a contrast to the stability of winter Arctic air, and skies tend to be clear with cumulus cloud. Thunder, however, is very rare; yet there is a record of a thunderstorm at SP6 (Russian drifting station) in July 1957 when half an inch of rain fell.

The North Polar regions are frequently invaded or occupied by air masses of maritime origin developed over the open waters of the North Atlantic or the North Pacific. The influence of maritime air from the Pacific is only felt in northern Alaska and in the Mackenzie district; even here its penetration is very rare in winter but it can produce very sudden rises of temperature, having crossed high mountain belts and producing therefore a föhn or chinook effect. In summer it is invading Pacific air that produces occasional very high temperatures in the Yukon and Mackenzie valleys, but on the coast cool, moist and foggy conditions result. From the North Atlantic maritime polar air penetrates to Greenland, southern Baffin Island, and Hudson Strait and far east into the Eurasian Arctic. This air is moist and unstable. In winter it is relatively warm and on reaching the Arctic lands carries this warmth with thick clouds far inland, causing drizzle or snow showers. In summer as it passes over the cold waters of the Arctic coasts it becomes completely saturated with stratus cloud and much fog. Inland, however, it once more becomes unstable and produces cumulus cloud and showers.

At the boundary between these different kinds of air masses we have fronts or frontal zones, where there is frequently an abrupt transition in wind, humidity and temperature. The mean position of these fronts is shown on the maps of Figs. 17 and 18. On them cyclones tend to develop and from this we can trace the average pressure patterns of summer and winter, the low-pressure areas being those of main cyclonic development.

Nevertheless it is true to say that throughout the year the major part of the North Polar region has fewer cyclones and more anticyclones than do latitudes further to the south, the exceptional areas being the coasts of the North Atlantic and extreme North Pacific. In winter anticyclones are usual over the North Polar basin with a maximum frequency off the northern coast of Alaska. Anticyclones are also frequent over the polar basin itself in summer. The maps, Figs. 19 and 20, show the mean pressure pattern in the North Polar regions in winter and in summer. In winter there is an average belt of high pressure extending from Siberia across the north of Alaska to the Yukon and Mackenzie region, at each end of which are developed anticyclones, with the Siberian one much the stronger. There is an average low-pressure region over the Aleutians and the Gulf of Alaska and a larger, usually deeper one, centred between Iceland and Greenland which extends from eastern Canada to Svalbard. From this system of average pressure eastern Siberia, Arctic Alaska, and the Mackenzie delta tend to have variable light winds, but much of the rest of the Arctic is affected by the Greenland–Iceland low which yields strong north-westerlies over the Canadian area, easterlies in Svalbard and south-westerlies in Europe. In spring there is a general decline in the intensity of both the high- and the low-pressure areas. The highest pressure has moved forward from Siberia to Alaska so that the Canadian archipelago and northern Greenland enjoys at this time its best weather. In summer a different picture is established. The pressure gradient is much

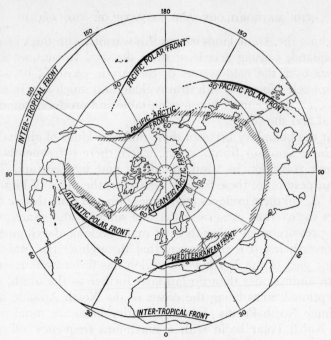

Fig. 17. Principal Frontal Zones in Winter.

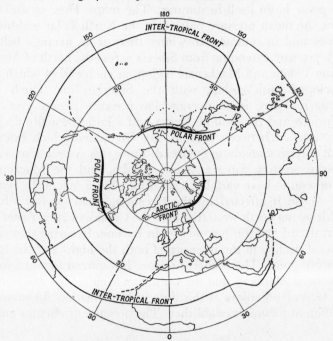

Fig. 18. Principal Frontal Zones in Summer.

less, since in summer there is the least contrast in temperature between the polar and the temperate zones. A weak high extends over the whole Arctic basin and the low-pressure area in the North Atlantic has migrated westward to the region of Hudson Strait. The autumn season sees a reversing tendency, the low-pressure areas moving back towards their winter locations and intensifying and the high-pressure area over eastern Siberia beginning once more to develop. It should be pointed out that these mean sea-level pressure maps are comparatively meaningless as far as the high land mass of Greenland is concerned, where, with its ice-cap, there is always a tremendous temperature differential between the interior and the coast. Greenland, therefore, is itself a cold air mass source and wind directions here are often controlled by entirely local and Greenlandic conditions.

The climate of Greenland can only be discussed as the climate of the ice-cap and the climate of the settled coasts. Within the latter there is a division, necessarily unsharp, between the south-west coast which is maritime sub-Arctic in character and the remainder which becomes drier and more Arctic as one progresses further north. Some details on the peculiarities of the south-west corner are given in Chapter 14. The changes in precipitation and mean annual temperature on the coasts are shown in the following table:

West Coast			East Coast		
Narssarssuaq	+2·0° C.				
Ivigtut	+0·6	120 cm.			
Godthaab	−1·0	60	Angmagssalik	−1·0° C.	90 cm.
Jakobshavn	−5·0	23	Scoresbysund	−8·0	30
Upernavik	−8·0	23	Myggbukta	−10·0	8
Thule	−12·0	8	Danmarkshavn	−12·0	16
			Nord	−17·0	5

Temperatures have been somewhat adjusted for recent warming trends.

On the ice-cap mean annual temperatures have been determined by borings to below the level where annual changes occur. The great bulk of the ice-cap has a mean temperature of below −18° C. (zero Fahrenheit) and in its highest part, centred around latitude 75°, this falls to about −32° C. (−25° F.).

Less is known about ice-cap precipitation but recent work by Diamond has shown that it is heaviest (forty to sixty

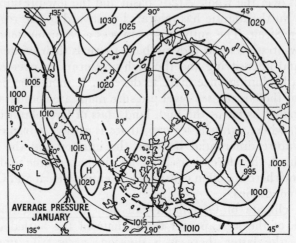

Fig. 19. Mean Surface Pressure in January (millibars).

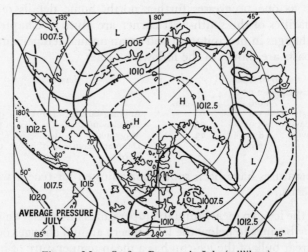

Fig. 20. Mean Surface Pressure in July (millibars).

centimetres water equivalent) to the west of the crest between latitudes 66° and 76° N. South of 66° N. precipitation is probably heavier to the east of the crest and in this area is probably as high. In the far north precipitation falls off sharply and north of 78° is generally less than ten centimetres of water.

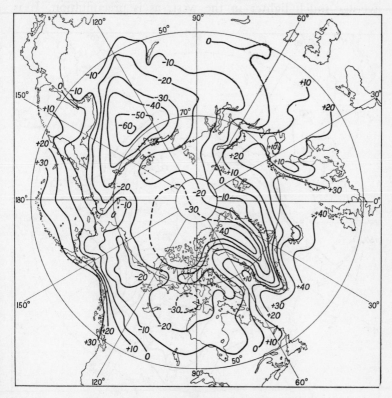

Fig. 21. Mean Air Temperature, January (° F.).

NORTH AMERICA

The prevailing low-pressure system that brings high precipitation to southern Greenland has a major role in the climate of Arctic North America. A less prominent role is played by the Aleutian low-pressure area due to the blocking effect, particularly in winter, of the western Cordillera. In contrast to these areas the polar basin itself is an area of relatively high pressure at the surface but in the upper air above ten thousand feet this is replaced by a relatively low-pressure area and around it the circumpolar westerly winds circulate continuously.

As a result of the north-west Atlantic low the eastern parts of North America tend to have a north or north-west wind system—often strong and persistent in winter. Winds are on average much lighter in the west, as is precipitation. It is

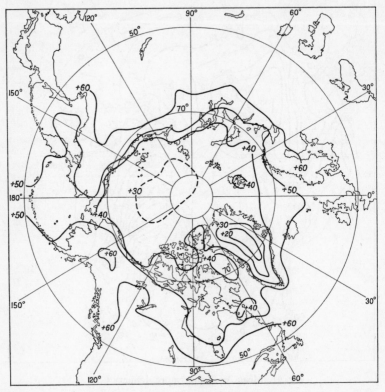

Fig. 22. Mean Air Temperature, July (° F.).

possible therefore to divide the North American Arctic into a stormy east and a 'Pacific' west, though long quiet spells are by no means infrequent in the east or blizzards in the west.

Mean temperatures in northern North America are shown on the maps (Figs. 21 and 22) for January and July, normally the coldest and warmest months. The coldest area lies over the northern rank of Canadian islands but a large gulf of low temperature extends southwards over Keewatin and another occupies the lower Mackenzie and interior northern Alaska. Near-by open water and occasional incursions of Atlantic air keep the coasts of Labrador and Baffin Island warmer. Hudson Bay, however, 95 per cent. ice-covered by the new year, has little warming effect. The fact of its near complete ice cover was first deduced from meteorological data when it was seen that the milder autumn temperature and heavy snowfall on its eastern shore ceased abruptly after the beginning of January. The Bering Sea has an even greater ameliorating effect on the western coasts of Alaska where mean January temperatures are higher than – 10° F. until the 70th parallel is passed.

Extreme temperatures are seldom below – 60° F., a figure often attained in the northern forest belt. However, neither extremes nor monthly means are indicators except to the scientific analyst of the character of American Arctic climate. Day upon short day of cloudless – 40° weather, with perhaps a ten miles per hour wind snaking ground drifted snow, will be succeeded by a one-, two-, or three-day blow when temperatures may rise 20° or 40° and the visibility be cut to a few yards. The changes are abrupt and the stable periods of weather average perhaps six days in length.

The summer temperature pattern shows clearly the division between east and west parts of the continent. Only a coastal strip in Alaska and western Canada is truly Arctic, but in the east the large cold-water areas keep the temperatures uniformly low except in the interior of the largest islands whence at present data are very scarce. Latitude plays a minor role and July temperature at Resolution Island at the mouth of Hudson Strait is normally lower than on the coasts of Ellesmere Island.

In the American Arctic only the eastern Hudson Strait area has a precipitation of any size as is seen in the map (Fig. 23). Most of the rest of the area has less than ten inches annually and in the extreme north five inches or less. Most of this is of course in the form of snowfall with a maximum in autumn and another often in April. Only at the latter season is the snow 'soft', a maximum snow cover depth is then obtained and cross-country travel can become laborious: at other seasons neither skis nor snowshoes are useful in the Arctic; the hard-packed wind-blown snow cover is an excellent walking surface.

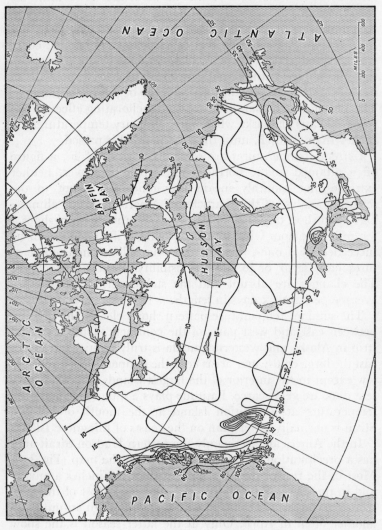

Fig. 23. Precipitation in Canada: isohyets in inches.

SIBERIA

Like North America the Soviet Arctic has regions of storminess and comparative quiet. The stormy province is the westernmost—the shores and islands of the Barents and Kara seas.

Atlantic influences, both the warm water drift and Atlantic polar-maritime air prevail here resulting in great variability in weather and higher mean winter temperatures than those further east. In the extreme west (Kola region) January temperatures average 20° F., and even far northerly Franz Josef Land has its coldest month mean only slightly below 0° F. Here the variability of the temperature (day to day means) averages 9° F.—nearly twice that of say Montreal or Leningrad indicating the changeable winter weather due to cyclonic activity. The daily temperature range is, however, slight. The maritime influence is also shown in the fact that usually February and often even March is the coldest month and precipitation is much higher than in regions of the Soviet Arctic further east.

When cyclones penetrate into these areas in vigorous form the coasts of Novaya Zemlya suffer from the 'bora'—strong winds of sixty to seventy miles per hour. On the western (Barents Sea) shore a strong easterly 'bora' results when high-pressure over the Kara Sea coincides with a vigorous depression in the southern Barents Sea. The 'bora' is rarer on the east coast and blows from the north-west when the high- and low-pressure systems are reversed. In each case the winds pass over the island picking up great quantities of drifting snow.

In spring there is a general improvement in cloud cover especially during the early part of the season but the average temperatures are below freezing and thaw occurs only in May. The cyclonic activity continues to decrease during the summer and this season sees very uniform conditions prevailing along the whole Soviet Arctic strip—much cloudiness and fog (twenty-five days in July and August), little daily amplitude in temperature which is kept low by the presence of melting ice and prevailing northerly winds. A shift of wind to the south will for instance lift the temperature at Yugor Shar some 20° F. but with this wind come the thickest advection fogs. Direct radiation from the sun, though tempered by the cloud cover, is still remarkably high (400 Cal./sq. cm.) only slightly less than mid-summer radiation in the Crimea.

Although September is a warmer month than June, in the second half of the month the mean temperature in the western areas falls below freezing and a dark and brief autumn sets in with only occasional thaws in October and November.

LAPTEV AND EASTERN SIBERIAN SEA REGION

In winter this region has a completely continental climate with little cyclonic activity, cloud or precipitation and low January and February temperatures in the range of −20° to −40° F. These, however, are still well above the temperatures experienced inland at this season in the enclosed valleys of Yakutia and southerly winds tend to drop the temperature 10° compared to those off the sea where ocean warmth is perceptible even through the ice cover. Winds are generally low but around the Lena delta are higher: occasional föhns can occur when Pacific air comes in from the south-east over the Kolyma lowlands.

Spring comes sooner than in the west with May temperatures warmer than those of the Barents and Kara seas and up to ten thawing days occurring on the average along the coast. Summer sees the uniform foggy conditions established that prevail elsewhere; but June is warmer than September and with prevailing northerly winds freezing temperatures can occur at any time. Nevertheless, absolute maxima in the seventies are recorded from the coast, and in the high sixties on the islands. More than half the year's precipitation occurs in the three summer months with one and a half to two inches in June along the coasts.

In September the temperature falls slowly due to open water conditions but in the next two months the drop is steep. Nevertheless, in November northern Yakutia is already colder than the New Siberian Islands.

CHUKHOT SEA

Further east Pacific influences begin to affect the Siberian Arctic and the climate becomes more comparable with neighbouring Alaska. The winter is warmer, cloudier and windier than the central Soviet Arctic as cyclonic activity develops on the Arctic front over the Bering and Okhotsk seas. Hence prevailing winds are north to north-east carrying cold Arctic air. Spring sees a similar temperature régime to that of the Kara Sea and as the cyclonic activity moves north fog and cloud increase. In summer maritime features increase but with prevailing south-east winds from the Bering Sea temperatures are lower than those farther west. Warm air from southern Siberia comes in but rarely and contributes strongly to the general fogginess when it does.

It is in this section of the Siberian Arctic that ice lingers close off shore the longest in summer and hence it is the most awkward portion of the North-East Passage for navigation. The late summer is best, as in autumn temperatures fall more slowly than in the Laptev Sea. Nevertheless, freezing-point is crossed two to three weeks earlier than in the Kara Sea area and autumn is bleak and stormy on Asia's eastern tip.

SPECIAL FEATURES

The duration and depth of snow cover are vital factors in man's transportation activities and these are discussed in Chapter 8. Some other elements of the Arctic climate, however, have very sensible and direct effects on human activities. As was pointed out at the beginning of the book one of the most distinguishing characteristics of the polar regions is wind-chill. It is a much better indicator of cooling conditions for men, houses and vehicles than temperature alone.

The original field research on a formula for wind-chill was done by Siple and Passell in the Antarctic and despite criticism and Siple's own doubts on the correctness of his result, it has received wide acceptance and in the present author's opinion is adequate for complete adoption. No formula can really cover the cooling capacity of men and inanimate objects, and wind and temperature are not the only parameters that are sensible. Solar radiation and humidity also contribute but cannot reasonably be worked into any simple formula. It should be noted that on or above the Arctic Circle in midwinter any temperature difference between sun and shade is purely psychological and people who talk about humidity with below-zero temperatures cannot know how little water vapour such air can hold.

Siple's formula reads that loss $= (33 - T)(10\cdot45 + 10\sqrt{v} - v)$ where T is the temperature in degrees centigrade and v the wind speed in metres per second and the nomogram shown in Fig. 24 is a simple way of reading off wind-chill from temperature and wind speed in metric and English-speaking units.

From this it will be seen that at a temperature of $+10°$ F. and forty-five miles per hour wind the wind-chill is 1,600, as sensibly bitter as $-35°$ with only five miles per hour wind speed. The map of Canada prepared by Thomas and Boyd from monthly mean data up to 1950 shows the January mean

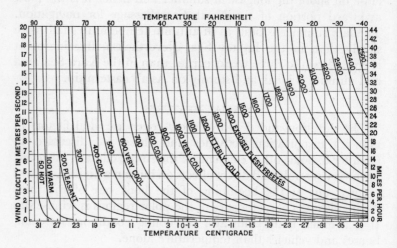

Fig. 24. Wind-chill Nomogram.

wind-chill of this figure 1,600 embracing all Arctic Canada as well as some sub-Arctic northern Manitoba where, however, the trees would noticeably break the wind. In contrast the Yukon and interior Alaska where violently low temperatures may prevail has, due to its comparative calm, much lower wind-chill values. Winnipeg's January wind-chill is greater than that of Dawson City as bus catchers on Portage Avenue probably realize.

The windiness of the eastern Canadian Arctic is shown by the 1,900 wind-chill isopleth enclosing Baker Lake (1,980) in Keewatin district. Nowhere in the remainder of the Arctic have we as yet found such high monthly wind-chill. In Siberia

at least one station, Ostrov Sagastyr on the Lena delta, has a
January mean wind-chill of 1,900 and from here to beyond
Cape Chelyuskin figures average 1,800 or more, but wind-
chill values fall off rapidly inland and Franz Joseph island
stations are in the 1,450–1,700 range.

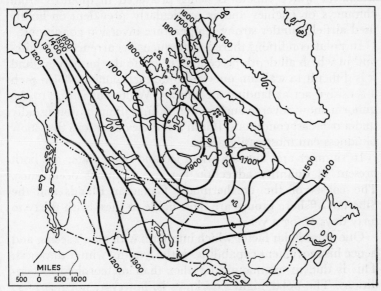

Fig. 25. Mean Wind-chill Factor, January.

VISIBILITY HINDRANCES

Although the polar region's clear air can provide the maximum possible visibility, meteorological conditions can cut it
to a minimum also. In the cold, dry conditions of the polar
winter the snow surface crystals, even when not freshly fallen,
are easily moved. A wind of about twelve miles per hour
(5 m./sec.) will start ground drift and as the wind speed increases the air will be filled with flying snow particles up to
a height of scores of feet with visibility cut to a matter of
yards.

Under such conditions aircraft landings and take-offs become
inhibited, dogs will not head into the wind, and even the next-
door house or the weather instruments screen may vanish.
The experienced Arctic man armed with a snow knife so that

he can build a shelter where he finds himself is never 'lost'—only the house is 'lost'.

Blowing snow can occur on up to a hundred days in the year in the areas of greatest wind. In calm conditions with a very low thermometer ice fog is the chief visibility hazard. This occurs whenever water vapour is being produced in quantity from chimneys or engines and is particularly prevalent on highly used airfields under strong temperature inversion conditions.

In polar conditions there is a frequent occurrence of 'white-out' in which all depth perception is lost to the human eye and it is difficult to walk on uneven ground let alone perform such a sensitive act as landing an aircraft. White-out is due to the uniform snow-covered surface and diffuse illumination usually under overcast conditions. It is in just these conditions that snow blindness can most easily occur.

In summer and autumn when ice and open water are both present in quantity advection fog is a frequent occurrence. The coasts of the northernmost Canadian islands and the Siberian offshore groups are most liable to these with thirty to forty days of fog a year.

One more Polar factor which interferes with man's seeing and hence his movement capabilities is the lengthy winter darkness. This is due to astronomical rather than meteorological conditions. The polar night's darkness is, however, not nearly so complete as many temperate dwellers believe. Civil twilight, during which for all practical purposes illumination is as good as when the sun is up, is defined as lasting until the sun is more than 6° below the horizon. There is still some adequate twilight therefore in latitude $72\frac{1}{2}°$ on the shortest day. A snow-covered surface is a very perfect reflector of any faint illumination and it is a fortunate astronomical rule that when the sun is lowest the opposed full moon is highest in the sky. And at the Pole the moon is continuously above the horizon for two weeks at a time. Even half moonlight on snow yields illumination sufficient for many hunting and travelling activities.

A treatment of the climate of the Arctic would not be complete without mention of recent trends of warming. During this century, at least up to the 1940s, the winter mean temperature has risen 8° C. in Svalbard, 4° C. in southern Greenland. The pack-ice area in the Greenland Sea has been reduced by 20 per cent. and since 1929 the Kara Sea has been always ice free in September. In the U.S.S.R. permafrost has been retreating northward at the rate of at least one kilometre a year.

The areas affected are not only those under the influence of Atlantic water, since similar changes have been noted in the Bering Strait region. Nevertheless, it is the North Atlantic area that has shown the most startling changes and the argument still continues as to whether the heat inflow is oceanic or meteorological.

The results have been, however, to make navigation seasons much longer, to increase the northern fisheries and in Greenland to change the whole pattern of life for the inhabitants. It would be disastrous therefore if the trend was reversed as some recent analysis tends to show. The Arctic is not so inhospitable as it was in the days of Franklin. But it is still very definitely Arctic.

FURTHER READING

Borisov, A. A., *Klimaty S.S.S.R.*, Moscow, 1959 (in Russian).
Dorsey, H. G., 'Arctic Meteorology', in *Compendium of Meteorology*, Amer. Met. Soc., Boston, 1951.
Petterssen, S., W. C. Jacobs, and B. C. Haynes, *Meteorology of the Arctic*, U.S. Navy, Washington, 1956.
Siple, P. A., and C. F. Passell, 'Measurement of . . . Cooling', *Amer. Phil. Soc. Proc.*, 89 (1945), p. 177.
Thomas, M. K., and D. W. Boyd, 'Wind-chill in Northern Canada', *Can. Geographer*, No. 10, 1957.

Chapter 4

LANDFORMS OF THE ARCTIC

THE study of the physical processes of the land surface in the Arctic is both helped and hindered by two main factors. We can see, particularly from the air, the ground pattern in a way impossible elsewhere, except in deserts, because of the lack of tree growth and of modifications by agricultural man. This is like lighting the laboratory. But we must remember that for a great part of the year the snow cover has a reverse, dulling, effect—obscuring outlines, particularly the shorelines, but again in springtime often revealing microrelief by the surviving drift pattern.

The three great controls on Arctic landforms are glaciation both present and past, permafrost, and the presence of ice and snow on land and water, these last producing surfaces that must be considered as landforms even though they may be temporary ones.

With massive land ice and its surfaces we will be concerned in more detail when considering Greenland and Antarctica: sea-ice is dealt with in the next chapter. One must stress, however, that for by far the greater part of the year the materials immediately underfoot on land, lake and river, are ice and snow. The snow blanket is very variable in thickness and texture; it piles up in the hollows and blows clear of the ridges: it may be soft in well vegetated and sheltered areas, iron-hard and fluted into yard-high *skavler* in exposed localities.

As was seen in the chapter on climate, Arctic snow has seldom a chance to retain a density lower than 0·3 except under calm conditions of spring snowfall and among taller vegetation such as long grasses of the *Poa* family and in dwarf willow and birch thickets. Elsewhere the wind takes charge. As a result snow forms are very similar to sand forms, ridges, dunes and the crescentic *barchans*, but a major difference from sand is the packing and cementing property of snow—once initially

66

emplaced by the wind it tends to resist further shifting; thus the features are smaller and more stable than those of the sand desert. Wind borne snow can erode its stabilizing forms, hence the windward vertical or overhanging faces of the *skavler* where erosion is strongest due to the heaviest load at the lowest point of the drift.

The snow cover of least thickness will be found on the tops of elevations and on steeper windward slopes. The greatest accumulations are in depressions and on leeward slopes. On flat plains only will the average snowfall be found and sometimes it is impossible to know if one is standing on tundra or lake without digging down to discover herbage or ice.

The presence of this winter-long stored precipitation means a powerful run-off in spring, waterlogging much of the ground and causing great changes in the volume of rivers—the impassable torrent of June may be a dry bed in September.

The break-up of the ice surfaces on lakes (as with the sea) is characterized by early melting around the shores while firm thick ice still remains in the centre. The small lakes are first to clear (and to refreeze in autumn). A spring air photograph of the tundra will show some lakes completely ice free, other larger ones with only a fringing water moat. Thus it is impossible to draw maps of mean equal dates of break-up (*see Plate 4*).

Both sea- and lake-ice exercise considerable influence on their shores. *Ice-shove* ridges up to four or five feet high are frequently found where the fetch of wind allows a powerful onshore movement of floating ice to be applied to unconsolidated deposits. The slope of the shore is important in deciding whether large ice floes will ground before reaching tide mark and how far beyond and above tide mark ice may eventually be pushed. On the shallow shelving north coast of Alaska ice-shove phenomena are few, but the north-west coast of King William Island has a steeply shelving shore backed by a flat plain. Here in 1833 Ross reported sea-ice to have travelled half a mile inland. In some areas where tidal range is considerable a noticeable feature is the development of a boulder reef at low-tide mark at the edge of major sea-ice disturbance in winter. At Pangnirtung, Baffin Island, this reef is a navigational hazard at higher stages of the tide (*see Plate 5*).

The discussion of snow and ice cover above must not be taken to indicate that the Arctic (as opposed to the Antarctic realm) is ice-covered all the year round. This is an all too popular fallacy. But as the severity of climate increases it is true that it becomes harder for the brief summer to get rid of the winter's accumulation and where glaciers are present it has in fact failed. But the very low precipitation of the high Arctic prevents a great snow accumulation so that though it is generally true that the snow line creeps downward toward the Pole, present-day glaciation may not be as well developed around the shores of the North Polar Sea as it is further south in mountainous regions with an abundant snow supply.

Thus a large portion of Peary Land (Greenland), starved of precipitation, is ice free though it is the most northerly land in the world. Moreover much of it appears to have been ice free throughout the Pleistocene period. Only a small fraction of the Arctic lands belongs to this unglaciated province—some of the north-western Canadian Arctic islands, much of Arctic Alaska, and the Siberian Arctic from about the mouth of the Olenek to Chaun Bay. In other parts of the Arctic at least two separate periods of Pleistocene glaciation have been recognized and the former extension of glaciers brought them not only down to sea-level but spreading out into the sea itself.

ICE SHELF

A peculiar polar landform which merits separate treatment is the ice shelf. Ice shelves are developed to an enormous extent in the Antarctic and will be considered in detail in Chapter 16, but the Arctic ice shelves of north Greenland and Ellesmere Island are in some ways unique.

To begin with they were discovered by their products—the *ice islands* observed in the North Polar Sea by reconnaissance aircraft which began increasingly numerous flights in 1946. Then the shelf is not a true land product; refreezing sea, as will be seen, has a good deal to do with its formation.

The ice islands were recognized in the polar pack not only by their great size—up to tens of miles in linear dimension, and height—twenty or more feet above sea-level, but by the astonishing linear roll pattern of trough and ridge shown on their surface, picked out in summer by meltwater in the hollows.

In conditions as they exist today on the fringes of the North Polar Sea the summer air temperatures are above freezing. Thus surface undulations are preserved and even accentuated by summer melt with the increased heat absorption of water—a process which does not happen in the Antarctic.

On the Ellesmere coast the rolled ice shelf (Fig. 26) has been studied of recent years; even the birthplace of one of the ice islands has been located from its jig-saw fit and here in fact the shelf is regrowing to fill the space. By 1954 this re-entrant had gained a cover of twenty-foot ice thickness as compared with the 120-foot thickness of its predecessor which presumably broke away in 1946. How is this shelf formed and how to account for the rolls? At present there is no connection at all between the existing land glaciers and the shelf. It is not glacial ice spread out as it reaches tide water nor can ice pressure account for the undulations. Furthermore owing to the apparent stationary or even advancing state of the Ellesmere glaciers it seems likely that for several thousand years there has been no overflow of ice from the land. So the shelf must grow *in situ*, as its youngest part has been seen in fact to do.

Wastage has been observed on its surface. The warm summer of 1954 took two feet of ice away and a camp-site of Peary's forty-five years before was found showing no appreciable surface accumulation. Coring in 1954 showed that 'the upper part of the shelf was built up by annual increments of water-saturated firn or by refrozen meltwater'—the lower part has probably been added by refreezing of sea water of low salinity to the under surface. Hattersley-Smith believes the whole must date from subsequent to the climatic optimum and may be only two thousand years old and at present in delicate balance.

The rolls are now attributable to past wind action at the build-up period. Current prevailing winds are westerly, parallel to the coast and to the rolls. The 'new ice' of the re-entrant has similarly oriented rolls but of a different wavelength, due to a difference in wind strength and snow supply. The process seems to be entirely analogous to the formation of longitudinal or *seif* dunes in sand as described by Bagnold. Once again we see the close resemblance between sand grains and polar snow.

The map (Fig. 26) shows the present development of the Ellesmere shelf. It is not large, only some hundreds of square miles. One other area, north-west Greenland, supports a similar feature which can logically be accepted as due to the same

Fig. 26. Ice-shelf Areas off Northern Ellesmere Island.

processes. This is the *sikussaq* of Koch in Sherard Osborn and Victoria fiords.

GLACIAL FEATURES OF EROSION

Past glaciation has had a profound effect on the present Arctic landscape and the familiar features of glacial erosion and deposition are rendered all the more visible by the absence of obscuring forests. The great ice sheets have been pictured as grinding over the face of the land and copiously eroding it. This conception must be treated with caution. It is probable that only when fast moving is glacier ice as powerful an eroding agent as flowing water, and it will be fast moving only where confined in a valley or near the edge of an advancing ice sheet. Once the edge has advanced well past a given locality erosion will once more be slight even if the thickness of ice above builds up to thousands of feet.

On the Arctic lowlands glacial erosion has been small: Flint suggests only some tens of feet. It did, however, tend to remove all pre-glacial unconsolidated material and soil and where the bedrock is highly resistant large areas of bare, ice-smoothed rock now appear on the surface, weathering very slowly and with the drainage almost entirely structurally controlled.

In the highland areas glacial sculpture has been more vigorous and we can see developed the usual horns and corries and the deep U-shaped valleys and truncated spurs that fast-moving ice streams have caused. Many Arctic regions present typical fiord coasts: the term fiord being here accepted as a glacially over-deepened inlet with some kind of a threshold shallow at its mouth.

Fiords are particularly developed in Novaya Zemlya, Svalbard, Greenland, the eastern rank of Canadian islands and Labrador. In Scoresby Sound (east Greenland) and Admiralty Inlet (Baffin Island) we have the longest fiords in the world, though it is likely that even greater ones would appear in the Antarctic if the ice cover were removed.

Few of the Arctic fiords have been studied in such detail as those of more temperate regions such as Norway. Particularly lacking are bathymetric data, but it would appear from such information as is available that most polar fiords are not as deep as, for instance, the Sogn Fiord.

GLACIAL FEATURES OF DEPOSITION

These may take the form of eskers, drumlins, moraines and the large expanses of unconsolidated glacially-derived material known as till. The esker is one of the most spectacular forms of glacial deposit and is splendidly displayed in the flatter tundra areas such as Canada. Here eskers, which consist of ridges of sand and gravel and were formed from englacial or sub-glacial melt streams near a decaying ice sheet's margin, trend up to 150 miles across the country (*see Plate 6*).

Though sometimes broken through by lakes and post-glacial rivers they provide natural routes across the country, have a great potential as a source of sand and gravel for construction, and are in fact often the only sure landmarks in an otherwise featureless plain area. Terminal moraines of any size are rare in the Arctic regions. They are present, of course, in the highland parts but, as they represent standstill positions of an ice edge, they tend to be absent from the central portions of ice sheets which lay over most of our region. They are undoubtedly well developed as submarine features off many Arctic shores where the ice sheets deposited their basal loads on the continental shelf.

The commonest glacial depositional feature of the Arctic is ground moraine or till often in drumlinated form. The

drumlin is a half-egg-shaped mass of till indicating the direction
of movement of over-riding ice and drumlin patterns are
developed in extraordinary profusion on the tundra plains.
Plate 7 shows a typical area in northern Canada where the
pattern has a controlling influence on the landscape dominating
the river and lake directions.

Large areas of the Arctic tundra, however, are covered
with ground moraine or till with no particular orientational
forms. There tends here to be a microrelief more subdued
than before the till was deposited, as the hollows have tended to
fill and the ridges to remain bare. Erratic boulders sometimes
of cottage size and appearance scatter the landscape. I recall
driving hopefully in the dusk for several miles towards one of
these rectangular erratics thinking it was the trapper's shack
for which I was making.

As an indirect result of the glaciation much Arctic lowland
was depressed under the ice load and before it could recover
was under the sea. This was particularly true of the areas
around Hudson Bay and in western Siberia. The erosion at
shore line seems to have been very small, but a great deal of the
ground moraine was reworked by the sea and particularly in
the limestone lowlands has produced a unique type of landscape.

This consists of a series of ridges of limestone fragments
usually dry and bare of vegetation separated by lakes or
marshy hollows which were the former marine lagoons. Where
the slope of a lowland is slight this type of raised beach country
can extend for scores of miles inland from the present sea margin.

Since deglaciation and the retreat of the sea normal erosive
processes have been at work on the Arctic landscape. Frost
shattering of rock material is of course the most important form
of weathering: chemical weathering is much subdued. Transport of load by the highly disorganized drainage left after
glaciation is slight except in the highland areas. In all areas
rivers are very variable from a maximum at spring flood to
feeble or non-existent for the major part of the year. Aeolian
weathering and deposition are present to some extent in the
limited regions where dry and fine unconsolidated materials
are present. Some loess deposits have been observed near the
Greenland ice-cap and in interior Alaska.

1. Captain Roald Amundsen (1872-1928)

2. Amundsen at South Pole, 14 December, 1911

3. Swiss Bay, Sam Ford Fiord, Baffin Island (lat. 70° 30′ N, long. 71° W)

4. Stages in lake-ice melting; rivers and lake shores melt first (*see p.* 67)

5. Ice-shore boulder beach (*see p.* 67)

6. An esker (*see p.* 71)

7. Parallel drumlins in northern Canada (*see pp.* 71–72)

8. Patterned ground – unsorted polygons (*see pp.* 81–82)

9. Patterned ground – unsorted stripes (*see pp.* 81–83)

The most important process of levelling by transport of material is mass wasting which far outweighs stream or wind action. This mass wasting varies from landslips and rock falls producing talus slopes in the highlands through all kinds of rock and soil creep to 'solifluction'—that is creep of saturated soil or rock material which can take place down slopes of extraordinary gentleness—as low as two or three degrees. Solifluction can occur in non-Arctic areas but it is particularly active in the region of permafrost where the upper surface of the frozen substratum forms a gliding plane.

Whole slopes may move under dry creep activated by frost-action, vegetation growth, or the removal of supporting fine materials by rain or wind. Each movement of individual stones and particles is bound to be resultantly downward. But when a whole mass of surface soil is saturated, as tends to occur when the summer warmth has percolated downward and melted the ice in it, the mass will flow. Often it forms lobes with steep fronts several feet in height where the ground slope eases off. Sometimes solifluction lobes are superimposed one above the other, sometimes where confined a solifluction stream will result. But whichever way this mass wasting arises it represents the most important levelling agency in the Arctic erosion cycle.

PERMAFROST

One of the characteristics of the polar regions postulated in Chapter 1 is the necessary presence of permanently frozen ground or *permafrost*. Only in south-west Greenland is it absent and the southern limit of permafrost dips far below the Arctic regions in North America and even more so in eastern Asia. It was for this reason, that it was present in the heavily forested taiga, that caused it to be regarded as a traveller's tale; but over a hundred years ago Middendorf's studies convinced the scientific world of its reality.

It is in Russia that the phenomenon has been most widely studied: North American interest was only aroused in the 1940s when wartime construction of buildings and airfields in the Arctic led to a realization of the difficulties of foundations and the need for permafrost surveys and special engineering practice.

Permafrost is defined as 'a thickness of soil or other superficial deposit, or even bedrock, at a variable depth beneath the surface of the earth in which a temperature below freezing has existed continually for a long time (from two years to tens of thousands of years).' Permafrost can be *dry*, when there is no ice as cementing material, e.g. in bedrock or dry sand; it is then of comparatively small influence on man's activities, except in mineral exploration drilling. Or it can be *wet*, the more usual condition in normal water-bearing soils or unconsolidated materials, when the void space between grains is occupied by ice. This is the condition that causes the troubles.

Permafrost of some degree underlies nearly one-fifth of the land surface of the world and affects much of Alaska and nearly half the territory of the U.S.S.R. and of Canada. Naturally its thickness varies with the severity of the region, being very deep in the high Arctic and thinning off to the south. It can be

(a) Continuous
(b) Discontinuous, where islands of unfrozen ground appear within the permafrost
(c) Sporadic, where patches of permafrost occur in generally unfrozen ground.

The diagram shows an idealized section across Canada.

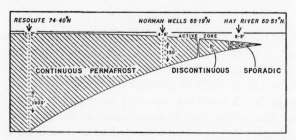

Fig. 27. The Permafrost Zone: idealized section from north to south in Canada.

At Resolute Bay the permafrost is over a thousand feet thick, at Yellowknife or Norman Wells about 150 feet, while at Hay River we are in the *sporadic* zone with patches of permafrost five feet thick.

In the diagram a zone of *annual thaw* is shown thickening

towards the south. This is an invariable concomitant of permafrost and is called the *active layer*—that which thaws during the
summer season. Other thawed layers may be present in the
permafrost and are known by the Russian term *talik*. Another
Russian term *pereletok* is given to a layer which for some reason
such as a very cold summer stays frozen within the normal
active layer.

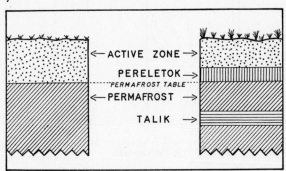

Fig. 28. Idealized Ground Profile to illustrate Permafrost Terms.

On the analogy with *water-table* we can term the upper surface of the permafrost the *permafrost table* which is as impervious
to water as the toughest clay and as resistant to pressure as many
types of bedrock *as long as it stays hard frozen.*

All the problems connected with permafrost are determined
by the local pattern of ground temperature. This is caused by:

(*a*) transfer of heat from the interior of the earth
(*b*) heat gains and losses at the surface.

The former is a comparatively steady function, the latter is
varied by daily and annual temperature fluctuations and by
other factors such as wind, evaporation, vegetation cover, snow
cover or the presence of surface water.

There is a lower limit to the depth of the temperature
fluctuations in the ground from these causes and this is termed
the level of zero amplitude. An inspection of the diagram
(Fig. 29) will show how there is an increasing lag in time between the results at depth and the causes (summer heat or
winter cold) at the surface. At the permafrost table the maximum temperature ($0°$ C.) is reached in October; lower still the

January temperature is highest, showing a lag of six months in the penetration of the warm wave. The warm wave and cold

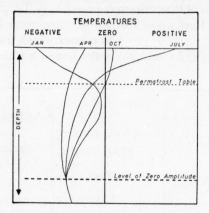

Fig. 29. Seasonal Temperature Variation
in the Ground.

wave are shown more clearly in Fig. 30 taken from investigations at Skovorodino on the trans-Siberian railway just north of

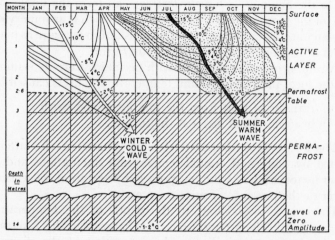

Fig. 30. Thermal Régime of Ground at Skovorodino, Siberia, 1928–30.

Manchuria in 1928–30: the 'waves' are seen to penetrate at about one metre per month. At a short distance below the permafrost table (2·4 metres depth) the annual variation is reduced to 1° C. and at a depth of fourteen metres all annual variation is obliterated—we have reached the level of *zero amplitude*.

Closer inspection of Fig. 30 will show that the condition of the ground at the end of November consists of an upper layer one metre deep already hard frozen; then a metre still just above freezing-point, and freezing temperatures moving upward below this from the permafrost table. This is the situation when surface heaving can most easily occur since the thawed layer on freezing must expand and is contained between upper and lower surfaces already solidly frozen.

This hydrostatic or 'cryostatic' pressure lowers the freezing-point of the soil and this, together with the latent heat of fusion given off, results in a pause at temperature 0° C. until the soil is all frozen. The duration of this pause is termed the *zero curtain* and its maximum is just above the permafrost table. At Resolute Bay, F. A. Cook studied the duration of zero curtain in both clay and shattered rock and gravel. In the former material it lasted twenty-five days and in the latter fourteen days at fifteen-inch depth. At Resolute Bay a deep boring carried out from 1950–3 inclusive revealed that permafrost extended to 1,280 feet in depth.

When the ground is of fine texture and contains a large amount of moisture, ice lenses are liable to form and grow by capillary attraction of the moisture in the voids.

It is this growth of ice lenses or the freezing of a large body of ground water blocked in some way from drainage, that causes the 'frost boils' so typical of permafrost regions. The ground is forced up by expansion of the ice; sometimes, if tree covered, tilting the trees so that a 'drunken forest' results; sometimes the ground ruptures and the water spills out to freeze on the surface into a *naled* (or *aufeis*) surface icing which can cover large areas and be slow to vanish in summer (Fig. 31).

The texture and water content of the soil determine to a great extent the thickness of the active layer. In the far north in moss- or peat-covered ground it may be less than a foot, but in lower latitudes and in sandy or gravelly ground it may be twelve feet or more in thickness.

The actual temperature of the ground at the level of zero amplitude is closely related to the mean annual air temperature.

Where this is well above (5° C. or more) or well below freezing-point it is a reasonable generalization to state that they are equal. But in the neighbourhood of freezing the latent heat factor ('zero curtain') causes deviations. Thus permafrost is exceptional with a mean temperature of 0° C. and in fact we

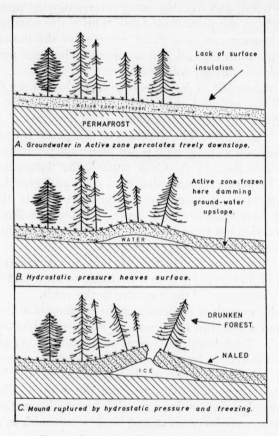

Fig. 31. Formation of Frost Boil and Naled.

can suggest approximate annual mean temperature limits for the three permafrost regions discussed earlier:

(*a*) Continuous   5° C. or lower
(*b*) Discontinuous   1·5° C. to − 5° C
(*c*) Sporadic   1·5° C. to 0

It is not easy to relate the boundaries of these various types of permafrost with the annual temperature isotherms on a map. To begin with, both factors, particularly the isotherms, have somewhat inadequate data. Fig. 32 shows the distribution as far as is possible at present. Future research will improve the detail on this map and perhaps we may be

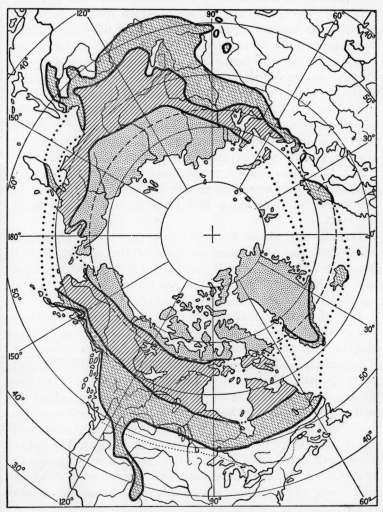

Fig. 32. Permafrost in the Northern Hemisphere: (*see table opposite*)
continuous; discontinuous; sporadic.

forced to modify the classification of permafrost types given above.

Sporadic permafrost can be induced artificially. It was discovered for instance, upon dismantling, under a long-used ice-storage house in Edmonton. But another interesting case of naturally induced permafrost is given in the case quoted below. The presence of a reasonably large water body such as a lake or a wide river, only the surface of which freezes in winter, results in an 'annual mean temperature' (of the water) above freezing-point. So permafrost may be absent altogether under it or at any rate the permafrost table will be driven deep. At Port Nelson during the preliminary work for the Hudson Bay railway a swamp whose bed was unfrozen was drained. During the first winter frost penetrated to a depth of eight feet, in the second to twenty feet, in the third to thirty feet. Here, at the level of the lower limit of permafrost in the surrounding area, it ceased. The normal permafrost condition under this region where the mean annual temperature was $-6°$ C. was re-established, and the rate of growth of the permafrost once the 'insulation' of the swamp had been removed was actually observed.

Permafrost is absent from under the bed of the Mackenzie River but has been found in some of the recently-formed islands in its delta. Under Hudson Bay it is presumably missing also and has been proved to thin out rapidly seaward from its 140-foot thickness at Churchill, Manitoba.

Permafrost has a considerable effect on the vegetation which the ground above it can support. Where the active layer is shallow only the shallowest rooted plants or trees can exist. Thus only in well-drained sandy soils will pines with their deep roots flourish. Black and white spruce, balsam poplar (not aspen), larch and birch are all capable of existing where the active layer is twelve inches or more deep, but the white spruce, birch and poplar require reasonably unwaterlogged soil and hence also cleave to the drier mounds and ridges. The impervious permafrost table is responsible for conserving the scanty moisture of the Arctic regions and results in a considerable cover of vegetation where otherwise would be an arid desert.

PATTERNED GROUND

This is the term suggested by Washburn, a leading investigator of the subject 'for the more or less symmetrical forms such as circles, polygons, nets, steps and stripes that are characteristic of, but not necessarily confined to, mantle subject to intensive frost action'. Patterned ground is not confined to the polar regions or to permafrost. It exists in many mountain areas, in the sub-Arctic and even in hot areas—the desiccated muds of ephemeral lakes show excellent patterns. But it is much best developed in the region of our study, forming a striking feature in aerial views and affecting considerably the summer foot-slogger who may sink into the porridge of mud-centred polygons or lacerate his footwear on the vertically set highly cleaved stones of their edges.

The five-fold classification given above by Washburn is augmented by a division of each into *sorted* and *unsorted* according to the differential positioning of finer and coarser material. Steps and stripes are typically slope phenomena, the term net is given to the group whose shape is intermediate between circular or polygonal. The net size can vary considerably from a few inches to a hundred yards and vertical relief proportionately. The illustrations (Plates 8 and 9) show typical examples of some of the groups in the series.

The sorted polygon is probably the commonest of the series. Polygons do not develop singly but appear to be the result of 'growth' of circles till they meet. They have typically finer material in the centres and coarse material at the edges but it must be stressed that the centre may be composed of merely smaller stones not necessarily clay or other truly 'fine' material. The size of the polygons tends to increase with the severity of the climate. The meeting edges of the polygons are characterized by tabular stones often on edge. These stony borders tend to narrow downwards in wedge form and in non-sorted polygons this edge often consists of a wedge-shaped mass of more or less clear ice (*see Fig. 33*).

Steps are patterned ground on a slope with a step-like form due to a down-slope border of coarser material embanking finer material above (if sorted) or of vegetation embanking relatively bare ground above (if unsorted).

G

Similarly stripes oriented downslope will be of parallel lines of stones and intervening finer material (if sorted) and of vegetated and barer ground (if unsorted).

Many hypotheses have been adduced for the formation of patterned ground particularly in the period succeeding the visit

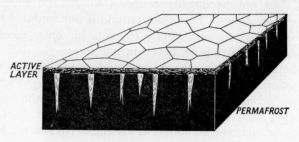

Fig. 33. Tundra Polygons.

of the International Geological Congress to Svalbard in 1910. In a critical examination of these Washburn has suggested acceptance of four principal and often inter-related causes—local differential heaving, cryostatic movement, and contraction due to low temperature and desiccation. The first two return us to the frost boil principle. Inequalities in the insulation provided by plant and vegetation cover will affect the local intensity of ground freezing and hence of heaving and segregation of ice. The repetition of this process will bring larger fragments to the surface and then move them downward and radially outward from the surface of the heave. The movement of moisture to ice-development areas may carry clay particles and hence concentrate the fines. The initial heaving may be best explained in permafrost conditions by cryostatic pressure (Washburn's term). By this is understood the 'progressive freezing from the surface downward to the permafrost table causing hydrostatic pressure in pockets of unfrozen material confined between these surfaces as in a press'.

With a given mantle the permafrost table is usually at a uniform depth which may explain the uniform size over a large area of the patterned ground produced.

Contraction due to drying or to lowering the temperature of already frozen ground will undoubtedly produce tension cracks forming a polygonal pattern. The centres naturally remain moister and on freezing will expand and cause an upward movement of clay particles. The coarser material must gradually be forced sideways until it lodges in the cracks which themselves may be enlarged by ice wedging. Thus the sorting process can occur again but it is probable that contraction processes are more closely connected with non-sorted patterns.

With steps and stripes gravity comes into play to cause the extension downslope of circles, nets and polygons on flatter ground. The transition between one and another form at change of slope can often be seen (Fig. 34). Both steps and stripes being

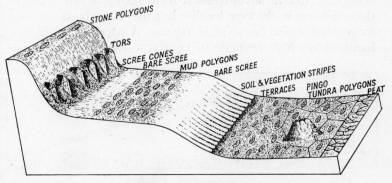

Fig. 34. Tundra Phenomena.

common in non-polar regions are less related to the permafrost than to the frost régime.

Another form of patterned ground consists of long (up to five hundred metres) cracks often with upturned lips and usually vegetation in the fissure running either parallel to emerged strandlines or at right-angles to them up and down the fall line. A tetragonal, often rectilinear, pattern thus develops. Some of the downslope fissures trend from areas where long-lasting snow beds could provide a seepage of ground water: the transverse fissures could likewise be caused by ground-water concentration at a rise in the permafrost table caused by the strandline ridge itself or a strip of insulating vegetation. In each case Washburn considers cryostatic pressure from the ground-water concentration would result in the fissuring of the surface.

PINGOS

A noteworthy landform of the permafrost region is the *pingo*. This is the Eskimo word for the peculiar conical hills in the area of the older deltaic deposits of the Mackenzie River lying east of the present delta. This is the 'type locality' for the feature. A pingo (Plate 11) is an ice-cored swelling rising from a lake or a former lake basin. It can be up to 230 feet in height though examples over a hundred feet are rare. Their summits are usually smooth and vegetated but sometimes they are ruptured and at times the whole centre has collapsed. Recent investigations have shown about 1,400 of these features in the type locality but they have been reported from many other Arctic plain regions. A borehole made in a hundred-foot-high example in 1954 revealed ice from four to

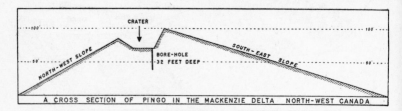

Fig. 35.

thirty-two feet below the depressed and ruptured centre with temperatures at the bottom of about 25° F. (Fig. 35.)

Porsild, the first to name these features, gave as the suggested explanation of their formation 'by local upheaval due to expansion following the progressive downward freezing of a body or lens of water or semi-fluid mud or silt enclosed between bedrock and the frozen surface soil in much the same way that the cork of a bottle filled with water is pushed up by expansion on freezing'.

The requirement of bedrock is unnecessary and unlikely. Following Porsild the pingo can be seen as an intrapermafrost swelling on a major scale starting as the diagram shows (Fig. 36) by the silting and desiccation of a lake at a time of strongly cooling conditions with increasing permafrost. As the insulating lake water diminishes the unfrozen bulb can take up the bottle shape shown following which the cork ejection would occur. This ejection may be slow, slow enough to allow the doming of the surface and its vegetation cover sometimes to remain complete, but often rupture would occur and the remaining water or muck be ejected. In the permafrost realm the vegetation cover is now sufficient to insulate the ice bulb from melting but in the collapsed cases sufficiently deep surface water perhaps formed in the centre crater to drive the frost level down and eliminate the ice core.

Pingos have also been described from Siberia where they have been termed 'bulgunniakh'. More recently they have been

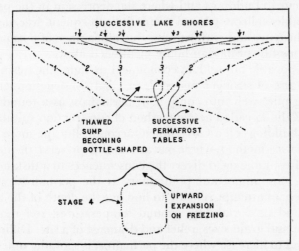

Fig. 36. Pingo Formation: the frost-boil explanation illustrated.

analysed by F. Müller in a monograph where he distinguishes between the Mackenzie type described above and an east Greenland type developing on valley floors in hilly country through a local *degradation* of permafrost and hence *increase* in ground water under hydrostatic pressure from the surrounding high land.

PERMAFROST ENGINEERING

Hitherto we have been considering the effects of permafrost on natural ground and vegetation. But it has a most important effect on man's activities, particularly those of engineering and construction. The astonishing sight of a two-storey wooden building in Siberia filled to the roof with ice, and with icicles hanging from its windows, is an indication of what can happen when man upsets the natural permafrost régime by tampering with the surface, loading it heavily or heating it. These activities result in driving down the permafrost table thus reducing previously frozen to thawed ground and allowing ground water to accumulate in the depression in the permafrost table. The ice in some frozen soils (and it may have a volume six times that of the 'soil') is a cement which gives rock-like qualities when frozen but when thawed changes the material into a liquid mass with no supporting power. Thus settling and complete failures can occur to buildings and where the depression in the permafrost table collects ground water its subsequent freezing can cause heaving and with rupture the appearance of a *naled* such as the ice-filled Siberian house mentioned above.

It is possible but seldom economical to 'fight' the permafrost by the use of stronger materials or rigid construction such as driving piles well into continuous permafrost as a foundation. Such is the so-called active method of construction suitable for heavy buildings on a Government account. But the more usual is the *passive* method, where one attempts to preserve the natural permafrost table or to divert the consequences to a distance.

The most important preliminary is the permafrost survey in which an attempt is made to find out the depth of the active layer and its variability, ground temperatures, soil moisture content and grain sizes, relief and drainage of a site. Difficulties will tend to increase where the permafrost is sporadic unless it is possible to thaw the ground altogether. Even bedrock is no sure foundation since it may be well-jointed and percolation of water into joint cracks and subsequent freezing can heave large masses of bedrock as the photo (Plate 11) shows of a ten-foot squeeze of a boulder at Churchill.

In all cases buildings are best located on gravel or coarse sand and the permafrost table can often be preserved by covering the surface with a pad of gravel which counteracts the depressing influence of load and heat. Insulation of floors and the use of an air-space under the building helps to prevent the heat leak. Such an air space can be closed in summer and opened in winter to *preserve* the permafrost.

In many lightweight northern buildings a floating foundation is used on the built-up gravel mat; thus the building re-sembles an 'ark' and settles as a whole rather than in parts, if settling or heaving should occur. This at least gets rid of the annoyances of doors that cannot close or walls coming apart from floors when differential movement takes place. For heavier buildings foundations anchored in permafrost are probably necessary. Piles may be driven into the permafrost for at least twice the depth of the active layer and attempts made to have them gripped in the permafrost by being roughened at this depth and *not* gripped in the active layer by smoothing and 'lubricating' them in this layer.

Other modifications to man's housing are dictated by Arctic conditions apart from permafrost and might well be mentioned at this point. The long axis of buildings should be parallel to the prevailing wind so that the snow drift piles on to the short wall. Doors should then be on the long, swept-clear, side and must always open inward and preferably into a porch. Insulation must be on an exceptionally high plane with adequate ventila-tion to prevent condensation on walls. And, with the ever-present risk of fire and the difficulties of fighting it, buildings should be well separated and all possible fire precautions taken.

Roads and runways present difficulties in the permafrost region for the same reason as do buildings. Here the golden rule is *fill* rather than *cut*. Fills tend to raise the permafrost table and prevent the evils of hollow formation. The location of roads will often be independent of the usual economics. It will be preferable to keep them to flat ground or to ridges avoiding all possible *cuts* and above all hillside cuts. The hillslope problem can be partly solved by upslope protection in the form of a ditch or bank where the induced dip in the permafrost table and resultant icing can form away from the road itself. Hillside icings across a road can put it completely out of action, since vehicles slide gently or violently off sideways. I have seen a whole convoy ditched in this way, each driver thinking he could negotiate it.

In any nucleated settlement in the permafrost regions the provision of water supply and disposal of sewage is an aggravat-ing problem. In ordinary heavy winter-frost regions it is possible to overcome the danger of freezing by burying pipes far enough below the surface. But this is of no avail when permafrost is present. In regions of sporadic and discontinuous permafrost *taliks* may be found which in themselves are aquifers and in which pipes can be laid.

The usual practice today is to use circulating water throughout the system, preheated at the delivery point to a sufficient

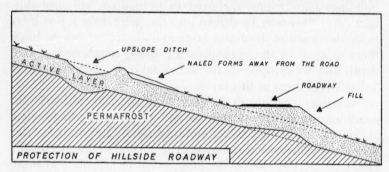

UPSLOPE DITCH

NALED FORMS AWAY FROM THE ROAD

ACTIVE LAYER

ROADWAY

FILL

PERMAFROST

PROTECTION OF HILLSIDE ROADWAY

Fig. 37.

degree so that on return the water is still above freezing. The speed of the circulating water is important; at Fairbanks, Alaska it is as high as three feet per second through the eighteen miles of mains in ground as cold as −10° C. in winter. The sewer pipes are laid alongside the warm water pipes often at shallow depths or above ground in wooden boxes heavily insulated. These are known as utilidors and of course if a settlement steam-heating plant is providing heat to the individual houses the presence of this pipe in the utilidor is a guarantee of warmth to the other utilities.

There are many other facets to permafrost engineering, but in a geographical text this short sketch must suffice to show the modifications to man's usual living practices imposed by this vital polar characteristic.

FURTHER READING

Brown, R. S. E., 'Permafrost in Canada', *Arctic*, 13, p. 163 (1960).
Crary, A. P., 'Arctic Ice-island and Ice-shelf Studies', *Arctic*, 11, p. 2 (1958), and 13, p. 32 (1960).
Müller, F., 'Beobachtungen über Pingos' (in German), *Meddelelser om Grønland*, 153 (1959).
Muller, S., 'Permafrost'. *Ann Arbor*, 1937 (Edwards).
Tedrow, J. O. F., and J. E. Cantlon, 'Concepts of Soil Formation in Arctic Regions', *Arctic*, 11, p. 166 (1958).
Washburn, A. L., 'Patterned Ground', *Bull. Geol. Soc. Amer.*, 67, pp. 823-66.

Chapter 5

THE ARCTIC SEAS

If there is one central fact about the Arctic region it is the sea. Its study is as important to the geographer as that of its adjacent lands—for its sheer size, more than twice the area of the Arctic tundras, for the fact that biologically it is more productive, and above all for the great difference between its character and that of other seas of the world. For here we have the frozen ocean, covered to a major extent by shifting, grinding ice: it is the truly shining sea with a radiance compared to which the glare of the sun-drenched doldrums is only a pale glimmer.

On its coast there is a blurring to the usual sharp boundary between land and water that one expects. Pytheas in his controversial northern voyage reached a point where 'the land, sea and air became as one'. Was this the edge of the pack ice in a summer fog?

In winter, landfast ice growing seaward is nearly indistinguishable from the snow-covered tundra plain inland, as aircraft radarscopes show all too unclearly. Even in summer some of the Queen Elizabeth group of Canadian islands are practically fused together by an ice cover. There is a development of the shallow continental shelf particularly off east Siberia and Bering Strait wider than anywhere else in the world. It is possible here to have less than a hundred fathoms of water four hundred miles from the nearest land.

As with the land, so with the sea areas it is difficult to define what we mean by the 'Arctic Ocean'. Dunbar has discussed the question of 'Arctic' and 'Subarctic' waters on a temperature and salinity basis, keeping the former for the cold waters originating from the upper layer of the North Polar basin and the latter for where there is a mixture of Arctic water with Atlantic or Pacific water. He goes on to discuss biological indicators which we will consider in the next chapter—and on the analogy of the tree line some biological limit would be a suitable boundary for us to use.

But in Arctic seas there is one overwhelmingly obvious

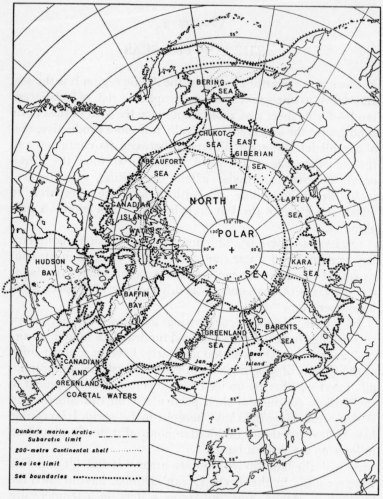

Fig. 38. The Arctic Ocean and its Constituent Seas.

physical factor and that is the presence of ice. If water temperatures and marine animals are variable in their distribution both seasonally and from year to year, even more variable is the ice limit. The line on the map (Fig. 38) shows only an approximate position of the edge of the ice at greatest extent. This swings far south into seas which from their summer characteristics and surrounding lands we cannot possibly consider polar —the Gulf of St. Lawrence and the Sea of Okhotsk among others.

So for the Arctic seas which will be discussed in this chapter some very arbitrary limits have been allotted following in the main the Morskoy Atlas, but adding the coastal waters around southern Greenland, south-east Baffin Island and Labrador, and the northern part of the Bering Sea.

These areas are shown on the map which should be compared with Fig. 5 showing the land boundary of the Arctic.

	Area in sq. km.	Area in sq. miles
North Polar Sea	4,700,000	1,800,000
Greenland Sea	1,200,000	465,000
Barents Sea	1,400,000	540,000
Kara Sea	900,000	350,000
Laptev Sea	650,000	250,000
E. Siberian Sea	900,000	350,000
Chukot Sea	600,000	230,000
N. Bering Sea	700,000	270,000
Beaufort Sea	450,000	175,000
Canadian island's straits	750,000	290,000
Baffin Bay	850,000	330.000
Hudson Bay and Strait	1,200,000	465,000
Baffin and Labrador coastal waters	200,000	75,000
S. Greenland coastal waters	150,000	60,000
	14,650,000	5,650,000

Our knowledge of these waters, particularly of the inner North Polar Sea, has been built up slowly with a greatly increased tempo after the Second World War. As recently as 1928 a map[1] showed the unseen (let alone unsounded) area as at least one and half million square miles. A few forays which had yielded scientific information had been made by Peary, Stefansson, Cagni and some Russian expeditions, but the main source of data was the three-year drift of the *Fram* from 1893 to 1896. In the Baffin Bay area Danish and American work had been quite detailed in the 1920s and 1930s.

Then came in 1937 the first of the ice-drifting expeditions, that of Papanin and his three companions, now called by the Russians SP1 (Severnaya Polyus 1). In 1939–40 the *Sedov* repeated, slightly to the poleward, the *Fram*'s drift and then

[1] *Problems of Polar Research*, A.G.S. Spec. Publ. No. 7 (1928), p. 3.

since the war there have been 'ice islands' manned by Americans and at least nine more drifting stations by the Russians. So the hydrographic and meteorological data from this area have been built up supplemented by other airborne temporary stations which have now at last elucidated the main factors of the North Polar Sea.

The diagram (Fig. 39) shows that beyond the wide continental shelf is a double deep basin, both parts exceeding four thousand metres in depth and separated by a ridge, the Lomonossov Ridge, first discovered by Gakkel' in 1948. This

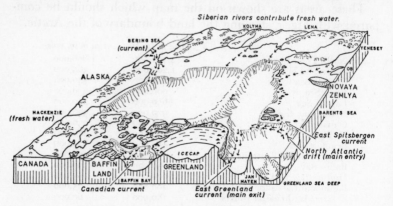

Fig. 39. Block Diagram of North Polar Basin.

runs from due north of the New Siberian Islands to the neighbourhood of Ellesmere Island. The ridge which averages about 1,300 metres below sea-level and thus is over 2,500 metres high with slopes up to twenty-four degrees lies just where Nansen guessed one might be. The 'Eurasian' half of the basin is deeper but smaller than the 'American' half and the continental shelf slope is astonishingly steep, as much as eighteen degrees in places.

A further inspection of Fig. 39 shows the deep-water door to the North Polar Sea where a ridge, once again of 1,200–1,300 metres depth, joins Greenland to Spitsbergen. To the south of this is the deep basin of the Greenland–Norwegian sea, itself separated from the main Atlantic deeps by the Wyville Thomson Ridge which runs from Greenland past Iceland to Scotland.

All other water passages to the North Polar basin, including the Bering Strait door can be seen to be shallow water ones, so we can perhaps consider the Arctic Ocean as a gulf of the Atlantic. It is certainly through this Atlantic door that the main exchange of water takes place both inward and outward and what is very important—the main heat exchange. Recent work by the Geophysical Laboratory in Leningrad[1] has shown that one-third of the heat transported from low to high latitudes is due to the oceans, two-thirds to the air. Opinions vary as to the amount of water transferred. The figures given by Sverdrup[2] do not take into account the Canadian Current outflow which has been estimated by Kiilerich[3] as 1·35 million cubic metres per second. In default of any over-ridingly authoritative figures the table below must be considered tentative.

Inflow		*Outflow*	
Atlantic	85%	E. Greenland Current	75%
Bering Strait (net)	8%		
Rivers	4%	Canadian Current	25%
Excess of precipitation over evaporation	3%		

Both totalling the order of 4·5 million cubic metres per second.

From this discussion and the figures shown in the diagram (Fig. 40) it is seen that the Atlantic water which forms the major

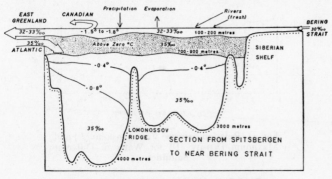

Fig. 40. Water Masses in the North Polar Sea.

part of the inflow is diluted and cooled so that the outflowing waters are quite different in temperature and salinity. The difference between warm saline Atlantic (or Pacific) water and

[1] Budyko, M. I., Comm. to Int. Assoc. Met., Toronto, 1957.
[2] Sverdrup, H. U. *et al.*, *The Oceans*, Prentice Hall, 1942.
[3] Kiilerich, A. B., *Medd. om Grønland*, 78 (5), 1939.

cold fresher Arctic water is stressed, because as we shall see
(Chapter 6) it is in the mixing zone, where both kinds of water
come together, that the greatest biological production occurs.
We must now turn to the processes of ice formation. The study
of sea-ice is fundamental to the movement of all-important
shipping in the polar regions and as Armstrong has said, 'The
main application of sea-ice studies is to shipping. There are
other applications; to aircraft seeking to land on ice, to vehicles
seeking to cross a frozen strait, to climatologists wishing to use
ice conditions as an index to climatic change, and to synoptic
meteorologists interested in the effect of ice on the dynamics of
air masses. But none of these is likely in the forseeable future
to eclipse the need of the shipmaster.'[1]

SALT-WATER ICE

In the polar regions of the world the sea itself, as well as the
lakes and rivers, freezes over. But it is harder to freeze the sea,

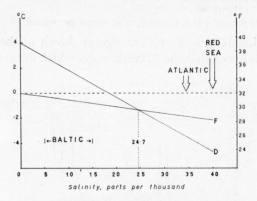

Fig. 41. Relation between Freezing-point (F) and
Maximum Density (D) for Water of Different
Salinities.

and to examine the reason for this we must go into the properties of 'salt' water which is very variable in salt content. In fact,
the salts of the sea can vary from almost nil in the presence of
much melting ice and in river estuaries to the 10 per cent.
content of the Dead Sea or, fairer comparison, the 4 per cent.
of parts of the Red Sea.

[1] Armstrong, T. E., 'Sea Ice Studies', *Arctic*, 7, p. 201 (1955).

The heavy waters of the Dead Sea must be a wonderful medium for a poor swimmer (poor floater, better) like the author, who sinks like a stone in fresh water. Density is the key and it is on the variations of density with salinity and temperature that the freezing process of the sea depends.

The graph opposite shows how freezing-point and maximum density vary for different salinities of water.

At a salinity of 2·7 per cent. the two functions meet—freezing and maximum density occur at the same temperature ($-1·33°$ C.).

Now we can see why it is hard to freeze really salt water. A lake of fresh water has only to cool to $+4°$ C. throughout for density currents to cease—any further surface cooling by the abstraction of heat into the winter air lightens the surface water —it stays on top.

But in saline water the exchange of layers by density movements goes on much longer since the major portion of the mass has to be cooled down considerably below zero centigrade before the cooling surface layers become lighter than the warmer layers below.

Of course vertical exchange of the water layers in the sea is slow and cooling may be fast: we do not have to cool the whole depth of the Atlantic to $-3°$ C. for the surface to start to freeze. But other complications also hinder sea-ice formation. Wave motion is usually much greater than on all except the greatest lakes and tidal motion also prevents the calm conditions required for the surface ice to knit into a sheet.

So we can expect sea-ice to start forming in estuaries (less saline), protected bays and other sea inlets (less waves), in regions of slight tide (e.g. the northern Baltic which is also extremely fresh).

When the freezing-point of our particular body of salt water is reached and further heat is removed under satisfactorily quiet conditions, ice crystals begin to form around nuclei in the water in a similar way to those in fresh water—and similarly the ice is fresh. As the crystals grow and interlock they enclose salt water between them and, growing at the expense of these pockets, abstract more water and leave an increasingly salt concentration behind.

Young ice therefore consists of a network of ice crystals enclosing pockets of brine which, with its freezing-point lowered with increased salinity, becomes steadily harder to freeze. Arctic temperatures will overcome this and actually precipitate the salts in crystal form, but most of the brine migrates—chiefly downwards into the water below—but some to the top where it 'wets' the surface of new sea-ice. This squeezing out of the salt content renders sea-ice seldom more than 5 to 15 per cent. salt if taken in bulk, and, as it ages, it gets fresher still. A summer surface thaw will wash away most of the remaining surface salt, and polar ice more than a year old is as near as human taste can detect 'fresh', making drinkable water, tea or coffee as polar exploring ships well know.

But we have run too fast over the life of sea-ice. Let us examine how it continues to form from the first stage of fresh ice-crystal formation.

As the surface accumulation of ice crystals grows the sea takes on a leaden oily appearance and the wind ripples disappear. This is termed *slush* in sea-ice nomenclature and if this continues to grow under quiet conditions *ice rind*, a thin elastic shining crust, will develop. Its thickness increases up to five centimetres, thereafter it is termed *young ice*, and the sea's frozen cover is assured unless broken by storms and tides. *Ice rind* can be broken by a small rowing-boat but woe betide the boat unless it is metal sheathed—the rind has a cutting action that will wear through the wood on the water-line in a matter of minutes.

Often *ice rind* and *young ice* are broken by storms and waves and the pieces thrusting violently against each other develop debris rims and form a well recognized variety, *pancake ice*; later this freezes together perhaps and its irregularity lasts till snow has smoothed the surface once again (*see Plate 14*).

So the young ice grows and always the process continues of the brine pockets being flushed out and the salt content becoming less. It is quite different to walk on young sea-ice than on fresh-water ice on a skating pond. First, the forcing out of brine makes the surface 'tacky'; it will never be smooth or 'glare ice' and not nearly so transparent as a frozen lake's surface, through several feet of which one can sometimes see the fish swimming. Second, it is elastic, an alarming property, bending and waving under the weight of a passing man or sledge.

The ice can be free floating or it can be *landfast*. The shallower protected bays start freezing first and ice builds out to seaward often to a fairly fixed limit each winter beyond which comes the shore lead, open water smoking with fog, and beyond that the freely moving pack ice.

The landfast ice must rise and fall with the tide which may be small in range in the Baltic and parts of the Arctic

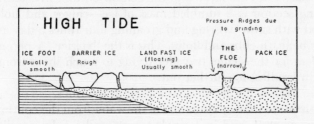

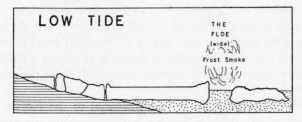

Fig. 42. Hinging of Fast Ice.

Ocean but which in Hudson Bay and Davis Strait is very considerable.

The diagram (Fig. 42) shows how this takes place.

Next to the shore, cemented to the ground, and aground at all stages of the tide, is the *ice foot*, often very smooth due to water overflow at particularly high tides with perhaps a bouldery barrier inland coated by iced spray in the earlier stages of the winter freeze (*storm ice foot*). It is broad where the coastal slope is gentle, narrow or absent where steep-to. Then comes the hinging part of the landfast ice, its shoreward edge aground at all tides, its seaward only at extreme low tide. Outside again, the remainder of the landfast ice is floating at all tides out to its edge. This '*floe edge*' is governed by winds and currents and the shape of the coast but it is often connected in a vague relationship with the twenty-five-metre depth contour (*see Plate 12*).

Here most frequently one sees the beautiful ice flowers, feathery hoar crystals deposited from the frost smoke over the relatively warm open water.

The diagram shows ideal or quiet conditions seldom met with in nature where autumn's frost is often accompanied by storm. The hinge lines or tide cracks are rarely simple lines, but where tides are large and the coastal bottom irregular, the hinging section is a tumbled mass of ice—ridges and hollows drifted with snow twisting and groaning four times a day as the water beneath ebbs and flows. This is the 'barrier', a perennial problem for the sledge traveller trying to reach shore from the smooth landfast ice further out.

Like fresh-water ice there is a limit to the thickness of sea-ice growth due to its own insulation of the water from the continuing winter air-chill, and in a single season under calm conditions it will seldom reach more than two metres. But under storm conditions broken pieces of ice will raft one over the other, pile up into great pressure ridges of tumbled blocks, and on projecting coasts and islands in the path of strong tidal forces thicknesses may build up scarcely to be melted by the summer warmth.

Much of the pack ice in seas marginal to the North Polar Sea and nearly all the fast ice is destroyed by the summer warmth. Sea-ice melts from within and from the surface; from within by the salt concentrations and from the surface by convection, first from the air and then from pools of water forming on the irregular surface. This water absorbs much more heat than the reflecting snow-covered ice around, so pools tend to deepen, voids appear in the ice where the brine concentrates are at work, and the final stage before dissolution sees the sea-ice honeycombed and rotten.

Zubov has calculated that the melting of the Arctic pack from nine-tenths cover to seven-tenths takes twice as long as the process from seven-tenths to five-tenths. The fast ice whose dissolution is slow until the mean air temperature reaches zero °C usually breaks out one, two, or three spring tides after this moment and joins the pack ice in the open sea. But often the ice foot is left clinging to the steeper shores and provides a precarious road for travellers for some further weeks.

THE NORTH POLAR SEA

It is in the North Polar Sea that the greatest development of sea-ice takes place, and here it has been closely studied.

There are three main sections of the ice to consider:

1. *Fast ice* growing outward from the shore, in summer joining
2. The pack ice (*Drift ice*), constantly on the move
3. The Polar Ice (*Arctic Pack*, Russian *Pak*)

The third section is the one that is unique and occupies the central part of the great double basin which is the North Polar Sea. Summer air temperatures in this region though just passing above 0° C. are insufficient to cause much melting and so the polar ice can become several years old. Due to its own powers of insulation it can increase little beyond three metres in thickness except where rafted piece over piece by pressure. But pressure calls for movement and the coverage is so nearly complete that much relative motion between pieces of polar ice is impossible; more rafting will take place in the pack ice belt (Group 2 above) where the shores or fast ice provide the 'immovable object' and there is more room for manoeuvre of the ice fleets.

But pressure ridges are fairly common in the polar pack especially since they are better preserved than in regions where greater thaws can occur. Due to its age and comparative lack of salt, polar ice is stronger and heavier than most pack ice, and level areas of young ice formed by the refreezing of leads in the polar ice are also found.

Beginning with the pioneer venture of 1937 when the four Soviet scientists led by Papanin were landed on smooth stretches near the North Pole itself, and increasing rapidly in the decade since the Second World War, many aircraft landings have been achieved on sufficiently level areas of the firm polar ice. It is certain that the most powerful modern ice-breaker could at great cost push its way into the polar ice but for the future exploration of the area we look now to the aircraft. Our earlier knowledge was gained from the explorers who sought to attain the Pole by sledge travel over the ice—the attempts from Svalbard, doomed because they were travelling hopelessly against the ice drift, and the attempts from the Lincoln Sea crowned by the journeys of Peary. But far more still was learned by the drifting expeditions of two vessels—Nansen's *Fram* in 1893–6 (intentional) and *Sedov* in 1937–40 (accidental). Both these crossed the Eurasian part of the polar ice over fairly similar tracks, and their observations, forty-four years apart in time, give an interesting comparison. For *Sedov* found the mean ice thickness reduced by one-third throughout its passage and the mean temperature higher by 4° C. Pondering in his cabin during the long nights of winter, Nansen propounded two important laws for the drift of ice relative to the wind in the northern hemisphere when unaffected by currents:

1. The ice is deflected 25° to 45° to the right of the wind direction.
2. It drifts at 1/50 the speed of the wind.

These laws were modified by Zubov after the *Sedov* drift to read:

1. Ice drift follows the direction of the isobars with high pressure to the right of the direction.
2. The rate of drift is proportional to the pressure gradient according to the formula $c = 13,000 \, dp/dx$ where c is the speed of drift in km./month and dp/dx the pressure gradient in mb./km.

Zubov's laws are essentially Nansen's, expressed in more scientific terms but we now understand that the rate of drift is considerably dependent on manœuvre room for the ice; very open pack ice (1/10 to 3/10) will drift three times as fast as very close pack ice (9/10 to 10/10) so the quantitative statement might be revised to read 'Ice drifts at 1/40 to 1/120 of the speed of the wind.'

But the polar ice is also subject to permanent currents which take hold when the wind is slack. In the Eurasian sector of the sea and crossing the Lomonossov Ridge the currents move from east to west, from east Siberian waters south of the Pole to the region of Svalbard. In the American sector a giant clockwise eddy occurs which has been discovered from the movements of recognizable 'ice islands'. This eddy may wash over the Lomonossov Ridge off northern Ellesmere Island and the ice it carries get into the grip of the Eurasian current system.

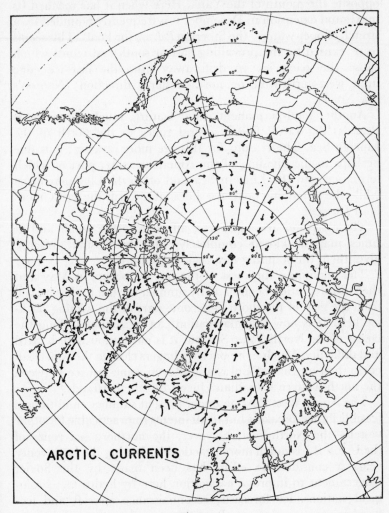

Fig. 43.

Combined, they then flow out strongly down the eastern coast of Greenland where we have a tongue of the polar ice annually exporting about one-fifth of its own mass.

The fast ice of the North Polar Sea grows out from the shores to a very variable distance. Over the shallow waters of eastern Siberia it reaches a vast extent, over four hundred kilometres, opposite the mouth of the Yana. Here when it has reached its maximum extension in December it is frequently bounded by a stretch of open water—the Siberian *Polynya* (or Pool). This seems to be caused by the prevailing east or south-east winds which cause the pack ice to drift away from the fast ice edge in a west-north-west or north-westerly direction (Nansen's law No. 1).

Another semi-permanent water feature, much narrower, is Peary's 'Big Lead' found several times to the north of the Lincoln Sea. The reasons for this are more obscure; it is due perhaps to the dividing of the American eddy, part of which forces ice into the Lincoln Sea and on to the Ellesmere coast while the remaining polar ice slides off towards the east Greenland Current.

These *polynyas* are, of course, affected by the winds and at times may be closed completely, but their usual presence gives them the standing of a regional feature.

The maximum thickness of the fast ice occurs in May and then disintegration begins and by summer the fast ice has moved from the grip of the shore to become part of the waning pack-ice belt. It is now that navigation can be resumed along the coasts of the North Polar Sea but it is navigation with hazard and difficulty. Much more pack ice lingers close to the American coast than on that of Eurasia and even some fast ice between the north-western Canadian Queen Elizabeth Islands.

The North-West Passage under present summer conditions is feasible for ice-breakers but to all intents impracticable for other vessels—the North-East, however, the northern sea route of the U.S.S.R., is much more practicable. During the last twenty years a considerable effort has been made by the Soviet Government to improve navigation here by hydro-meteorological stations, ice forecasts, reconnaissance aircraft and ice-breaker convoying of merchant ships.

Asiatic rivers pour fresh water into this route facilitating ice melting and removal offshore during summer, delaying freezing in the autumn through heat accumulation, but speeding it later due to the low salinity. Two types of ice forecast are made by the Arctic Institute of Leningrad. The first predicts the state of ice in general terms for several months ahead and it is with this that Soviet scientists are dealing in an attempt to correlate ice amounts with meteorological conditions and with sea temperatures in other regions, particularly the

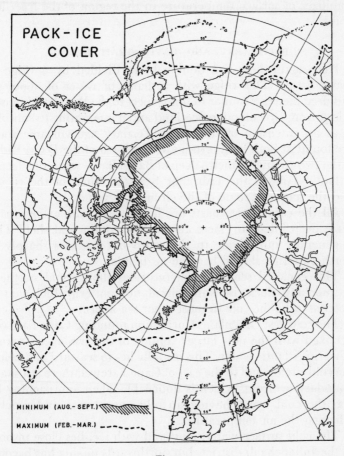

Fig. 44.

Norwegian Sea. The short-term forecasts, with which the navigator is more concerned, cover in greater detail the regions themselves and are devised from local observational factors.

We see from this that the meteorological conditions influence the ice situation but the reverse is true of the North

Polar Sea as a whole. The presence of this large area of ice is a major factor in the climate of the northern hemisphere. In effect, in winter the sea represents an extension of the continents free of any mountain barriers which could impede the air circulation. In summer, the area of the polar ice is a profound stabilizer of surface temperature in the region of the freezing-point.

BAFFIN BAY AND DAVIS STRAIT REGION

Here again there is a double basin divided by a ridge at Davis Strait. This ridge with a depth of water of about six hundred metres is similar in this respect to the Wyville Thomson Ridge from Greenland to Scotland and it is tempting to consider it as an extension of this, since Tertiary age volcanic rocks are found at both land terminations. North of the Davis Ridge is the two-thousand-metre deep of Baffin Bay—south the deeper Atlantic Gulf of the Labrador Sea, the 'sink' of the region and the source of some of the circulating water.

All the containing coasts are fiord coasts with extensions of these deep inlets in places cutting the continental shelf. This is generally quite wide in the south but narrows sharply in northern Baffin Bay to become negligible.

This enclosed sea area demonstrates the normal northern latitude anti-clockwise water circulation pattern which we will observe to be the rule in most other sea areas.

The cold east Greenland Current on rounding Cape Farewell is mixed with the now larger volume of the Irminger Current of warm Atlantic water. This initially lies to seaward and below the cold stream and to the east of Cape Farewell there is a sharp boundary or 'front' which is noticeable when approaching by sea, the cold water having an oily appearance and quickly affecting the air temperature.

The cold surface water, cluttered with ice, lies close inshore in the Julianehaab district, but northwards mixing has become so advanced that the current is thenceforth warm, keeping the next section of the Greenland coast virtually ice free all year. To it is added Labrador Sea water and the combined current moves on up the Greenland shelf. But between Godthaab and Holsteinborg most of it turns westward above deeper water leaving a weakening stream to bring warmth to the Greenland coast as far as Melville Bay. Solar heating in summer gives an average surface temperature as high as 9° C. in Disko Bay, despite the fact that this is a breeding ground of icebergs.

In Baffin Bay beyond the ridge the lower layers of water are very still. From the three major northern inlets, Smith, Jones and Lancaster sounds, comes the Canadian Current of cold Arctic water which travels mainly down the Baffin Land coast but swings out widely in latitude 72° as an inspection of Fig. 43 will show. The conflicting currents in this area cause a late-lasting concentration of pack ice—the 'Middle Pack' of the nineteenth-century whalers.

Between Lancaster and Smith sounds is a curious area known as the 'North Water', very ice free at all seasons and where the summer temperature on the surface is in excess of 5° C. This was the goal of the Baffin Bay whaling fleets to reach which the ice-filled waters of Melville Bay had to be crossed. The explanation of the North Water is still obscure, but the immediate cause must be continual vertical mixing currents.

South of the Davis Strait Ridge the Canadian Current continues at an average rate of six to twelve miles per day carrying with it much of the pack ice from Baffin Bay and icebergs from the Greenland fiords. Many of the latter strand on the shallower banks—the author has counted a hundred or more giants in sight at a time from a Baffin hill-top. Off Hudson Strait it is joined by another outflowing current and continues as the cold Labrador Current till it is lost off the coasts of Newfoundland. Here, winter pack ice upsets local navigation and in early summer the icebergs finally melt after reaching the main Atlantic shipping lanes.

HUDSON BAY AND STRAIT, FOXE BASIN

This is a large very enclosed water system, mainly shallow, occupying an area of crustal depression under a very recent ice load. There are tongues of deeper water extending from Nottingham Island towards Churchill and Melville Peninsula: a sill across from Charles Island to Cape Dorset separates the inner area from the rather deeper trench of Hudson Strait. Even here, there are only a few holes over four hundred metres in depth.

There is a slight admixture of Atlantic water from the Labrador Sea into the outermost part of the system, Ungava Bay,
and it is believed that some of this influence has been felt of
recent years in Hudson Bay itself. On the whole, though, this
consists of cold Arctic water with intense stratification in
summer when much fresh water is poured into its southern half
and surface temperatures in these low latitudes rise to 8°,
9° or 10° C.

The currents follow the anti-clockwise pattern prevailing
in an enclosed northern sea. Icebergs from the Canadian
Current move in along the south coast of Baffin Island, but
seldom further than Big Island. The outflowing current from
Hudson Strait swings around Ungava Bay and presses strongly
against its eastern shore before escaping to the Labrador coast.

Knowledge of ice conditions in the bay, apart from the
summer season, was surprisingly chaotic until only 1949 when
a piece of work that can be described as a scientific detection
story was carried out. Inhabitants on the low shores could see
the fast ice growing seaward and beyond the floe edge misted
with frost smoke. The general belief was that beyond this was
mainly open water in midwinter. Geographers at McGill
University, especially Burbidge, became convinced from
meteorological evidence that this could not be so. The prevailing
westerly winds brought heavy precipitation (snowfall) and
warmer temperatures to the eastern or Quebec shore until the
end of December as would be expected if open water in quantity
were present. But conditions changed sharply in January;
snowfall slackened and the temperature gradient from east to
west coast vanished.

This seemed to show that after the new year the bay had
become virtually 100 per cent. ice covered and for meteorological purposes was 'land'. Air reconnaissance in the succeeding
few winters after publication of this theory vindicated it precisely.

Little of this large expanse of ice cover finds its way out of
Hudson Strait, the vast majority rots *in situ* with the summer
warmth. Later in the season, Foxe Basin ice moves out along
the Southampton shore and often blocks the strait again
temporarily. In unfavourable years, however, this tends to stay in
place, particularly on the west Baffin coast, which can often be
quite unnavigable. In 1957, the Canadian Eastern Arctic

Fishery's vessel *Calanus* was unable to move at all from her winter quarters on Rowley Island.[1]

BERING SEA AND STRAIT, CHUKOT SEA

This region as one of the portals of the North Polar Sea needs a more detailed treatment. The Russians exclude all the Bering Sea from the 'Arctic Ocean'. Dunbar shows only the north-west corner on the Siberian shore as composed of 'Arctic' water. For treatment in this volume, the Bering Sea north of latitude 59° has been included, this parallel joining points on both coasts which we consider polar from the landward point of view.

This area certainly includes waters of purely Pacific character-istics; on the Alaskan side, the summer surface temperatures reach 8° to 10° C. with a salinity of less than thirty parts per thousand. This can be attributed largely to the run-off of warm, fresh water. Much colder water is found on the Siberian shores. The lower waters are more uniformly cold, but here we have no great depths to contend with: the northern part of the Bering Sea is shallow and flatter than any land area of com-parable size.

There is a summer current flowing from the south-east corner of the Bering Sea through the straits and then anti-clockwise around the Chukot Sea. But this is believed largely to cease during winter at which time the ice cover is more or less co-extensive with the area of the continental shelf. But this current pushes back the pack-ice limit to 72° or 73° in the Chukot Sea in summertime and is instrumental in clearing the roadstead at Nome at a date around 1 June.

Further east, the main North Polar Sea ice approaches close to Point Barrow at all seasons. Only a narrow gateway over shallow waters allows access to the east in summer, and in winter the polar pack grounds and piles up to awe-inspiring proportions at this northerly tip of Alaskan territory.

BARENTS SEA

Among the Arctic sea areas we are considering, that of the Barents Sea is most important commercially, owing to its well-developed fisheries. It is another 'special case' and it is

[1] *Arctic*, 10, No. 4, p. 245 (1957).

mainly shallow though much of it is deeper than two hundred metres. A four-hundred-metre deep boundary would place all of it on the continental shelf, however, with the exception of an entrant, Bear Island Channel, which extends to 30° E. longitude.

It is in this deeper channel that warm Atlantic water persists through the winter and it is believed to be the refuge for fish which come out to feed on the shallower banks when the warm water spreads over them in the summer months.

The warm Atlantic Current flows continually northwards past Vest Spitsbergen where, as was noted earlier, it forms the main inflow into the North Polar Sea. A cold counter-current flows south around the eastern shores of the Svalbard group.

The other branch of the Atlantic Current, the North Cape Current, along the Norwegian coast is responsible for the well-known ice free gulf which allows shipping to reach as far as Murmansk all through the year without hindrance from surface ice but, as those who took part in wartime convoys knew to their cost, through areas where temperature and other weather conditions are exceptionally wintry.

The normal ice limit is shown on the map (Fig. 44); it retreats north-eastwards from here during the summer until the southern approaches to Franz Josef Land may be cleared and only the east shores of Svalbard remain at all icebound.

OTHER SIBERIAN SEAS

In the other subdivisions of the ocean north of Siberia the familiar pattern of anti-clockwise orientation is weakly present, southward on the western island limits, northward on the eastern. The map (Fig. 62) shows the main ice areas persisting in summer with which the Soviet ice forecasting system has to be concerned. The development of winter fast ice and the Siberian *polynya* have already been mentioned (p. 102 above).

TIDES

The term Mediterranean has been applied to the Arctic Ocean in what may be called a propaganda vein. But as far as tides go, the term is consistent for in the North Polar Sea and its Asiatic subdivisions and the western American sections, tides are slight, seldom exceeding a foot or two in range and dependent tremendously on offshore or onshore winds which produce more significant low and high water.

In Baffin Bay, Hudson Bay and the southern Barents Sea areas, however, Atlantic tidal influence is felt and the tidal surge in two inlets, Ungava Bay and Frobisher Bay is as powerful as anywhere in the world.

Hudson Bay west coast tides run from twelve to fifteen feet but only a quarter of this value on the eastern shore. Hudson Strait has tides from twenty to thirty feet at springs but Ungava Bay and Frobisher have recorded up to fifty feet. The effect of this semi-daily rise and fall on the winter ice cover is tremendous, the hinging barrier is very rough and broken and the spring icefoot becomes a veritable ice cliff at low tide.

Once north of the Davis Strait Ridge tides become less and six to nine feet is a more usual spring's range.

In the Barents Sea the stream coming from the west causes tides of spring range twelve to eighteen feet on the Murman Coast.

CHANGES IN THE SEA CONDITIONS

As with atmospheric transfer of heat it has been observed that there have been striking changes in recent years in the marine circulation between tropics and poles. This appears to have been negligible in the Pacific Bering Sea gateway and to have been effective only in the Atlantic exchange. The main sources of evidence are the ice conditions in Vest Spitsbergen, Greenland Sea waters off Iceland, and in the thickness of ice cover and of the upper cold layer of water in the North Polar Sea.

Vest Spitsbergen was considered approachable for only three months at the beginning of this century. Now the sailing season has extended to practically six months.

In the Greenland Sea waters, Koch has analysed the conditions from 1898–1939. He shows severe ice seasons to have been 1918, 1917, 1907, 1934, 1912 and 1906 and mild ice seasons, 1933, 1925, 1930, 1931, 1904, 1936. The swing to mild conditions is obvious from these dates. In Iceland itself during 1880–99 there were only two light ice seasons, in 1900–19 there were eight and in 1920–39 seventeen seasons.

The *Sedov* drift forty-four years after that of the *Fram* showed the average ice thickness had diminished by a third from over three metres to over two metres and the upper layer of cold Arctic water from two hundred metres to a hundred metres.

Another event, the cause of which may be linked to warming of the Arctic Ocean, is the apparently unusual release of 'ice islands' from the Ellesmere shelf in the 1930–40 period.

As Dunbar has pointed out, a large increase of warm water addition must be balanced by increased outflow which, for a period anyway, must be of cold water. The Canadian Current would be increased in volume and would press more strongly against the Baffin and Labrador coasts and into Hudson Strait. This would result in just the opposite of an ameliorating effect, but if the increased circulation faltered in the 1940s the subsequent cooling effect is likely to be felt most in west Greenland and Svalbard waters while the Canadian eastern Arctic may warm up before the general cooling takes over.

If the Atlantic inflow should continue powerfully for a prolonged period there is the possibility that the upper layer of cold water in the Arctic Ocean would be completely flushed out, which would have a sudden and startling effect on the climate of the north as a whole and particularly to east Greenland and the Canadian east.

Russian oceanographic work on sediments in the North Polar Sea during the last few years has tended to show that this process has occurred in the lengthier past together with periods when *no* Atlantic circulation reached the Arctic Ocean at all.

FURTHER READING

Armstrong, T. E., 'The Ice of the Central Polar Basin', *J. Glaciol.*, 3, p. 105 (1957).
Billello, M. A., 'Formation, Growth, and Decay of Sea Ice', *Arctic*, 14, p. 3 (1961).
Dunbar, M. J., 'Eastern Arctic Waters', *Bull. 88*, Fisheries Research Bd. of Canada, Ottawa, 1951.
Koch, Lauge, 'The East Greenland Ice', *Meddelelser om Grønland*, 130, No. 3, 1945.
U.S. Navy Hydrographic Office, *Oceanographic Atlas of the Polar Seas*, Part 2, 1958.
Zubov, N. N., *The Ice-drift of the Central Part of the Arctic Basin*, Amer. Met. Soc. Translation, Cambridge, Mass., 1953

Chapter 6

ARCTIC FLORA AND FAUNA

ALL life and particularly that of man—primitive man earning his subsistence from his environment, is dependent ultimately on plants. Yet as we shall see in the next chapter the Arctic natives make little direct use of plants but their food, land and sea game, derive their existence from the herbage of the land and the minute plant life of the ocean. This latter is surprisingly rich, attaining a development in polar waters equal to or greater than that of any other marine areas. But the land vegetation is poor, both in quantity and in the number of species present.

By definition our polar regions lie beyond the limit of real trees: the area and its vegetation are described by the Finnish word *tundra*, meaning *barren land*. The tundra plants belong to five main groups:

1. Lichens, either on rocks or in mats on the ground
2. Mosses
3. Grasses and grass-like herbs
4. Cushion plants
5. Low shrubs.

There is an almost complete lack of *annuals*. Climatic conditions provide such a short growing season that the annual's life processes cannot be completed: there exists therefore a uniform régime of *perennials* which spring into life briefly each summer and remain dormant—in hibernation—for up to ten months of the twelve. But what seems to the human eye, jaded by the black and white winter-long landscape, a sudden rapid flowering, a burst of colour, is in fact, a rather slight if hurried affair. The very low annual growth rate is in fact the dominant factor of polar vegetation.

This is demonstrably obvious in some of the woody plants such as willow and juniper where annual rings can be counted in the stem (but with a microscope only). Examples have been noted of thumb-thick junipers four hundred years old. In terms of weight increase of plants Wilson has shown that the Arctic willow (*Salix arctica*) has on Cornwallis Island, N.W.T., an annual increment of about one-third the total plant weight; in temperate climates such an increase can take place in less than a week. Similarly the productivity of Cornwallis Island— the weight of plant material per unit area produced in a year— was of the order of 1 per cent. of that of a temperate climate region.

This very low growth rate seems due in great part to low temperature assisted by winds. Wind-chill is just as discouraging for plants as for man and houses. Shelter from wind will result in a much greater temperature at the surface of the plant's leaf; here particularly the reduction of wind speed near the ground makes for success for the *dwarf* vegetation, and curtails expansion upward. An extreme variation of temperature was observed by Wulff in Pearyland (latitude 82½° N.) on 19 May. With an air temperature of −12° C. a recording of +3° was made within a tuft of saxifrage, +10° within a cushion of dark coloured moss. Only still conditions with no air mixing could give such results from which we can see how Arctic plants can spring to life with below-freezing screen temperatures. The earliest flowering saxifrage (*Saxifraga oppositifolia*) has always amazed me by appearing to flower as soon as the snow cover exposes it to view. Thus the publishing of 'frost-free periods' for given northern stations is a useless exercise. Air temperature *per se* is not the determining factor.

Porsild quotes a case showing the incredible hardiness of some Arctic plants (in this case Richardson's willow). After a week of spring thaw the catkins were ready to expand when nearly three weeks of heavy frost returned, freezing the twigs solid so that they broke off at a touch like icicles. Yet on the reappearance of spring conditions, apart from such breakages, no apparent harm had been done and the willows flowered and ripened seed.

Wind-chill is not the sole factor inhibiting the tundra plants' growth. Arctic soils are also relatively infertile, although many soil constituents are present in normal quantities, they are deficient in nitrogen. The local precipitation seems to be rather

. Frozen strait, Franklin, N.W.T.

11. Boulder block raised by frost action (*see p.* 77)

. Ice-foot (*see p.* 97)

13. Pancake ice; in distance, Erebus volcano, Antarctica

14. Pancake ice, off Cape Evans, Antarctica (*see p.* 96)

free of combined nitrogen, leguminous plants are rare, and the nitrifying bacteria in the soil are inhibited in their activity by the low soil temperatures. Where nitrogen is present in quantity the comparative luxuriance of vegetation is startling. The well manured slopes below a cliff bird colony carry a lush growth and the orange splash of *Caloplaca elegans* the nitrophilous lichen. So too do *perching knolls*, even on exposed ridges where manuring by birds or foxes, who regard them as lamp posts, again results in an increased growth of herbs and the coloured *Caloplaca*.

Owing partly, however, to low nitrogen value and also to the long periods of sunlight in high latitudes where photosynthesis continues for twenty-four hours, the sugar level of plants is high—what scarce vegetation does exist is nutritious fare for the herbivorous animals.

Faced with the limiting factors of wind-chill, low nitrogen concentrations, the disturbance of the soil by permafrost, and scanty rainfall, tundra plants have developed many ways of overcoming their difficulties. Competition is with the physical factors, seldom with rival plants as is usual in more favoured regions.

Most species take several years from seed germination to their first flowering season and many in fact do not rely on seed production for propagation but on various means of vegetative reproduction—underground budding for instance from creeping rootstocks.

For protection against desiccation and drifting snow and sand, many of the cushion plants hide their wintering buds by having them under the soil or within the mass of dead leaves of former years. In this way the buds are enabled to bloom and mature seed in a month or so once the summer comes, and while the seed is maturing new buds are developing and food is being stored in the subterranean stems. Yet some grasses which rely on wind-borne seeding for reproduction do grow tall stems projecting above most of the winter snow cover so that the winter blizzards will spread far afield the seed which has not matured and lost its husk until the autumn.

We can divide the tundra vegetation into six main plant communities in three groups.

I

1. Fell field (*fjaeldmark*) communities. Here the vegetation is 'open'—it is so scantily developed that the ground is never covered with a complete sward but individual plants are scattered over its surface. We can distinguish:

(*a*) The rock desert community with crustaceous and foliose lichens (rock tripe) growing on the rocks, and between them other lichens, mosses and cushion plants, such as moss campion (*Silene acaulis*) and various saxifrages. One of the most pioneering plants of all, often the first to colonize a glacier's moraine, is the yellow Arctic poppy (*Papaver radicatum*).

(*b*) Gravel flat communities. On the frequently flooded areas of braided streams, often covered by persistent icing (*naled*), the short growing season again restricts vegetation to the hardiest of the colonizers.

2. Tundra communities. Here the vegetation is more continuous, the winter's snow protection more complete. We distinguish:

(*a*) Dwarf shrub—heath tundra. The creeping willows, dwarf birch and berry-bearing members of the *Vaccinium* family are interspersed with Arctic heather (*Cassiope*) and a carpet of mosses and 'moss' lichens (*Cladonia*). This is the most diverse of the plant communities and the most colourful area of the tundra.

(*b*) The grassland tundra. On the damper and rawer soils and on alluvial flats of former rivers and lakes, grasses and sedges predominate with, in the wetter parts, great development of sphagnum moss and cotton grass (*Eriophorum*). Where differential frost heaving in wet mineral soil is dominant the typical tussocks (*niggerheads* in Alaska, þufur in Iceland) are developed. Each tussock which can be a foot or more in height, has a core of heaved mineral soil and a tuft of dead rhizomes and leafbases on the top and sides. It can afford one of the more abominable walking surfaces in the tundra area.

(c) Willow and alder thickets. Where abundant summer water is available as on stream banks and below late-lasting snow patches, the nearest approach to forest and the best source of wood supply in the tundra will occur. Associated with the willow bushes are fireweed (*Epilobium*) horsetails (*Equisetum*) and sedges and grasses.

3. Shore communities. There is a normal development of salt-tolerant grasses and sedges in tidal flats in the Arctic together with the sandwort (*Arenaria*) scurvy grass (*Cochlearia*) and the sea pink.

PLANT LIFE OF THE WATERS

Small, shallow freshwater lakes which lose their ice cover early and warm up rapidly in summer have a quite rich plant life including many vascular forms. But in the cold water of larger lakes vascular plants are rare and in the sea are replaced with a rich microflora, algae and diatoms.

Cold water and especially water recently melted from ice has a high concentration of trihydrol [polymerized water molecules $(H_2O)_3$] which has been demonstrated as having a beneficial effect on the growth and division of plant cells. Moreover cold water can have a higher concentration of dissolved gases CO_2 and O_2. In the latitudes of the long day photosynthesis can go on continuously provided the sun's energy is not impeded by thick ice. We see in fact a positive brown staining of the waters around the pack ice and in pools on its surface when in August the diatoms are multiplying at a tremendous rate. And in places where there is considerable vertical interchange with upwelling currents nutrient salts may be brought to the surface.

Shoreline marine plants are rare in Arctic waters, the larger seaweeds are too often rubbed from their moorings by ice, but some kelp beds flourish and in the regions of ice free water around the sub-Antarctic islands some of the largest algae in the world are found.

WILDLIFE

Because of the lack of vegetated ground there are no truly land animals or birds in the Antarctic regions. Here the life is

entirely marine with an occasional overflowing on to the land
or ice of breeding penguins and sleeping seals. But in the north
we have in addition to the rich life of the seas a considerable
land fauna as well—like the plants few in species but with
sometimes large numbers of an individual species such as the
lemming, the caribou, or the mosquito.

Sea temperatures remain fairly uniform throughout the year
—the marine mammal's layer of subcutaneous fat (blubber) is a
sufficient protection against the chill of the icy water. But on
land in the Arctic the animals have to submit to wide fluctuations of temperature and by various means have to adjust
themselves to this. These means may be divided into three
groups:

Hibernation or dormancy.
Migration.
Fur covering (or feathers).

The best-known fur bearer is the Arctic or polar fox (*Alopex
lagopus*). This beautiful little animal with his long *guard* hairs
and short underwool is so well protected against the chill (a
value of about 10 clo units) that Scholander has shown it has
no need to increase its 'metabolic rate', i.e. move about for
warmth, until the temperature falls below −40°. Its problem
is more how to lose heat in comparatively warm conditions but
like several other animals it has a summer coat of notably less
insulating quality. The musk ox (*Ovibos moschatus*) is another
example of the adaptation of fur—over his woollen undercoat
(from which excellent woollen stockings have been made)
come the long guard hairs up to two feet in length which,
trailing almost to the ground, hide his feet from view. Not only
do northern animals generally have better winter coats but
they cover more of them; less of the skin around nostrils or feet
is bare and ears and tails of most species are shorter and more
furred than those of their southern relatives. The ptarmigan
even has the soles of his feet feathered.

Many northern animals grow a white winter coat to replace
a browner summer pelage. This is often cited as protective
coloration against a background of snow, but it is likely again
to be a physiological adaptation for warmth since the cells
normally filled with pigment hold instead air with its powerful

insulating qualities. The hair of the caribou which in its warmth-to-weight ratio is still the best clothing material known, is thicker at the tip than at the base, thus entrapping more air, and also contains many air cells within the hair stem.

One of the surprising exceptions to the white-coat rule is the raven who persists in wearing his majestic black plumage all through the Arctic winter. The raven can be taught to speak. His first words in the Arctic would be, I am sure, 'My feet are *freezing*.'

Hibernation or dormancy during the cold months is the method used by some animals. The lemming spend the winter under the snow surface, sometimes dormant in grass nests, sometimes active but invisible. They tend to store food over against the cold season—others store fat and relapse into a proper hibernation but there is a northern limit to the hibernators owing to permafrost and the tremendous length of the winter so that practically the only true example is the Arctic ground squirrel (*Citellus parryi*).

That entirely Arctic animal the polar bear (*Thalarctos maritimus*) is not a true hibernator. Most males (except it seems, in the Hudson Bay area) and younger bears are out on the pack ice all the year round, only the female who is expecting cubs dens up and lapses into a partial sleep while her cubs are born—one of the perils of the Arctic is to break through the roof of a mother bear's cave when the young ones, born minutely small, are still in with her before they move out to find food again.

To turn to the invertebrate world dormancy in some form, seldom the adult one, is the rule. Most of the Arctic insects spend the winter in a larval or even egg form—it seems an unkind twist of nature that they can survive at all, but were it not for their presence there would be none of the insect-eating smaller birds which enliven the summer tundra with their twenty-four-hour song.

These birds are typical of the migration habit which enables many Arctic dwellers to escape the winter's blast. Only the snowy owl, some ravens and some of the ptarmigan remain throughout the year on the tundra. A few sea birds stay much of the time in pools of open water that persist in tidal rip areas but this is really an exception to the rule that animals with sufficient mobility move south for the winter. Birds are the most mobile, next come the marine mammals. But as was noted above it is not the cold these latter are fleeing, it is the danger of ice forming over their heads. Two of the seals have learned to live with even this situation, the jar seal (*Phoca hispida*) and the bearded or square-flipper seal (*Erignathus barbatus*). They maintain breathing holes through the ice, often along lines of weakness, by means of their clawed front limbs, and caves are scratched out within the ice and its snow cover and above water. Some walrus persist in Arctic waters where tidal currents prevent or lessen ice formation but again many of these with the members of the whale family move to more ice free seas.

Few land animals have the capacity to travel far. The musk ox seldom leaves his native valley. The best-known migration is that of the caribou. Many tales are told of the countless numbers of *la foule*, their hooves clacking, passing the early tundra travellers. But the caribou's migration though usually southward into the trees, where they exist within a few hundred miles of their summer range, is a search for winter pasture—the lichen-rich (reindeer moss) areas, particularly well developed in the forest—tundra transition zone, not an escape from the climate. On Svalbard, Greenland, and many Canadian Arctic islands they remain the year round.

In the Antarctic where the life is essentially marine there tends to be a migration movement northward in winter. The few land areas in summer are crowded with penguins and other breeding birds but one of these, the emperor penguin, seems to defy all reason by breeding in midwinter. Their eggs are laid on the bare fast ice and hastily moved into a breeding 'pouch' above the parent's feet to be there incubated in darkness and deeply subzero temperatures. As the bay ice breaks up in the succeeding summer the young birds, still unable to swim properly, float out to sea on their home. It is this delayed growth that probably forces these birds to breed at this extraordinary season.

PREDATOR PREY RELATIONS

In the polar world the usual division of animals into vegetarians and predators prevails. A schematic chart shows the food relationship of some of the major groups. The Arctic wolf stays close to the caribou herds, the bear's main food is the ring seal, the fox's the lemming, though in places where the lemming or other small rodents are missing they make do with ptarmigan or hares. Often the fox is a camp-follower of the bear, feeding on the scraps of seal or fish left by him.

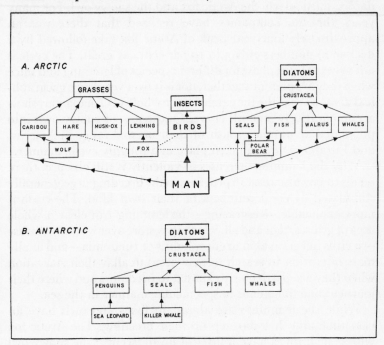

Fig. 45. Polar Food Chain.

In the Antarctic where the land-based food chain is absent the overwhelming importance of marine crustacea is shown. Man is shown as missing from the chart here though this is only true of native hunting man, economic man is now a serious predator on the whale population and was in the recent past on the seal group. On the Antarctic land the penguin and seal are safe hence their (as yet) lack of fear of men, though penguin chicks have plenty to fear from predatory southern birds.

CYCLES

An interesting point concerning the numbers of certain Arctic animals which has received a good deal of study is a cycle of abundance and scarcity. The basis of this three- to four-year cycle is the number of rodents—lemmings, mice and voles, as in the American sub-Arctic regions it is the varying hare (*Lepus americanus*) that results in a nine- to ten-year cycle.

The lemming cycle has repercussions in numbers of its pre-dators, particularly the Arctic fox and the snowy owl. For many years the fur companies have realized that there was an approximately four-year peak of Arctic fox take followed by a decline to numbers only 5 to 10 per cent. as great. The cycle is not necessarily in phase for different species of lemming and mice when they are present together, nor is it over very large geograph-ical areas so that the fur catch for the whole of Canada may show a comparatively smooth curve. Outbreaks of snowy owls into populated areas much south of their normal range in America and Eurasia have also taken place in a roughly cyclic manner.

Why the lemming increases so violently is still obscure, there seems to be an increase in progeny, in the breeding urge generally stimulated by great numbers of their own kind. The crash is more explicable, overgrazing—the lemming can clear a whole area of grasses, root and all, which they store over winter—disease —a virus infection akin to encephalitis or tularemia—and finally mass migration in search of new areas to allay their starvation when they are particularly exposed to predators and where their journey sometimes ends in spectacular manner in the sea.

While the lemmings are abundant foxes and owls have an easy time and they too step up their breeding. The Arctic fox will at such times have a litter of up to twenty; the snowy owl will raise seven or eight young. But with the lemming crash comes their famine; the owls may move southward, the less mobile fox must reduce his numbers—once again by a combina-tion of starvation and disease.

In these pages we can discuss only some of the geographical facts of polar life—certain distributions, the importance to man and such attempts as have been made toward a rational conservation of the wild life resources.

The two main forms of lemming are *Lemmus*, which remains brown all year, and *Dicrostonyx* which changes to a white coat in winter. They occupy very similar ranges though *Dicrostonyx* appears to prefer drier ground to *Lemmus*. Both are absent in Svalbard and in Greenland from Scoresby Sound round the south to latitude 81° on the west coast. In north and east Greenland we have *Dicrostonyx* only: in Scandinavia *Lemmus* only. Their importance to man is entirely indirect—from the commercial value of their predator, the Arctic fox.

The Arctic hare and the ermine, both again of very limited importance to man, are absent from Svalbard; the former is very widespread in the northern Canadian islands.

One of the most decidedly Arctic animals which cannot claim close relationship with other species in temperate latitudes is the musk ox (*Ovibos moschatus*). The generic name indicates scientific doubt as to whether he belongs to the sheep or the cattle. When J. M. Wordie brought young musk ox to Britain in the 1920s the animals languished for some time in Aberdeen while the railway officials argued as to whether they should travel under the regulations for sheep or for cattle. The musk ox has a natural enemy in the wolf and against this has developed the hollow square defence with cows and calves protected by a ring of bulls who make occasional short aggressive charges. But this defence is unavailing against man—even man armed with bow and arrow alone. We find today therefore the musk-ox range limited to virtually uninhabited Canadian Arctic islands and north and east Greenland with one or two pockets on the Canadian mainland where man is a rare visitor.

The caribou with its domesticated relative the reindeer, is the most important land animal to the Arctic natives. In Eurasia west of the Yenisey, domesticated deer have virtually displaced the wild ones, and the latest estimate from the U.S.S.R. is that the northern (Arctic) part of the range is fully utilized. But in North America and Greenland there have been up till recently no attempts to introduce reindeer pastoralism, and never any attempt by the Eskimo to tame the wild caribou. In these areas there has been over the past century an alarming and accelerating decline in the caribou population. Published estimates by the Canadian wild life authorities for the barren ground caribou (excluding those of Baffin Island and the Queen Elizabeth Islands) are:

1900	1,750,000
1948–50	670,000 reduction of 60% in 50 years
1955	277,000 reduction of 60% in 5–7 years

This terrible decline has been attributed to many causes, predation by wolves, disease, burning of lichen range and over-hunting by the native use of rifles. The weight of evidence is that the last is most important, but there have been disastrously low calf crops in some years in the 1950s, 1950, 1951 and 1955 all being well below 10 per cent. increase. Since it has been estimated that predation and disease cause a loss of 9 per cent. and human utilization 12 per cent., it is obvious that nothing less than a 21 per cent. calf increase will stop the decline, let alone build up numbers again (*see Plate 17*).

An estimate of the Alaskan caribou population for 1942 was 500,000 (on the decrease), and recent observations in the Queen Elizabeth Islands indicate that caribou are less numerous than musk ox which have enjoyed Canadian protection since the 1920s.

The depletion of this vital polar wild life resource has completely altered the lives of some of the native inhabitants. Whole groups of inland Eskimo have starved or have had to move: the source of winter clothing on which many North American inhabitants depend has dried up. Legislation has been proposed to prevent the killing of calves at any time, females from 1 January to 31 July and the use of ·22 rifles, which can maim more often than kill, or the feeding of dogs on caribou. Something of this kind is essential, otherwise the caribou, harried by wolves, by the parasitic warble fly which lays eggs in its hide, but above all by often unthinking man, will soon go the way of the buffalo. Although large concentrations of individuals often obscure the fact, the general *productivity* of Arctic land is slight; wild life resources may very easily be depleted.

MARINE LIFE

We have seen that vegetable and animal life on land in the Arctic is comparatively slight and in the Antarctic virtually non-existent. But in the seas of both polar regions life is abundant, reaching a maximum at the ice-edge or the mixing zone between polar and warmer waters which is unexceeded elsewhere in the world. At a time when population pressure is causing widespread concern among those interested in man's food supply, much attention is being focused on the potential of the world's oceans. In the polar regions this has always been so—the Eskimo of the north, with a small number of inland caribou hunters excepted, and the white commercial hunters of the south, depend on the ocean produce—only to a limited extent on the produce of the land.

The chain of marine food supply is founded on the floating microscopic plants—the phytoplankton. Next link is the group

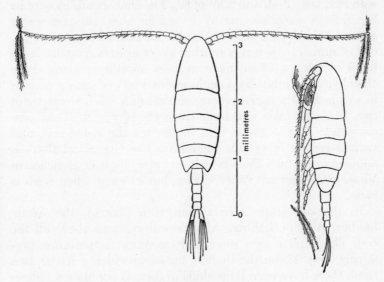

Fig. 46. Calanus.

of creatures, the animal plankton, feeding directly on this—particularly the crustacea, amphipods and copepods. The illustration (Fig. 46) shows one of these most important polar creatures, *Calanus*.

Many of the cold-water plankton crustacea grow larger than their near relatives in warmer seas and this is true of fishes (nekton) also. This appears to be due not to speed of growth, which is in fact slower, but to delayed sexual maturity.

FISH

In truly Arctic waters the fish play a minor role compared to the marine mammals in the human economy.

But the reverse is true in seas where there is an admixture of warmer Atlantic or Pacific waters. Here in the Barents Sea and off south-west Greenland where this admixture takes place over a fairly shallow bottom we have very rich fisheries.

The most truly Arctic fish (*the* fish, *ikaluk*, in Eskimo) is the Arctic char (*Salvelinus alpinus*) a member of the salmon family with red, tasty flesh and a lot of fat. The char spends most of its life in fresh water coming to the sea for a few summer weeks after about the fifth year of life. At this time of year, or at the end of summer when it is waiting to get upstream again, large hauls of fish are often made in river mouths or along shore close by. The author has caught one this way of sixteen pounds in weight but the more average size of adult fish is a quarter of this. In Arctic lakes and large rivers the lake trout (*Cristivomer namaycush*) is also found and in the sea the polar cod, and various species of cottids (sculpins). The Greenland shark is another fish which favours colder water, its liver is richer in Vitamin A than any other species, but its meat when fresh is toxic.

In the sub-Arctic waters many fish abound, the Arctic halibut, Atlantic halibut, Atlantic salmon, and above all the cod. The latter is very susceptible to water temperature, preferring 2°–4° C. on the shallow banks on which it feeds. As a result there have been large shifts in the cod population following changes in the marine circulation. One such example is the rapid growth in cod numbers off south-west Greenland during this century but a significant change has been noted in recent years—the cod were smaller in the 1950s than in the 1930s and were moving southward again, a reversal of the earlier trend.

MAMMALS OF THE SEA

The large sea mammals are the most conspicuous members of the polar wild life and are all of them of direct importance to hunting man. Ruthlessly exploited in the past it is with these creatures that some of the more successful attempts have been made of recent date to conserve existing stocks and provide a continuing supply. We are concerned with three zoological sub-orders each of three families.

Sub-order			Family
1. *Pinnipedia*	(a)	*Otariidae*	Eared or Fur seals
	(b)	*Phocidae*	Hair seals
	(c)	*Odobenidae*	Walrus
2. *Odontoceti*	(a)	*Physeteridae*	Sperm whales
(Toothed whales)	(b)	*Delphinidae*	Dolphins
	(c)	*Ziphiidae*	Bottlenose whales
3. *Mysticeti*	(a)	*Balaenidae*	Right whales
(Baleen whales)	(b)	*Rhacianectidae*	Grey whales
	(c)	*Balaenopteridae*	Rorquals

The fur seal family lives only on the edge of our region both north and south and has been seriously harried by man. In the Bering Sea we find the rare northern or Steller's sea-lion, *Eumetopias jubata*, but far more evident is the Alaska fur seal, *Callorhinus ursinus*. This animal breeds in extremely limited localities, the Pribilof and Komandorski islands of the Bering Sea and along with man is perhaps the only creature of which censuses are taken. In the winter the fur seals spread out over the northern Pacific but in summer they haul out on the island beaches to breed with standing room only. They are intensely polygamous, the huge males collecting a harem of much smaller females, who after a year's gestation have just delivered their pups. They were seriously reduced in numbers prior to 1911 when an international agreement limited their slaughter to the three-year-old (or thereabout) young males during the breeding season. On the U.S. controlled Pribilofs the herd has recovered to numbers of about two million from a low of not much more than 5 per cent. of this.

The southern fur seal, *Arctocephalus australis* and other kindred species has suffered much more, and there is now no real annual take of skins. Their chief haunt in past times was the South Shetland Islands where in two years after discovery, 1821 and 1822, 320,000 skins were taken and in ten years they had been nearly exterminated. Other locations of this seal are Macquarie Island, Marion Island, Kerguelen, the South Orkneys and South Georgia; in each of these areas they have been reduced from tens of thousands to a few hundreds of individuals. In more temperate southern islands such as Lobos Island and Gough Island their fate is more secure due to modern conservation regulations.

The hair seals of polar waters are listed below (*see also Plate 23*):

(*a*) *Arctic*
1. Harbour seal   *Phoca vitulina*
2. Jar or ring seal   *Phoca hispida*
3. Bearded seal   (square flipper) *Erignathus barbatus*
4. Harp seal   (saddleback)   *Phoca groenlandica*
5. Hooded seal   (bladder nose)   *Cystophora cristata*

(*b*) *Antarctic*
1. Weddell seal   *Leptonochytes weddelli*
2. Crabeater seal   *Lobodon carcinophagus*
3. Ross seal   (rare)   *Omnatophoca rossi*
4. Sea leopard   *Hydrurga leptonyx*
5. Sea elephant   *Mirounga leonina*

The first three are the universally distributed wintering seals mentioned above, those of most use to the Eskimo, as will be described in the succeeding chapter. The next two are migratory seals which have been exploited commercially by white men. The harp seal is widely spread in the Atlantic–Arctic area in summer and moves in late autumn to breeding grounds on the pack ice in the White Sea, the Greenland Sea, and the Gulf of St. Lawrence. It is here in March that the annual slaughter averaging half a million of adults and young (white coats) alike took place. Recent falls in the numbers taken has led to realization that there has been serious over-exploitation. The bladder nose seal, also breeding on the Greenland Sea pack ice, is less common and is seen in summer in numbers only around the Greenland coasts.

In the Antarctic seals have no enemies on land save man and after even a century of experience of the latter's ruthless habits are still 'tame' and can be approached without difficulty. The sea leopard is a large animal reaching over a thousand pounds in weight and preys on penguins in the water. The sea elephant resembles the fur seals in its gregarious and polygamous breeding habits and has been similarly hunted to near extinction in many former haunts on all the sub-Antarctic islands, but with present protective measures it now appears to be holding its own.

The remaining pinniped is the walrus, divided into two species, the Atlantic and Pacific. It is a habitant of the shallow waters, feeding on clams and other bottom fauna which it can root up with its ivory tusks. Once again its habit of hauling up on shelving, rocky benches in certain favoured localities has proved a fatal attraction to the hunter and its numbers have been vastly reduced. In certain areas, particularly northern

Foxe Basin where it remains the year round, it is still an important resource for the Eskimo.

The history of both Arctic and Antarctic seas is closely bound up with the pursuit of the members of the whale family which include in the blue whale, not only the largest existing animal but the largest in the world's long history. Some of this story with the present economic situation of this world industry will be given in a later chapter—for it is in the Antarctic that the industry exists today, the northern seas have been nearly emptied by centuries of pursuit. Two groups of whales are of concern to us and these are listed below with brief notes on their present distribution.

ORDER CETACEA

Sub-order *Odontoceti*
Family *Physeteridae*

Physeter catodon	Sperm whale	Chiefly tropical waters but males in summer penetrate to the Bering Sea, Davis Str. and the South Shetlands

Family *Delphinidae*

Grampus orca	Killer whale	Arctic and Antarctic
Delphinapterus leucas	White whale	Arctic only
Monodon monoceros	Narwhal	Arctic only, not now Siberia

Family *Ziphiidae*

Hyperodon ampulatus	Bottlenose whale	Summer only in Greenland and Barents Sea areas

Sub-order *Mysticeti*
Family *Balaenidae* (Right whales)

Balaena glacialis	Biscay whale	Rare or extinct
Balaena mysticetus	Bowhead whale	Arctic seas
Balaena australis	Southern right whale	Sub-Antarctic seas to New Zealand

Family *Balaenopteridae* (Fin whales)

Balaenoptera borealis	Sei whale	
Balaenoptera physalus	Finback whale	All can be seen in Arctic waters but chiefly in the Antarctic
Megaptera nodosa	Humpback whale	
Balaenoptera musculus	Blue whale	

Only the *Delphinidae* (dolphin family) will be mentioned here. First we have the killer whale, a black-and-white monster with its high 'danger signal' back fin which in fortunately small numbers haunts both the northern and southern seas. Its chief food is seals and other small whales, often driving them close inshore in terror as it has done before now to men caught on the pack ice in dangerous proximity to this puffing killer.

The white whale or beluga (only white when it is adult) and the narwhal are both of some importance to northern natives

and to the outside world. At times confined in autumn by growing ice into small pools a great killing can be made described by
the Eskimo as *savssat*. The great delicacy is the outer skin or
maktak which is eaten raw, boiled or 'pickled'. This peculiar
skin is the dolphin family's weakness if stranded ashore as it is
very susceptible to the sun and the animals can die of sunburn
in a few hours. The white whale inner hide is the porpoise-hide
of commerce that provides the finest bootlaces. The narwhal
has an extraordinary ivory tusk up to nine feet in length of
spiral growth and representing actually an enlarged canine of
the upper jaw. This was the unicorn's horn of medieval commerce more prized than gold as it had an antidotic effect on
poisons. So they alleged in those days when poison was an
occupational hazard of medieval courts.

In considering the importance to man in the polar regions of
the wild life we cannot leave out two other important groups—
the birds and the insects. The northern tundra, comparatively
silent in its long winter whiteness, springs to life and sound with
the arrival of migratory song-birds, waders, auks, gulls, ducks
and geese, and the less desirable sound of the humming of
countless mosquitoes. And in the Antarctic the bird life, particularly that of the penguins, provides one of the few pleasures
and humours of the lifeless continent.

The ducks and geese and auks and their eggs provide a minor
but welcome change of diet to the northern natives—in the past
the gyrfalcon of Greenland was an important article of medieval
trade reaching the hands of Arabian princes from (originally)
the Norse settlers.

But the insect life, vital for the smaller birds which breed on
the tundra and raise their broods on the plentiful insect fare, is
one which most directly affects man—essentially the mosquito.
Parts of the marshy tundra can become uninhabitable except by
a man most psychologically adapted to the mosquito-filled air
and immune by long experience to their bites. 'Cold and mosquitoes—these two miseries never come together' is an Eskimo
saying. The fact is that mosquitoes are very temperature-sensi-
tive and as latitude increases, the season during which they will
fly and bite diminishes. In North America it becomes virtually
nil at latitude 74° when the number of hours at 50° F. (10° C.)
or higher, the biting threshold, are very few. Wind is another

5. King penguins, South Georgia

16. Husky dog

7. Caribou bull, chewing piece of discarded antler to get lime (*see pp.* 121–122)

18(i). *Cassiope tetragona*

18(iv). *Rhododendron lapponicum*

18(ii). *Salix arctica*

18(v). *Ranunculus glacialis*

18(iii). *Campanula uniflora*

18(vi). *Saxifraga aizoides*

inhibitor of mosquito activity but because it can blow the insects considerable distances, area control by lethal sprays on the tundra seems not feasible. Modern repellants now give good protection to the exposed skin for several hours but only if the subject avoids heavy sweating.

Mosquitoes are the most evident of insect life on the tundra, the other biting flies such as blackflies (*Simulium*) and deerflies (*Tabanus*) are confined to the forest or its immediate vicinity. But butterflies, spiders and bumble bees all thrive during the brief Arctic summer and the pools and damp soil are full of other insect life such as the springtails.

Much of the importance of the wild life to man will be brought out in the next chapter. But in addition to providing him with food the animal life brings some dangers. Direct danger is slight—like other animals in the world they tend to fear and avoid man. But the polar bear, particularly on the Arctic Ocean and uninhabited northern islands, can mistake man for his more usual dinner—walrus in the water, when provoked, can and do attack small boats—the killer whale is always worth giving a wide berth. Some indirect dangers come from transmissible disease. The northern mosquitoes are fortunately not vectors of malaria or other disease. But the polar bear is highly susceptible to trichinosis and as recently as the Second World War, parties have succumbed to this disease from eating insufficiently cooked bear meat. Its liver too is toxic, a fact well known to Eskimo who will not feed it to their dogs. Only recently has this toxicity been found to consist of an over-concentration of Vitamin A.

Compared to life in the tropics or other parts of the world man has little to fear from the rest of natural life which is as fascinating as anywhere.

FURTHER READING

Bliss, L. C., 'Adaptations of Arctic and Alpine Plants to Environmental Conditions', *Arctic*, 15, pp. 117–44 (1962).

Polunin, N. V., *Circumpolar Arctic Flora*, Oxford Univ. Press, 1959.

Porsild, A. E., 'Plant Life in the Arctic', *Can. Georg. J.*, March, 1951.

Elton, C., *Voles, Mice and Lemmings*, Oxford, 1942.

Rousseau, J., 'Les zones biologiques de la Péninsule Québec-Labrador', *Can. J. of Botany*, 30 (1952), pp. 436–74.

Rodahl, K., *Hypervitaminosis*, A. Norsk Polarinstitutt Skrifter, 95 (1950).

Scheffer, V. B., *Seals, Sealions, and Walruses*, Stanford Univ. Press., 1958.

Wiggins, I. L., and J. H. Thomas, *Flora of the Alaskan Arctic Slope*, Arctic Inst. of N. America Spec. Pub. 4 (1962).

Wilson, J. W., 'Arctic Plant Growth', *The Advancement of Science*, 53 (1957), p. 383.

Chapter 7

NATIVE PEOPLES

No native peoples were found in the Antarctic continent when this was first reached by white men in the nineteenth century. Too long a stretch of stormy sea separates it from the closest land, Patagonia, which was the furthest penetration of the native American.

But around the Arctic Mediterranean there has been for several millennia a thin sprinkling of peoples, diverse in tongues and probably in racial origin, but unified by a great similarity of material culture. This culture by means of which these tribes have been able to exist and combat the harsh conditions of tundra life is well deserving of close attention—the later literate invaders such as the Norsemen, Russians and even twentieth-century Americans, Canadians and Danes have found much of it worth while adopting.

The race most studied and whose culture is most highly adapted to the conditions is the Eskimo and these people will be described in greater detail. But across the Eurasian Arctic fringe are distributed other peoples whose way of life is very similar. The basis of existence is fourfold—fishing, hunting sea mammals, reindeer herding and dog driving. The first is almost universal, the second and third are to some extent alternates, the last only developed in part of the polar circumference. We can in fact draw a diagram (Fig. 47) which illustrates the dominance of reindeer herding in the 'west' and its absence in the 'east'. An exception to ·this is the twentieth-century growth of reindeer herding among the Chukchi of the Anadyr basin. These two terms, 'west' and 'east', must be used when considering northern native peoples. The gap comes between Greenland and northern Europe, the dispersal centre was on the Eurasian continent to which America was an 'eastern' appendage.

The racial division of the northern peoples is fraught with

the usual dangers of this concept. We can distinguish linguistic groups but within even such races as Eskimo or Lapp there are such diverse appearances that it is impossible to dogmatize on their racial origin. For convenience the following major groupings will be termed 'races'.

1. Lapps.
2. Finno-Ugrians.
3. Tungus-Manchu.
4. Yakut-Turkic.
5. Palaeoasiatics.

We can be fairly certain that groups three and four are recent invaders of the Arctic fringe; two and five (which latter includes the Eskimos) were perhaps the original inhabitants

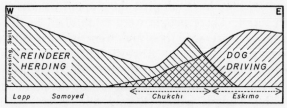

Fig. 47. Relative Importance of Reindeer and Dogs from Western Eurasia to North America.

of Asia's northern fringe. The Lapps are a separate mystery: at present their language is Finno-Ugrian in type but is likely not to be their original tongue. Some authorities put them as the descendants of the first colonizers of their home area, the Komsa Stone Age folk.

The Finno-Ugrians are represented today by the Nentsi (Samoyeds of former description) spreading from the Kola to the Taimyr peninsula. From here east the two recent invaders Tungus-Manchu—the Evenki, and the Yakuts speaking a Turkic tongue are intermingled up to the mouth of the Indigirka with the less nomadic Yakuts occupying the choicer river valley sites. East of here come the Palaeoasiatic tribes—the Oduly (Yukagirs), Chukchi, Koryak, Aleut and Eskimo, the last two predominantly represented on the American side of the Bering Strait.

For lack of any reliable history, traditions or valid archaeological evidence we may speculate that the Palaeoasiatic peoples followed the tundra region of Europe and Asia as it moved slowly northward with the retreating ice. And on reaching the sea coast they developed there an addition to their culture, the hunting of sea mammals. Or this latter phase may have developed in the Eskimo 'heartland', the Bering Sea, and spread east and west through these people of similar origin. Certainly the domestication of reindeer, one of the big forward steps in man's mastery of nature, developed far to the west in the north European area. The decline in reindeer herding technique eastward, till we find it absent altogether from the Eskimo territory (until recent introduction) indicates this.

The invasion of the Palaeoasiatic realm by Finnic people, the Samoyeds, may have brought in this deer culture, the more eastern invasion of the Tungus-Manchu people, now mainly deer herders, may have adopted this pursuit on arrival in the northern forest. These people were established in the middle Lena from at least A.D. 1000 and were in turn subjected to invasion by the Yakut people from·the Turkic steppe heartland, the Sayan mountain region, at the time of Mongol expansion from 1300 onwards. Thrust west and east by the more advanced Yakuts, the Tungus tribes (Evenki and Eveni) themselves displaced the Palaeoasiatics further west and further east in Asia. In the west only a small pocket (the Kety) now inhabit the middle Yenisey but in the east the Palaeoasiatics are still dominant and were in the Chukchi tribe at least sufficiently powerful to resist for some time the Russian penetration of the seventeenth and eighteenth centuries.

In more detail the approximate distribution of peoples is shown on the map (Fig. 48) It will be seen that the Eskimo have only a toehold on the Asian shore, the Aleut even less on the Komandorski Islands alone, and this a historic settlement of previously uninhabited islands.

Nearly all these Siberian 'races' have representatives further south within the forest fringe. Many in fact are reindeer herders who move seasonally on to the tundra and winter in the taiga: only some are permanent coastal dwellers and it is among these that the typical circumpolar culture survives which is best demonstrated by that of the Eskimo.

In the Eskimo we have one of the most remarkable adaptations of the human race to a peculiar set of geographical conditions. It is worth while to examine this in some detail, but it should be pointed out at once that the last decades have profoundly altered the Eskimo way of life in all the regions that he inhabits. The human geographers' interest is thus twofold— first to relate the primitive Eskimo's physiological make up, his material and social culture with the environment, and secondly to observe the changing conditions caused by the impact of modern technical civilization.

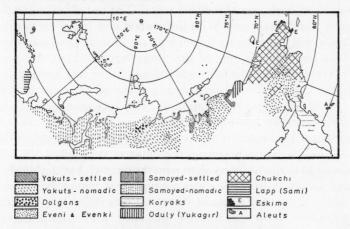

Yakuts - settled	Samoyed-settled	Chukchi
Yakuts - nomadic	Samoyed-nomadic	Lapp (Sami)
Dolgans	Koryaks	Eskimo
Eveni & Evenki	Oduly (Yukagir)	Aleuts

Fig. 48. Native Inhabitants of Northern Eurasia.

Although there are many considerable divergences, a standard physical type of the Eskimo race is easily describable. He is short, but not so short as, say, the Japanese. It is the legs and arms that are short with the torso long and very power- fully built. The head form is long with a ridged skull and massively developed cheekbones and lower jaw. It is on the cheekbones and around the eyes that the Eskimo quickly puts on fat and the epicanthal fold of the eye is not always present and is less strongly marked than in most 'Mongolian' races. His hair is black and coarse and body hair is comparatively sparse. Most Eskimo belong to the 'primitive' O blood group, lacking either A- or B-group elements. Although externally they appear to be broad nosed, the bony nasal passage is one of the narrowest known. This is the only obvious character which can be an advantage in a cold climate, but in addition, from recent experiments, the Eskimo race appears to be more

resistant to cold exposure, and to be able to digest and assimilate
fat to a greater degree than any European.

The original material culture of the Eskimo people on which
much has been written was an ingenious adaptation of the
limited materials available. His country is typically devoid
of wood, except drift wood, and the use of metals was originally
very slight. Meteoric iron in north-west Greenland and native
copper in northern Canada were used sparingly but there was
no smelting technique for either metal. The use of soapstone for
vessels was widespread. With little wood and less of metals the
Eskimo was even more dependent on animal products than
were many other people of the Stone Age. Perhaps the most
important of these products was animal fat for fuel, used in the
blubber lamp and consisting mainly of seal oil but sometimes of
the oil of fishes and other animals. This ingenious device, the
kudlik, is used for heating his dwelling and for cooking and it is
said that a good Eskimo wife is one who is skilled at tending the
lamp and particularly during the hours of sleep when she will
wake up at frequent intervals to trim the moss wick of the blubber
lamp. Yet even this device was not universal among the Eskimo
culture. In interior Canada where oil was difficult to obtain,
the blubber lamp was missing and their winter houses were
either totally unheated or were warmed by the burning of
sparse willow bushes.

Two Eskimo words—Kayak and Igloo—have attained
international currency. The kayak, the ultra-light fast sealskin
boat is one of the most refined objects of the Eskimo culture. It
is at present found in its best development in Greenland and
has ceased to play a part in much of the rest of Eskimo territory.
Yet even in a part of Greenland the skill in kayak making had
been lost at one time in history, and it was reintroduced in the
1860s by Baffin Island immigrants into the Thule district.
This is the only district in Greenland in which the ·winter
snow-house or igloo is still known. The finest development of
snow-house building is in the central Canadian Arctic and skill
in its construction diminishes again westward from here. The
classical igloo, as made by the best builders is an unbeatable
piece of architecture, combining strength, insulation and speed
of construction. The method of building from snow blocks cut
vertically in a well-formed, uniform snowdrift is shown in the

accompanying illustration. Once the key block is in, which will be less than an hour after the beginning of construction, and the chinking of the cracks completed from the outside with loose snow, the structure will ·be strong enough for a man or at least a boy to stand on the roof and will be warm enough with mere body heat inside to maintain a temperature 40° or 50° warmer than the outside air. In Alaska and Greenland where the art of snow-house building was not practised, the sod

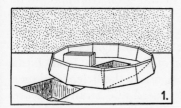
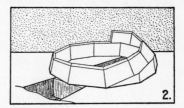
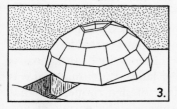

Fig. 49. Stages in the Construction of an Igloo.

dwelling or autumn house (Qarmat) was used—a semi-underground dwelling usually skin-roofed (as were the summer tents) which had fair insulation qualities but damp and un-hygienic compared with the temporary house of pure snow.

For clothing the Eskimo's main reliance was on the skins of caribou and seal. The former make the finest and warmest winter garments of extremely light weight and were also used for sleeping skins and occasionally, even for tent material among the interior tribes. The back sinew of the caribou is used for sewing and also for the construction of snares. Sealskin, in addition to making clothes, particularly the ubiquitous summer sealskin boot, has an immense number of uses. The skin of the larger seal, the square flipper, is used extensively in place of rope as sealskin line for sled lashings, traces for dogs, whips, etc.

A sealskin inflated and plugged is used as a bladder attached to the harpoon line for supporting big sea game. Seal intestines are used for translucent window material and also for constructing the kayak suit which enables the kayak rower to be completely weatherproof.

Various other animals have their minor uses. From bearskin are made special soles for winter boots which can be extremely quiet while crossing sea-ice when seal hunting in winter and provide also good insulation against the cold. Another use of bearskin is as the wiper for applying ice to the underside of sled runners. Musk-ox horn, though now very rare in Eskimo territory, has a variety of uses, due to its springiness, as scoops and spoons and the flexible arms of fish spears. Even birds have their uses—in some parts, particularly the Belcher Islands in former days, birdskin shirts were used and swan's feet are manufactured into a variety of bags including tobacco pouches. Whalebone, that is to say the ribs of the larger whales, was used for sled shoeing and sometimes for the rafters of autumn houses.

Vegetable products form a comparatively slight factor in the Eskimo's material culture. The resinous cassiope (Arctic heather) was extensively used for summer fuel, and moss is important for the wick of the blubber lamp. Peaty material was used for 'mudding' the undersurface of sled runners so that it would easily take a final ice surface. The eating of any vegetable materials was rare though berries, such as the blueberry, were collected and eaten in summertime. But essentially his diet was a purely meat one and the necessary vitamins were obtained by the consumption of liver and various intestinal parts of the animals, slightly, if at all, cooked. With meat the essential ingredient in the food supply, both for the family and for their dog team, the hunting of animals was the supreme and daily task. Seals, walrus and even white whales and narwhal were hunted in summer from the kayak. In wintertime the seals were patiently waited for at breathing holes, in spring they were stalked over the ice as they lay resting but scarcely sleeping on the surface. The caribou were hunted mainly with bow and arrow and occasionally with spear at particular crossing places of rivers or sometimes driven by means of men, and stone cairns, into a narrowing killing place. Fish were speared in the rivers in summer and jigged for through the ice in wintertime. Smaller game was the target of women and boys. Snares were set for the lesser animals, ducks and geese were hunted by the children. Egg collecting formed a brief occupation during the nesting season of summer. In thinking of the hunting methods and in fact the animals of the chase, it must be remembered that the Eskimo territory is widely diverse, varying from the unfreezing fiords of south-west Greenland to the interior tundra of Alaska and Canada. Essentially the hunter must be a nomad, although there are certain areas where the game is always plentiful and, in former times, where the caribou always passed on migration. Movement is necessary to gain the better hunting grounds and for an expanding population to reach new areas. It is only, as we shall see, in modern times that the Eskimo has tended to settle in concentrated communities.

SOCIAL CULTURE

Although the old order has changed everywhere in the twentieth century, in order to understand how the Arctic native can adapt himself to the present clash with white culture, it is necessary to examine his early social organization. In this respect the Eskimo probably resembled many of the earlier Stone Age cultures in that there was no real tribal organization of any kind. The family or, at most a few families was the largest organized group. Sometimes these would be centred about a man of particularly strong character, a good hunter, or in modern times the skipper of a boat's crew of men. Sometimes he would be a conjurer or shaman, one who was able to play on the superstitions of his fellow men. But this is not the place to go into the religious beliefs and mysticism of a primitive people. The important thing to remember is that the Eskimo with his social organization was and is psychologically adapted to this country of harsh environment. Nothing can be more comforting to the white man out with an Eskimo in an Arctic blizzard with night coming on, when he sees him after the first layer of blocks of a snow-house has been built, calmly take time off to strike up and light his pipe before continuing with the shelter which is essential for survival.

The primitive Eskimo had four important psychological attributes. First he set a high value on skill and to him skill meant particularly skilled hunting. The Eskimo's wealth was in his skill and in the songs he could sing about his achievements. He valued a white man who came into his territory, not for his own skills but for how he showed up at those of the Eskimo. A white man might be a magnificent radio operator but he was not considered highly unless he could shoot straight. Secondly the Eskimo set a low value on possessions. As a nomad all the family belongings could go on a komatik or in a single oomiak, (the larger skin boat). This resulted in essential honesty, not only because possessions were valued low but everyone knew what everyone else owned. Similarly, there was no building up of capital for the future which resulted again in the lack of thinking of tomorrow, which we consider one of the Eskimo's failings. These first two attributes together—his high value on skill and low value on possessions—resulted in considerable generosity and feasts to give possessions away. It was considered something fine to be in the position of giving material possessions away to one's friends. It showed off one's skill and one could sing a song about it. This results too in the difficulty the Eskimo has in understanding land as property. He can only regard land as subject to temporary usage rights and this has created difficulty in organizing registered trap-lines in places in the Canadian Arctic. The third great attribute was the importance of group survival in this fierce environment. This results in many things that the white man thinks of as wrong. There is considerable primitive communism, one may say, among the Eskimo people, the sharing of food when it is scarce. Female infanticide used to be practised when girls were less important to the survival of the group than were the potential hunters, the boys. Again there was the killing, or at least assisted suicide, of old people who were still loved but who had become a drag on the survival of the group. A feature resulting from this attribute together with the second is what we think of as loose sexual morals. The Eskimos are not possessive about their wives or their husbands. On occasions when it is suitable, they are quite prepared to trade one with the other. Nor are they so possessive about children, although their love for children is tremendous. There is therefore an exceptional number of adoptions, again often for purposes of convenience when one family may be too large and another be wanting children. This created difficulties when the R.C.M.P. were first trying to register and make a census of the Eskimo of northern Canada. A cheerful-looking family of four children might consist of—1. the husband's son by a former wife; 2. the wife's child by a former husband; and the remaining two adopted from so-and-so, a neighbour who had gone away on a trip. The fourth very important psychological attribute is extreme passiveness in personal relations. This results in an apparent lack of emotion; the emotion is present but is something that should not be shown. It is a desire, in effect, not to show oneself in a different mood from those around one. For instance, you may be bereaved but your companions have not been. Therefore you should not show emotion about the bereavement. In the same way, the Eskimo has a distaste for giving orders. He will not say, 'shut the door!' More likely he will say, 'One feels here that there is a draught somewhere.' Or even, when working a boat, instead of saying, 'Let go for'ard!' he will say, 'perhaps it is about time that the anchor was dropped.' They give, in effect, few orders to children and yet the children do seem remarkably disciplined and good. Much of this is due again·to the lack of possessiveness which is the normal cause of strife among white children. Family ties are in fact especially important in the Eskimo culture, the family being the essential cultural unit.

ESKIMO ARCHAEOLOGY

The pre-history of the Eskimo people, their origin and their relation to other native American races, is a subject which has been studied intensively in the last fifty years. We should remember that the Eskimo, who were encountered by the Norsemen, were the first of the New World natives to be seen by Europeans, yet in the central regions of northern Canada some tribes had had no contact with the white man prior to 1910. The study has been complicated by the great extent of the Eskimo's present territory, occupying, as it does, something like six thousand miles of coasts. Yet, within this territory there is, at the present time, a remarkable uniformity of language, culture, and race—unique perhaps among the primitive peoples of the world. Although much work has been done at the two extremes of the Eskimo settlement area, the Bering Strait region and in Greenland, there has been, until recent years, a large gap in our knowledge from the central Canadian territory. Yet it was here, on the Fifth Thule Expedition of 1922–4, that the first modern work on Eskimo archaeology was accomplished by Therkel Mathiassen. On the coasts of Hudson Bay, he demonstrated an early culture which he named the 'Thule Culture', based largely on the hunting of the great sea mammals, especially the whale. The 'Thule Culture' has now been traced all the way from Bering Strait to Greenland and appears to have originated in the former area and spread rapidly across the present Eskimo settlement area within the last thousand years. A return movement to Alaska took place even more recently and it is this wide, rapid diffusion of the Thule people from whom the present Eskimo stock seems descended that can account in large part for the present uniformity of language and culture.

We can, it seems, term the Bering Strait region the 'heartland' of the Eskimo people. Here always was and still is a rich hunting area with an abundance of seals, walrus, whales and fish, as well as access to the previously large herds of caribou in interior Alaska. Here, on the coasts and islands of the Bering Strait and Sea, grew up a culture highly artistic at first, though degenerating later, which by modern dating techniques we can put at more than two thousand years ago. The Bering Strait, once a land bridge, and still shallow today, at some period after the close of the last glaciation became open water deep enough to admit the passage of the large sea mammals, including whales, into the North Polar Sea and, for a period, it would seem that the movement of whales across northern Canada and through the Archipelago was a continuing process until rising land and the worsening climate of the Little Ice Age put an end to this access.

But before the development of the ancestral culture, the Old Bering Sea Culture, from which developed the Thule migration, there were earlier races of supposed Eskimo characteristic in the area, and earlier migrations. In 1948, at Cape Denbigh in Norton Sound, Giddings discovered an ancient culture—the 'Denbigh Flint Complex'—which is dated at six thousand years ago. The finds here included burins, end-scrapers, finely chipped side-blades, and lamellar flakes, and show definite affinities with European palaeolithic and mesolithic materials.

Other older Eskimo cultures have been discovered in eastern Canada and in Greenland where the material finds show close resemblances to those of the Denbigh Flint Complex, although undoubtedly separated by a gap of several thousand years. Prominent among these cultures is the Dorset Culture of eastern Canada, now also proved from Greenland as well. This was first named after the locality in southern Baffin Island where it was described by Jenness. It was undoubtedly older than the Thule Culture in places such as eastern Canada, where settlements of the two groups overlap, and it seems reasonable to hazard a guess that the earlier inhabitants of Greenland prior to the Norse arrival were of Dorset type, whereas the Thule people only reached Greenland at the same time or even later than the Norsemen. The Dorset people were apparently ignorant of the bow drill, the holes in their implements being cut or gouged, no evidence has been discovered of any cultural material in connection with dogs, nor did the Dorset people appear to be capable of hunting the larger marine mammals. The age of this culture, although comparatively recent perhaps in eastern Canada and Greenland, is still very little known but from the existing evidence the Dorset people appear to have left the Bering Sea region before the Old Bering Sea Culture had come to full flower. The linguistic change which will be referred to later, which occurs south of Norton Sound in Alaska, would appear to indicate that the present-day Eskimo peoples of these parts and even more so the Aleuts, speaking a different language again, were similar diversifications of the Bering Sea 'heartland' peoples, perhaps coeval with the migration of the Dorset group to further eastern lands.

During the historical period of white contact with Eskimo peoples many local variations of culture and way of life have been noted, some of which have given origin to different theories of the spread of Eskimo people. It was believed at one time, for instance, that the present small group of Eskimo inhabiting north-east Siberia were a recent backwash across the Bering Strait. Yet it seems that many place names along the Arctic coast, much further west than the present area of Eskimo occupation, belong to their language rather than to that of the Chukchi and, in fact, the Chukchi have an oral tradition of driving out a former coastal people. In the central Canadian

Arctic a method of seal-hunting in winter through the breathing holes has been developed, which appeared to be unique. But this is possibly only a special adaptation of the much wider general seal-hunting Eskimo technique. Similarly, in this region the use of snow-houses is much better developed than further east or further west where the skills may have been lost, due to the not so vital necessity of the knowledge. One particular group which has puzzled the investigators is the now sadly depleted caribou-Eskimo group of interior Keewatin. Among them all contact with the sea and the use of the blubber lamp had been lost, and one investigator argued that the present coastal-dwelling Eskimo had come from the interior and learned to hunt the sea mammals from an original caribou-hunting past. This theory is now discredited and the caribou-Eskimo are seen to be a specialized group who have moved inland following their favourite meat, until in the recent years of this present century that meat has vanished. Further investigation is vitally required from central northern Canada and from Siberia but the pattern of Eskimo pre-history now seems to be coming into view of an Asiatic origin, centred originally on the heartland of the Bering Sea with at least two and probably many more thrusts to the south and to the east, the last of which, the Thule thrust, has given rise to the modern Eskimo peoples with their peculiar uniformity.

LANGUAGE

Their language gives us very little clue to the genetic origin of the Eskimo. It appears to have no connection with any other Amerindian tongue, but some attempts have been made to prove a slight connection with the early Indo-European tongue, in which case the original contact can only have been in western Eurasia. The Aleutian language, though obviously connected, is certainly so distinct as to be considered a separate language, this evidence agreeing with recent carbon dating to show that the early Aleutian peoples must have lived three thousand years ago, since when all speaking connection with their Eskimo cousins has been lost. In the Bering Strait there is also a sharp distinction between Eskimo as spoken to the north of Norton Sound, which is very similar to the tongue of Canada and Greenland, and the language south of Norton Sound, the distinction having been likened to that between English and German, and the period of separation estimated at anything up to two thousand years. This helps the idea that the Thule migration took place subsequent to this date and is responsible for the uniformity in tongue right across from northern Alaska to Greenland. Knud Rasmussen, a native Greenland speaker, was completely intelligible at Point Barrow when he spoke there after his crossing of North America in 1924–5.

The language itself is poly-synthetic and has been regarded by Birket-Smith as resembling organic chemistry, since in both it is possible from a small beginning to build up imposing complexes by a logical application of definite rules. Despite a fairly complex grammar, there is no real distinction between nouns and verbs, nor does Eskimo suffer from genders, but despite many primitive characteristics, it can form abstract ideas and, although the vocabulary is comparatively limited, in things that matter to the Eskimo, such as seals and snow, the richness of shades of meaning is extraordinary. And certainly in Greenland, where there has been a long tradition of literature in the Eskimo tongue, modern phrases have been adapted to modern conceptions and a proper literary language has emerged.

THE NEW AGE

The description of Eskimo life and culture, which has been given above, is one of several decades ago. An entirely new way of life has been thrust on this northern race in recent years and the problem today is one of adjustment to the clash between the white culture and the Eskimo's culture. The influx of white men and ideas into the Arctic territories has been of very recent date, chiefly as the result of the Second World War. In the Soviet Union the integration of native peoples with the Soviet way of life has been a steady and deliberate policy since the revolution. In Alaska, in the spirit of free enterprise, things have been allowed to take a rather haphazard course, but the white man's ideas and civilization are now firmly implanted. In Greenland many years of miscegenation of the races and a slow paternalistic approach to the integration of the native people with a more modern way of life has resulted more favourably. In Canada, with its smaller, widely scattered population, there has been a generation (some thirty years) of limited contact, with the fur trade as the basis of economic change, until again the explosion of white ideas and peoples which took place during the Second World War. A return to the primitive way of life for any native people is impossible however much the sentimentalists may regret it. It should be remembered that the primitive life was full of discomfort, hardship and danger, and the people died young. The peculiar triumph of the Eskimo over the environment was cruelly expensive in human happiness. Here, however, we have a people physically and psychologically adapted to this environment, far more so than any white immigrant will ever be, and it is up to the governments concerned to ensure that this people, suitably adjusted to modern technology and needs, is able to take its continuing place in habitation of this vast region. After many years of population stagnation or even decline, the advance in medical help has resulted now in an expanding population, expanding too fast for the food resources of the area. In addition, in Alaska and in Canada and also in Greenland there has been a tremendous decline in the numbers of caribou, the skins of which are of such importance for winter clothing. As yet domestic reindeer herding has in no way been able to take the place of the caribou hunt. The fur trade, once the only economic means of earning a cash income for the Eskimo, has also been liable to considerable fluctuations and now a perhaps prolonged depression. In all the political areas of the Eskimo realm the food supply can no longer support the population and a large and increasing proportion must be wage earning, and for the sake of the corporate life and particularly schooling, now so urgently required, concentration in larger settlements is also essential. This has already taken place to a great extent in Greenland, where fishing and sheep farming industries are well established and it is happening in other parts of the Eskimo territory at airfields and mines. Frequently now the head of the family has become an electrician, a miner, or a carpenter, though many will undoubtedly remain as hunters dependent on the natural living resources of the country. Education takes at least a generation to catch up and only Greenland has so far had this opportunity. As with many primitive peoples throughout the world, primary education for all should come before secondary education for a few, but how seldom is this rule applied. But, given the opportunity and with a wise governmental control, there is no question that this cheerful, happy race of people can and will successfully undertake a great portion of all the work required in the lands which they now occupy.

FURTHER READING

Acta Arctica, Vol. 12 (1960), Copenhagen, various authors on archaeology and anthropology.
Birket-Smith, K., *The Eskimos*, London, 1936 and 1959 (rev. ed.).
Lantis, M., *Eskimo Childhood and interpersonal Relationships*, Seattle, 1960.
Rudenko, S. I., *The Ancient Culture of the Bering Sea and the Eskimo problem*, translation, Univ. of Toronto Press, 1961.

Chapter 8

TRANSPORTATION

TRANSPORT is the key to the polar world. Efficient transport has been the most important factor in the long story of exploration. It is just as vital today for the scientific research which is being carried out in the great expanses of interior Greenland and Antarctica and in the North Polar Sea, as well as in small-scale detailed work under the difficulties which the polar climate imposes. The settlements which have been established depend almost entirely on their transportation lifelines and on the machines or animals which can move between and around them. It is on the economics of transport that all plans for mining or for exploration work depend, though for the latter 'economic' may be the wrong term to use. The cost of transport definitely enters into the picture of civilian activities such as the Eskimo on his trap-line, the doctor making his rounds of an enormous scattered community, mines and airfields. For certain civilian exploration activities the cost, though important can scarcely be termed 'economic' and of course for military operations in the polar regions cost is seldom an item which is carefully considered.

Therefore, as in any other region of the world, water transport is still the cheapest answer and air transport, now so widely used in the polar regions, by far the most expensive.

The polar climate imposes considerable limitations on transport and certain very definite modifications of our normal ideas. The waterways, the rivers, lakes and even the seas are frozen for an increasing time as one moves poleward. Permafrost results in widespread swamps in the summer time, and the in-between seasons described as 'break-up' and 'freeze-up' are particularly difficult for the operation of aircraft. Another limitation is the darkness of the polar winter as exemplified in the difficulties experienced in two relief organizations, for the Papanin Expedition of 1937–8 which had to be rescued in

January from its floating piece of pack ice in the east Greenland Current and the more recent relief of the United States' floating station 'A' in the North Polar Sea itself, also in mid-winter darkness. On the other hand, there are certain advantages given by this severe polar climate. Many forms of land travel become easier when the ground is hard and covered with snow. It is well known that greater weights can be hauled on sleds than can be carried. The many lakes, when frozen and snow-covered, provide useful landing surfaces for aircraft and, where snow is slight, as for example in eastern Siberia, wheeled transport can operate on very slightly prepared roads in wintertime where movement is impossible on the softer ground of summer. But another factor, not so often considered, is the difficulty of maintaining in operation any equipment—not only transport equipment, and the cardinal rule for operation in the polar regions is simplicity. The more complicated the equipment is the more there is to go wrong, and under blizzard conditions the simplest task of maintenance can become impossible or at least miserably prolonged.

In former times the Arctic natives' means of travel was by canoe, boat, dog team and reindeer sled; none of these is yet superseded and they will continue to be used for many years to come. Roads and railways are still practically non-existent and we have the curious situation where people are familiar with multi-engined aircraft and ten thousand horsepower ice-breakers and yet have never seen a train or a motor-car. The greatest revolution in polar travel is the use of aircraft which have made rapid movement possible in an area where travel used to be the slowest and most difficult in the world.

OVERLAND TRAVEL

Summer overland travel away from the navigable rivers is still primitive. Where the ground is either swampy lowland or ice-capped mountain, man's aids are limited to pack transport (horses, reindeer, dogs) or to man himself. It is difficult for a man to carry his outfit and food for a period longer than two weeks and still maintain reasonable travel speed. The trained porter, particularly the Canadian Indian, can carry tremendous loads, three hundred pounds or more, for the short distances on portages between waterways. Pack dogs can carry thirty to forty pounds, horses four times as much but grazing for horses (and reindeer) can only be expected in certain areas and vegetable fodder is bulky and heavy. As Bertram has said in the *Technique of Polar Travel*—man should choose a carnivore as a beast of burden, and the dog has an additional advantage of being able to store protein which man cannot.

When the ground is frozen and snow-covered, travel conditions on the tundra are greatly improved. The sled in various forms has been developed wherever man has lived with the snow but although the gliding resistance of sled runners on warm snow is low, it increases rapidly as the temperature falls so that special techniques have to be employed at very low temperatures to relieve the strain of hauling for man or for beast. This in essence is to use ice as one of the surfaces either applied to the sole of the sled runner, or to the trail as in the iced ruts used by loggers.

Manual sled-hauling has been developed mainly by white explorers, particularly the British naval Arctic expeditions and South Polar parties. Some astonishing feats have been performed this way. McClintock, one of the greatest technicians in this field, covered thirteen hundred miles in 105 days on the Franklin Search around Melville and Prince Patrick Islands. Shackleton, assisted at the start by ponies, on his South Polar journey of 1908–9, covered sixteen hundred miles in 120 days. On average going, a man can haul up to two hundred pounds on a sled, but man-hauling is a terrible drudgery destructive of any mental effort, dangerous in the sense that exhausting labour makes it almost impossible to keep clothing dry. The failure of Captain Scott to return from the South Pole while Amundsen did is a tragic proof of the difference between men and dogs as hauling animals. Amundsen, covering a slightly shorter distance, reached the Pole in eight weeks, his party fresh and well fed, able to increase its speed and even dawdle on the return. Scott arrived in eleven weeks, worn out by hauling on short rations. His party's speed failed on the return and they were overcome by starvation and winter.

Dogs are still the mainstay of light travel in much of North America and in the eastern parts of Siberia and have been used extensively also in the Antarctic. The husky dog of the Arctic is a natural selection breed. Occasional crossing with wolves undoubtedly occurs but is much rarer than romantic literature suggests. He is large and sturdy, weighing from sixty to a hundred pounds with thick hair three to six inches long, ears erect, eyes slanted, with large thick padded and hairy paws. All sorts of colours exist—black, white, wolf grey or tan, and combinations of these (*see Plate 24*).

In a sled-dog it is stamina that counts. He can pull an average of a hundred pounds on a sled day after day for

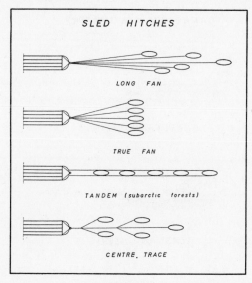

SLED HITCHES

LONG FAN

TRUE FAN

TANDEM (subarctic forests)

CENTRE TRACE

Fig. 50.

twenty to thirty miles and with a negligible load cover a hundred miles or more in a single day's run. And in all but the severest weather of Antarctic winter he is able to sleep unprotected allowing the drifting snow to cover him completely (*see Plate 25*).

There are many styles of driving and many designs of sled. The chief of these are:

1. The short Greenland sled and short fan hitch.
2. The long Canadian komatik with long fan or individual hitch.
3. The Alaskan basket sled and centre trace hitch with the dogs in pairs behind a single leader.

4. In the Antarctic, the Nansen sled with the dog team arranged in centre trace hitch with certain modifications is the usual type.

These variations have been developed for different and good reasons. The Greenlanders' usual travel is over the smooth ice

CANADIAN   KOMATIK

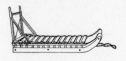

GREENLAND   SLED

ALASKAN   SLED

MODIFIED   "NANSEN"   SLED

Fig. 51.

of fjords. The Canadian komatik is for use on tundra and sea-ice but greater distances are travelled, heavier loads carried and rougher ice encountered—hence the long sled base.

The horse and reindeer are still used considerably for sled

hauling, the former almost invariably over prepared roads on which a sled load for a team horse will average about 1,500 pounds. But ponies from Iceland and Siberia have been used in the past on long ice-cap journeys such as Koch's Greenland crossing in 1912 when they hauled between seven hundred and a thousand pounds.

The reindeer will only haul up to three hundred pounds. In Lapland it is still extensively used before the boat-shaped sled known as a 'pulk' but it is also considerably used in Siberia. It is only in the present century that cross-country travel in the polar regions has become mechanized.

Shackleton and Scott experimented with primitive motorized devices in the Antarctic. Now giant caterpillar tractors are used and many types of 'snowmobiles' and aerosleds have been developed. For economic efficiency the wheeled vehicle is greatly superior to the track-layer but requires smooth trails. However, a surprising amount of ordinary wheeled transport is used in eastern Siberia over well-frozen, roughly cleared winter roads which are quite impassable in summer. In the low temperatures to be expected in polar operations considerable difficulties appear in the operation of mechanical vehicles. First there is a problem of cooling mixtures and here the air-cooled engine has considerable advantages. Although cold weather lubricants have been devised, there is continual difficulty in the steady congelation of oils as the temperature falls. The standard electric battery will produce very little power at sub-zero temperatures and even natural rubber tyres become brittle and difficult. So, in fact, do all materials and the brittleness of metals at low temperatures causes a great deal of breakage with the concomitant difficulty of repair. It is of interest to contrast the various types of engine and their efficiency under these conditions.

The most usual type is some form of standard automobile petrol-driven engine. This suffers from difficulties in cold starting with thickened lubricants, low-powered batteries and fuel evaporation. But it is reasonably light and will weigh perhaps four pounds per horsepower. The diesel engine cannot approach this power-weight ratio but it can be made independent of the electrical battery. Perhaps the most suitable engine for polar operations is the gas turbine which obeys the cardinal rule

stated above of mechanical simplicity. There are far fewer
bearings so thick-oil trouble is very much lessened. It can be
started by special cartridges and therefore made independent
of the electric battery and a wide range of cheap fuels is available for its operation. The great advantage in cold weather of
the gas turbine is the fact that its power and efficiency rise
rapidly as the temperature falls. For example an engine rated
at 200 h.p. at a temperature of plus 40° F. may develop 380 h.p.
at minus 40° F. Moreover, its power-weight ratio is better even
than the petrol engine.

For the purpose of really heavy freight hauls there is nothing
superior to the diesel track-layer. This has low speed but great
hauling power and trains of sleds, weighing up to a hundred
tons or more, allow a great deal of fuel to be carried. The tractor-train is therefore independent for very long distances, well
over a thousand miles or twice the distance of an average unsupported dog team and considerable comforts can be provided
in the way of cabooses or *wannegans*, sleeping and eating
quarters hauled along together with the train of fuel and pay-
load sleds. In severe cold the diesel engines are usually run
continuously and with reserve drivers and sleeping quarters
operation can carry on day and night so that along a marked
trail a hundred miles can be covered in the twenty-four hours.
Such heavy tractor-trains have been used extensively in the
Alaskan tundra for oil-search operations, for the transference
of mining equipment in east Greenland and in the Antarctic
where the United States Byrd Station was established overland
from Little America by a heavy tractor train. But in many polar
transport operations a requirement has grown up for a faster,
lighter passenger vehicle which can be an improvement on the
comfort, speed and efficiency of the dog team. These are the
vehicles which now go by the generic name of 'snowmobile'
and many versions, civilian and military, have appeared in this
field. They vary all the way from slightly modified agricultural
tractors, such as the Fergusons which Sir Edmund Hillary used
on his supporting party in the British Trans-Antarctic Expedition, and in three of which was made the third overland
journey to the South Pole, to the sleek-looking propeller-driven
'aerosled'. These latter are used more extensively in the level
lake country of Finland and Canada where great speeds can be

obtained on the most perfect surfaces. But on the whole their use on rough trails is limited and the power required and fuel consumption are very great. Wegener, the German explorer, used them on the Greenland ice-cap in 1930–1. His Finnish aerosleds fitted with a 112 h.p. engine had to be hauled by dog team on to the higher and smoother sections of the ice-cap, but once there they operated efficiently, and on one occasion achieved 180 miles in nine hours with a thirteen-hundred-pound load. The Germans continued military experiments during the war on aerosleds but came to the conclusion that an uneconomic horsepower-per-ton ratio was required for efficient starting from a stop when the runners tend to freeze down. This freezing down of runners is a problem present with any type of heavily weighted sliding surface on snow, whether it is aircraft ski or a simple komatik. A powerful jerk, preferably with a sideways slewing movement is required to start the sliding. It is helpful, for example, for ski-fitted aircraft to run up on wooden rollers or a kerosene-soaked cloth before coming to rest.

There are several types of snowmobile—the half-tracked vehicles where the front or steering axle rests on skis, the fully tracked vehicles where steering is done by the braking of one track and the articulated fully tracked vehicle. An example of the first type is the Canadian-built 'Bombardier', now considerably used in the Canadian Arctic, of the second type the 'Weasel' or Canadian snowmobile and of the third type the larger 'Sno-cat', as used recently on the British Trans-Antarctic Expedition. The articulated track is an improvement over the shorter wheel-based full track vehicle, since for steering purposes a length-to-breadth ratio of more than 1·6 is inefficient in the former type. All these snowmobiles aim at low ground pressure for use in snow and pressures below one pound per square inch have been achieved. This is very desirable for operation in deep, soft snow or on the marshy tundra in summer-time. For winter operation in the tundra or on the ice-caps such low pressures are unnecessary. The problem there is to overcome the iron-hard snowdrifts or *skavler* which can cause very rough going. Hence the desire for increasing the wheel-base and therefore the advantage of the articulated track vehicle. Most of these snowmobiles use standard automobile engines up to 200 h.p. but fuel consumption is high and as yet a vehicle has not been found which can improve much on the distance of an unsupported journey compared to the performance of a dog team. For the doctor, surveyor and the explorer they have considerable value since they can travel fast, particularly on

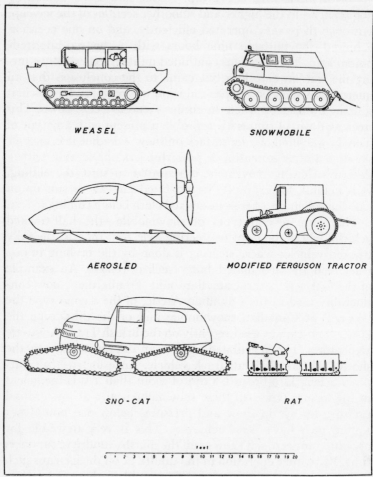

WEASEL

SNOWMOBILE

AEROSLED

MODIFIED FERGUSON TRACTOR

SNO-CAT

RAT

feet

0 1 2 3 4 5 6 7 8 9 10 11 12 13 14 15 16 17 18 19 20

Fig. 52. Some Types of Oversnow Vehicles.

good going and do not consume 'food' when idle. But in really difficult country with steep slopes and on rough sea-ice the superior flexibility of the dog team is still apparent. Many of the recent large-scale vehicle expeditions in polar regions have, in fact, been dependent on air supply for refuelling. The 'Weasels' used by the French Greenland Expedition were air supplied in the establishment of their central ice-cap station and in the long journeys made over the Greenland ice-cap. So also were the snowmobiles on the Canadian military exercise—'Muskox'—in 1946 and in part the trans-Antarctic expedition. It should be remembered that the supporting party, led by Sir Edmund Hillary, did not put in the fuelling caches by means of his tractors. His tractor journey was to act as a receiver for air-supplied fuel caches. A great deal of the research and development of these types of polar vehicles has been inspired by the military, where there is a continued requirement for a useful transport means for small bodies of troops and light weapons. The Canadian and American military forces have recently developed two other vehicles—a light one, by the Canadian army known as the 'Rat' which can be manhandled or parachuted since it weighs only fifteen hundred pounds and is capable of carrying six hundred pounds of cargo and towing an additional thousand pounds. The United States army has developed something more equivalent to the heavy diesel tractor train which is termed 'the overland train'. This is a series of linked-wheel trailers with up to fifty-two wheels, ten feet in diameter and all driven. This return to wheels rather than tracks recalls the *Snow Cruiser* which Byrd attempted to use in the Antarctic in 1934. This particular vehicle was grossly overweight, however, for its four large independently driven wheels, and got no further than a mile from the ship's side. The table below shows certain characteristics of some of these snowmobile types.

TYPES OF SNOWMOBILE

	Weasel	Canadian Snowmobile	Muskeg	Sno-cat	Ferguson
Engine (cyls.)	Studebaker 6	Cadillac 8	Chrysler 6	Chrysler V8	Diesel
Developed h.p.*	75	110	115	200	30
Ground pressure, p.s.i.	1·9	1·5	0·75	0·75	1·3
Miles per gal. under load	0·8 to 3	0·8 to 2	1·0 to 2	0·8 to 2	1·1 to 1·8
Usual hauled load, tons	2	3	2	5	1 to 2

* Note developed h.p. reduced to half at ten thousand feet as on Antarctic plateau (*see Plate 26*).

The areas in which long-distance mechanical vehicle transport has been greatly used in recent years are the major ice-caps of Greenland and Antarctica. These present additional transport difficulties in the presence of the ablation zone surrounding the Greenland ice-cap where glacial surface streams and snow swamps are present, and on both ice-caps the problem of crevasses. The latter are the particular bugbear of ice-cap travel. In Greenland recent French and British expeditions have both lost 'Weasels' down crevasses. In the Antarctic Mawson, as long ago as 1912, lost one of his companions with his dog team and nearly all their food and we are all familiar with the pictures of crevasse trouble experienced in the British Trans-Antarctic Expedition. The particular trouble on these polar ice-caps is that snow bridges across the crevasses are always in dangerous condition equivalent to those of early winter in the Alps. They seldom become firm in the way that Alpine crevasses do in late spring. Heavy vehicles of course are especially vulnerable. Various means have been devised to try to overcome the danger. 'Weasels' have been driven with ropes attached to the steering mechanism and pedals, and vehicles have been roped together as are a team of mountaineers on an alpine glacier with strong, round-the-body cables. A recent journey of particular interest was the 650-mile trail from Little America to Byrd Station, one of the interior I.G.Y. Stations established by the United States. The supply train for this consisted of thirty-seven-ton D.8 Caterpillar Tractors, hauling over forty tons each. A scouting vehicle, a 'Weasel' fitted with a 'crevasse detector', went ahead of this convoy. The crevasse detector operates by pushing, thirty to forty feet ahead, electrodes (hemispherical metal sectors) which measure the electrical impedance of the snow and ice surface and therefore detect air gaps. It was capable of recording crevasses when the snow bridges were less than ten feet thick. In one particular section of the trail, seven miles long, some thirty-six major crevasses were encountered and, to make them safe for the heavy tractor train they were bulldozed in solidly.

WATER TRANSPORT

When ice or below-freezing temperatures are not present, there is nothing very peculiar about polar water transport. In midsummer ordinary sea-going freighters operate in Hudson Bay and to the mouth of the Yenisey and stern-wheel river craft ply on the great northern rivers. But certain areas of the world are always ice-guarded—e.g. all the Antarctic continent, except for the tip of the Graham Land peninsula, and the east coast of Greenland, and to navigate these waters special vessels are required. The true ice-breaking ship operates by sliding up on the ice and crushing it with its weight. Various devices are used to increase this crushing weight—ballast tanks which can be flooded, either to weight the bows or to rock the vessel from side to side if it becomes fast on top of the ice. We can classify these special vessels as follows.

A. *Ice-breakers*, specially designed, broad in beam, with ice-breaking bow and heeling tanks, the horsepower-per-ton ratio greater than one.
    (*a*) Heavy ice-breakers, 10,000 h.p. and upwards
    (*b*) Auxiliary ice-breakers, 4,000 to 10,000 h.p.
    (*c*) Port ice-breakers, around 2,000 h.p.

B. *Ice strengthened ships*. The Finns have listed six classes of ice-worthiness. Two examples are:
    (1*a*) Specially designed ice vessels, e.g. the *Sedov*, *Norsel*, *Magga Dan*
    (1*b*) *John Biscoe*, a strengthened, ordinary vessel (converted naval net-tender).

The first real ice-breaker was *Yermak*, built in Britain for Russia in 1899 to the idea of Admiral Makarov. This veteran of the Arctic seas was certainly still in action in 1957. It is since 1940, however, that ice-breaker building has really gone ahead. Steam engines have now been mainly replaced by diesel-electric motors and the latest ice-breaker, the *Lenin*, built in Russia, is powered by a nuclear plant. The table on page 158 gives examples of some of the older as well as the later ice-breakers.

In addition to the difficulty of forcing a way through the polar pack ice another danger is the deposition of ice on ships operating in low air temperatures. Particularly vulnerable are the distant-water Arctic trawlers operating in the Greenland Sea and Barents Sea. The problem here is ice top-hamper caused by freezing spray when the air temperature is lower than $-2°$ C. 'Green' water will not freeze readily unless trapped by choked scuppers, and at very low temperatures (below zero Fahrenheit) spray will consist of ice crystals and will not adhere. Recent design of such ships has attempted to eliminate as much as possible the top-hamper on which the spray can freeze and a tripod mast has been found much preferable to the normal foremast with standing rigging. The danger of the situation has been illustrated by the fact that on a seven-hundred-ton trawler over a hundred tons of ice can form with a centre of gravity thirty feet above the level of the deck (*see Plates 27, 28*).

	Built in	For (country)	Year	H.P.	Tonnage	Propulsion
(a) Heavy						
Yermak	Britain	Russia	1899	10,000	5,000	Steam (coal)
Krassin	Britain	Russia	1917	10,000	10,000	Steam (coal)
Stalin	Russia	Russia	1938	10,000	11,000	Steam (oil)
North Wind (4)	U.S.A.	U.S.A.	1944	10,000	6,500	DE
Labrador	Canada	Canada	1954	10,000	6,000	DE
D'Iberville	Canada	Canada	1953	10,000	10,000	Steam (oil)
Kapitans (3)	Finland	Russia	1954/6	10,000	5,500	DE
Glacier	U.S.A.	U.S.A.	1955	21,000	8,300	DE
Moskva (2)	Finland	Russia	1959	22,000	13,000	DE
Lenin	Russia	Russia	1958	44,000	16,000	Nuclear
(b) Auxiliary						
Gen. San Martin	Germany	Argentine	1954	6,600	4,500	DE
C. D. Howe	Canada	Canada	1950	4,000	2,500	Steam (oil)
Karhu (3)	Finland	Finland	1958	7,500	3,400	DE

Despite the advance in ice-breaker construction, where vessels powerful enough to drive through almost any known ice now exist, many people have considered the possibility of avoiding ice altogether by going under it. In 1958 a new chapter in polar transportation was written. The United States' nuclear-powered submarine successfully traversed the North Polar Sea, thus justifying the passionately advocated views of Sir Hubert Wilkins, ever since his attempt to do this in 1931. Nuclear power, making propulsion independent of large quantities of air, was the key to this success, but another vital adjunct was a new navigating device, the 'inertia navigator', designed originally to control high-altitude guided missiles. This instrument records sensitively and automatically changes of direction and speed and is therefore a built-in dead reckoner, supplementing the gyro compasses and magnetic compasses (comparatively useless here) carried by the vessels. U.S.S. *Nautilus*, bearing the famous name of Jules Verne's creation and Wilkins' vessel, sailed under 1,800 miles of ice in ninety-six hours from off Point Barrow to the Greenland Sea in the first days of August. In the same month U.S.S. *Skate* went from the Greenland Sea to the North Pole and thence to the United States' drifting station Alpha where it made one of its nine surfacings, another being very close to the Pole itself. As was expected, the underside of the polar ice proved to be far from smooth. A projection of 125 feet below surface was recorded in the Chukot Sea. In the Bering Sea and other shallow areas the problem in fact, is to find adequate room between the ice and the sea bed: a submarine valley, off Point Barrow, gave *Nautilus* an entry to the deeper North Polar Sea. Almost immediately after this striking advance in polar transport, plans are being laid for nuclear-powered submarine tankers and the polar Mediterranean may soon be utilized commercially in this way with tremendous distance-savings between, e.g. Tokyo and Europe.

INSURANCE

One problem in connection with the use of polar waters by private commercial shipping is that of extra insurance rates, due to the risks for thin-skinned vessels of icebergs and pack ice and for all ships of fog, snowfall and deck-icing. The underwriter is a statistician first and foremost. If a large number of vessels continue to use a route with safety, the rates will come down but if one out of a handful of vessels is lost, they will go sharply up. Continual pressure by the users on the underwriters is necessary but scientific arguments are not very helpful. It is numbers that are required.

Certain areas of the world (*Polar Record*, 8, p. 425) are subjected to 'warranty', i.e. extra rates. What these rates may be cannot be indicated simply, but one case in 1956 showed that a vessel sailing to Svalbard in December had such a high premium demanded that it was in excess of the freight income. The ship had to proceed, in effect, without insurance. This is one of the best-used commercial polar routes. Another is the Hudson Bay route to Churchill, Manitoba which came into full use in 1931 as a route for grain vessels after the completion of the Hudson Bay railway from the prairies. The Hudson's Bay Company and naval craft had been sailing this route for 250 years but ordinary merchant ships here were something new. As the route slowly gained in use, the extra premium charged has fallen considerably though spasmodically as shown in the following diagram.

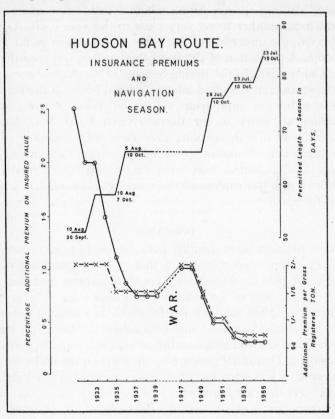

Fig. 53.

AIR TRANSPORT

Flight through the cold air of polar latitudes in itself presents no great problem and in fact the dangerous icing conditions are less frequently met with than in, for example, northern Europe where the critical temperatures of zero to plus 25° F. are often encountered at normal flight levels. But to start engines in extreme cold takes time and special heating equipment, and shelter for planes is difficult but very necessary when repair

9. Woman, aged about 70, from Mackenzie delta

20. "Copper" Eskimo woman from Victoria Island

ESKIMO TYPES

21. Half-breed "Copper" Eskimo with wife and adopted daughter, Victoria Island; Caribou skin clothing, with wolf skin hoods

22. Eskimo women cutting up slabs of whale blubber

23. "Square flipper" seal (*see p.* 126) being cut up to make skin line, Southampton Island, N.W.T.

and maitenance work have to be carried out. The chief problems in connection with polar flying are concerned with landing surfaces. The tundra with its many lakes offers opportunities to ski-equipped planes in winter and float-planes or flying-boats in summer. Ice-caps also provide smooth landing grounds but regular airfields for wheeled aircraft are few and far between and have to be kept clear of snow in wintertime and are subject to frost-heaving in summer in the permafrost region. Nowadays more and more landings of heavy wheeled aircraft are being made on ice surfaces, a good example being the American air base for the I.G.Y. in McMurdo Sound in the Antarctic to which planes flew directly for the first time from New Zealand. A rough rule for safe ice thickness is given by the following formulae:

$$\text{Lake-ice} \quad T = 4 \cdot 05 \sqrt{W}$$
$$\text{Sea-ice} \quad T = 8 \cdot 10 \sqrt{W}$$

where T is the thickness of ice in inches and W the weight in tons.

Jet-assisted take-off has been considerably used in some cases, for example the American landings at the South Pole, where their I.G.Y. Station was equipped with a weight (all air landed) greater than the weight landed by sea for any pre-war Antarctic expedition. Another danger of the ice-cap flying is the 'white-out' conditions prevalent with an overcast sky and no feature on which to sight a horizon. Many cases have occurred in the last few years of aircraft crashing or even landing unexpectedly and gently on the ice-cap surface when in 'white-out' it was impossible to tell ice from air. The British North Greenland Expedition had an additional 'home' provided at its central ice-cap station when a *Hastings* aircraft delivering from low altitude 'flew in' during white-out conditions. A point of interest that has emerged from the many recent ice landings is that on smooth glare ice at minus 40° the braking effect on wheels is nearly as good as it is on concrete, in striking contrast to the conditions for ice landing, when the temperature is near freezing-point. The use of JATO (Jet Assisted Take-Off) has been found very necessary not only on soft snow conditions but on the ice-caps where high altitude radically lowers the horsepower of internal-combustion engines for take-off. Almost all the successful take-offs from the high

M

Greenland ice-cap or Antarctic plateau have been achieved by the assistance of JATO.

Since the early 1920s very great strides have been made in northern flying both in North America and in the Soviet Union. It was in these days that the 'bush pilot' era began, the pioneer flyers operating with single-engined ski and float-planes and with no complicated radio aids to navigation. Skis and floats are on the whole limited to smaller aircraft, though the ubiquitous DC3 (Dakota) has been fitted with both and as long ago as 1937 the Russians landed four four-engined ski-equipped aircraft at the neighbourhood of the North Pole for the Papanin expedition.

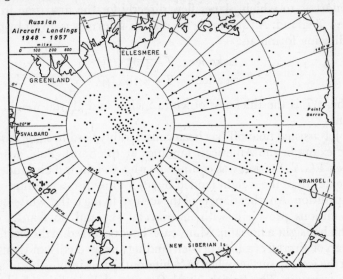

Fig. 54.

Now, however, wheeled aircraft are being used directly for landings on prepared and unprepared snow and ice surfaces and the accompanying map (Fig. 54) shows the enormous number of Soviet landings in connection with the scientific survey of the North Polar basin that have been made over the last ten years. Interesting experiments have been carried out recently by the United States Air Force on landings on natural sites in northern Greenland. Here there are places where, as at Brønlund's Fiord, Nord, Centrum Lake and Polaris Promontory, old, dry lake beds give natural smooth landings for heavy wheeled aircraft. An additional feature of north Greenland is that certain lakes into which large arms of the ice-cap protrude, carry perennial ice which remains thick enough and strong enough throughout the summer again to support heavy aircraft, but in these cases the surface usually becomes too irregular in the summer thaw for safe, wheeled landings. The presence of these natural airfields on or near the transpolar route from Europe to Alaska is important in the case of emergency alternates being required. It should always be remembered, however, that the cost of aircraft transport is tremendous and at the present date that of the even more versatile helicopter is more costly still. Helicopters are being used now on both American and Soviet ice-breakers as 'spotters'. Before the air age the masthead gave the widest view that a skipper could have of ice conditions ahead of him, but helicopters are now being used to a great extent for survey work on the tundra where, in the absence of high relief ground with dangerous air currents, they are in their element. The Geological Survey of Canada has called on helicopters to a considerable degree for the mapping of the vast North-West Territories, discovering that even though the cost of helicopter transport is tremendous the cost per square mile mapped becomes lower than by the traditional methods of surveyors in canoes and on foot. In 1958 the Geological Survey of Canada used a lightweight aircraft in a mapping programme of the Parry Islands. This was a Super-Cub PA18A fitted with special large tyres at five pounds pressure. In covering nearly twenty-four thousand square miles landings were made on unprepared ground at 249 different places. Only once was it impossible to land the geologists within ten minutes' walk of their desired objective. This performance is not far short of that of a helicopter but in addition the running costs were much lower and the range of the aircraft permitted it to be flown to and from high latitudes whereas a helicopter needs to be transported to a near-by base.

COMMERCIAL ROUTES IN THE ARCTIC

The great development over the last few years has been the establishment of truly trans-Arctic commercial flying. We have seen how, as far back as 1922, Stefansson in his Wrangel Island adventure believed in the possibility of such flying, and in 1928

Wilkins demonstrated a flight from Alaska to Svalbard. In the 1930s, when aircraft range was comparatively limited, the trans-Atlantic route considered was one using the stepping stones of Iceland, Greenland, Baffin Island, and the same route was developed and to a small extent used during the Second World War for short-range fighter aircraft travelling from North America to Europe. As the range of large commercial air transport increased, so it became possible to eliminate the small

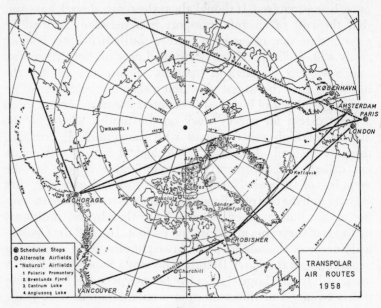

Fig. 55.

hops and initiate nearly or truly Great Circle routes between destinations across the northern hemisphere. As the table opposite shows, from 1954 to 1957 four major airlines established routes from western North America to Europe over the Baffin Island, Greenland route, often described in the Press as transpolar but not in fact travelling to any great extent north of the Arctic Circle. But in 1957 Scandinavian Airlines established a truly transpolar route from Copenhagen to Tokyo via Anchorage, Alaska with alternate landings at Nord, Thule and Resolute Bay. This route saves some two thousand miles between Europe and Japan but is still far from the true Great

Circle which would, in fact, be via the mouth of the Yenisey and then across eastern Siberia.

1954	S.A.S.	Los Angeles to Copenhagen	now via Frobisher Bay
1955	C.P.A.	Vancouver to Amsterdam	,,
1957	Pan Am.	San Francisco to London	,,
	T.W.A.	Los Angeles to London/Paris	,,
1957	S.A.S.	Copenhagen to Tokyo*	via Anchorage
1958	Air France	Paris to Tokyo	,,
	K.L.M.	Amsterdam to Tokyo	,,

* In November 1956, four hundred Scandinavian athletes travelled to the Olympic Games at Melbourne by this route in six aircraft.

As we have seen, it is now politics rather than technics which prevent complete Great Circle flying over the Arctic basin. Although the range of aircraft has now rendered landings in the true Arctic unnecessary on the scheduled flight, emergencies will always occur and alternate airfields will be required together with organized rescue service in case of a plane being forced down. It will continue to be important to provide weather stations throughout the area to forecast conditions for the trans-polar route and here those nations controlling Arctic territory have a duty to perform which is so far being carried out efficiently and with co-operation.

NAVIGATION

The polar regions produce some extra problems in navigation both in the air, on sea and even on the land since the bare tundra, when inadequately mapped, and in wintertime even if good maps are provided, can impose difficulties similar to those of the open sea. The main factors are:

1. In the neighbourhood of the magnetic-dip Pole, the magnetic compass becomes entirely unreliable, the vertical force is all-powerful and the horizontal force, on which direction depends becomes extremely weak. Where its value is less than 0·04 gauss even the best magnetic compass is suspect.
2. The gyro-compass is fairly adequate for ships but in aircraft travelling at high speeds precession is too rapid for accuracy. *Nautilus* had to take great care not to make sudden changes of direction when in high latitude to avoid upsetting the gyro-compass direction.
3. Radio-range beams are few and far between and are liable to quite queer distortion within the belt of maximum aurora.

4. Radar location of gently sloping shorelines when the sea is ice-covered is extremely difficult.

5. In high latitudes there are complicating twilight effects when it is easy to be flying west at the same speed as the sun and thus maintaining a lengthy period of twilight when no astronomical bodies are visible.

6. In high latitudes the lines of longitude (meridians) are converging so rapidly that an alternative method of indicating direction instead of true (north, etc.) is very desirable. Such a method, the Greenwich Grid, was devised by W/C Maclure, R.C.A.F., in 1941 and has now been universally adopted for the area to poleward of 70° latitude.

A polar stereographic chart is substituted for the Mercator of lower latitude and on this gridded chart directions are measured as Greenwich 0° to 360°. Greenwich 0° is the southerly direction of the Greenwich meridian for the North Polar area (the northerly direction of the Greenwich meridian for the South Polar area).

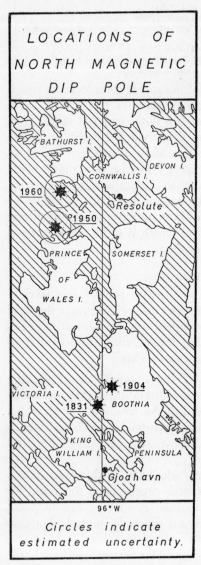

LOCATIONS OF NORTH MAGNETIC DIP POLE

BATHURST I.
DEVON I.
CORNWALLIS I.
1960
°1950
Resolute
PRINCE
SOMERSET I.
OF
WALES I.
1904
VICTORIA I.
1831   BOOTHIA
KING
WILLIAM I.   PENINSULA
Gjoahavn
96° W

Circles indicate estimated uncertainty.

Fig. 56.

The formula connecting 'True' and 'Grid' direction reads Grid dir. = True dir. + long. W. (or − long. E.) ± 180°. On the gridded polar chart isogonals of magnetic variation with respect to grid direction appear much simpler than they would on a true direction chart since, although still bunched at the magnetic-dip Pole, the second bunching at the geographical Pole is eliminated.

The position of the north magnetic-dip Pole has been an interesting problem in scientific research and in exploration. It is the point where the horizontal force of the earth's field is nil. But it cannot be adequately described as a point, rather as an area whose radius is perhaps twenty-five miles on a magnetically quiet day and fifty miles or more during magnetic storms. J. C. Ross was lucky in that he seems to have stood for twenty-four hours at about the centre of the area at his time (June 1831) when it was at 70·1° N. 96·8° W.

Amundsen came not so close on foot, but his observatory work over two winters within 150 miles established the position for 1905 at 70·5° N. 95·5° W.

Since 1945 the Dominion Observatory with field parties and at a permanent observatory at Resolute Bay has established a new position for 1950 at 74° N. 100° W. and concludes that a secular drift of about five miles per year slightly east of north is taking place so that the predicted centre of the area for epoch 1960 is 74·5° N. 99·6° W.

The south magnetic-dip Pole, to establish the approximate position of which was the same J. C. Ross' first task in 1839, is also in motion and is not antipodal to its northern counterpart. Sir Edgeworth David's party in 1908–9 reached its then vicinity in 72·4° S. 155·3° E. During the I.G.Y. its approximate location was 70° S. 145° E. not far from the French inland station Charcot.

For high-latitude operation by land, sea, and especially by air it is still vitally important to be able to map-read and take astronomical sights and bearings. Probably half the aerial disasters in the north of recent years are due to neglect of these old-fashioned navigational factors and reliance in all too faithful measure on radio and other modern aids.

Trans-Arctic commercial flying has arrived—how about trans-Antarctic flying? An examination of the globe in the

southern hemisphere shows that Great Circle routes do exist
between the centres of population in South America, South
Africa and Australia which, if not crossing the South Pole,
reach or touch the Antarctic continent. In the 1960s distances
involved are even too great for present aircraft but as the
range of aircraft increases such lengthy flights will become
possible—but will they be used? At the moment there is perhaps
little demand for direct and frequent air communication between the southern centres themselves, but undoubtedly the
Antarctic at its coasts provides reasonable landing fields and

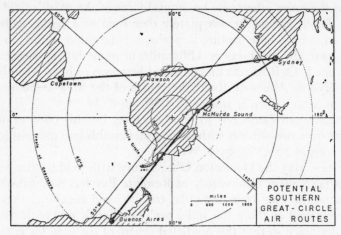

Fig. 57.

adequate weather conditions for alternates or stop-overs for
the southern routes. At the moment these lie well in the future.
Much of the length of these Great Circle routes would lie over the
stormy Antarctic ocean and the provision of adequate weather
stations and rescue services will be considerably more difficult
than in the Arctic. Many of the sub-Antarctic islands are now
provided with weather stations but the pattern of them is very
open and life in a Weather Ship in the sub-Antarctic seas would
be perhaps the most uncomfortable prospect in the world.

FURTHER READING

Armstrong, T. E., 'Insurance Against Ice Risks at Sea', *Polar Record*, 8, p. 421.
Calvert, Cdr. J., *Surface at the Pole*, New York, 1960 (McGraw-Hill).
Maclure, K. C., 'Polar Navigation', *Arctic*, 2, p. 183 (1949).
Morley, J. P., 'Icebreakers, Their Construction and Use, *Polar Record*, 11, p. 6 (1962).

Chapter 9

POLITICAL GEOGRAPHY OF THE ARCTIC

A GREAT deal has been written in the years since 1945 on the political and strategic importance of the Arctic. To the political geographer these areas offer several points of special interest. International power politics demand the control of territory by a sovereign power for the sake of its economic value (e.g. minerals, food), for its strategic value as an area from which to threaten another power or as a base for defence, and in the past but less often nowadays, for prestige value or for the avowed purpose of 'protecting the natives'. Political sovereignty has been established by discovery, conquest, purchase, or gift or just gradual peaceful penetration. We have had all these means of obtaining sovereignty in the Arctic, including mere peaceful penetration, of which Greenland is a very useful example. This sovereignty needs to be maintained by effective occupation and must be recognized by at least a modicum of other powers.

Discovery and its attendant rights is perhaps the vaguest basis of all claims. We have as an example here the rights of Great Britain in the discovery of the North-West Passage district islands subsequently transferred by Britain to Canada. We have had conquest in north-east Siberia by the Russians and purchase by the United States from Russia of Alaska. Finally in addition to the gift of claims to the North-West Territory's islands by Britain to Canada, we have a twentieth-century example of the allotment of the Svalbard Archipelago to the sovereignty of Norway by the League of Nations.

One complication present in many other parts of the world is missing in the polar regions. There is no Arctic Nation. Greenland, perhaps, is the nearest equivalent, but it is difficult to envisage a demand for autonomy from its twenty-five thousand people, nor can one forsee any agitation for a Greater Eskimo Land which would include the four separate political sovereignties at present inhabited by branches of the Eskimo people. We are left at present with five nations claiming political sovereignty of Arctic territories, and during this present century anyway, such disputes over political rights as have occurred have been settled by peaceful arbitration and not by a resort to force. But in past history, this was not always the case. Hudson Bay, in the seventeenth and eighteenth centuries, was an area in which the struggle for colonial territory between Britain and France was mirrored. There were naval battles in the Bay and frequent exchange of control over the scattered fur-trading posts. Similarly, in the great whaling days of the early seventeenth century, Vest Spitsbergen was the scene of rivalry between Dutch, Danish and British whaling ships, naval vessels often accompanying the merchant fleets and ensuring 'protection' over their nationals' activities.

CANADIAN ARCTIC TERRITORY

This region is mainly an inheritance from the independent Hudson's Bay Company's Rupertsland and from British naval discoveries in the direction of the North-West Passage. The transfer to Canada came about in a rather curious way. In 1870 a United States citizen desired to mine mica in Baffin Island and applied in turn to the appropriate agencies in equally surprised Ottawa and London. It was actually not until 1880 that Britain officially transferred her rights to the young nation of Canada which was rather slow to make any move effectively to take up the allotted sovereignty. This came early in the twentieth century when Captain Bernier began to make formal annexations and proclamations on his northern voyages and to collect with considerable difficulty whaling and trading licences. Portions of the northern islands, however, had been explored and discovered by Norwegian and United States expeditions. In 1930, the Canadian Government paid over a hundred thousand dollars to the heirs of Otto Sverdrup's estate 'in recognition of his discoveries'. As far as United States' rights to what are now considered Canadian islands, no government claim was ever made, but certain United States citizens denied Canadian sovereignty for a long time and refused, for instance, to observe the game laws established for the North-West Territories. Commander MacMillan was one of these and officers of the R.C.M.P. were, in fact, placed on board his

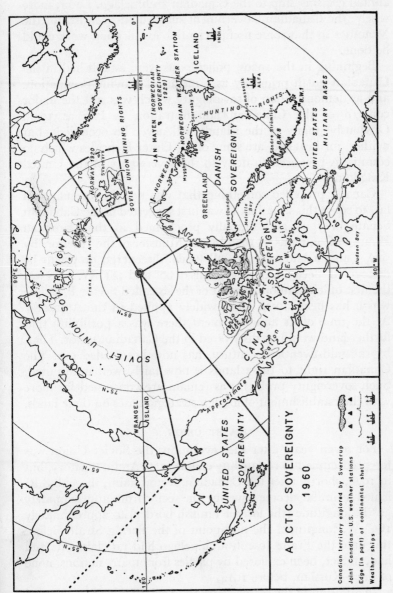

Fig. 58.

ARCTIC SOVEREIGNTY
1960

Canadian territory explored by Sverdrup
Joint Canadian - U.S. weather stations
Edge (in part) of continental shelf
Weather ships

annual cruising ship to the Canadian archipelago. Later, more wisely, the Canadian Government substituted scientists for the Mounties so that some useful scientific exploration work could be done.

Beginning in the 1920s, police posts were established in the Canadian north primarily as a means of proving occupation, and as demonstration of sovereignty which was still the major concern of the Canadian administration as late as 1945. Obviously, many of the islands will never be occupied—but neither, for instance, are some of the Outer Hebrides which no country is prepared to deny to the sovereignty of the United Kingdom.

Canada proposed something that was new in international law to cover this situation. It was first suggested in the Canadian Senate in 1907 and formally proclaimed in the Canadian House of Commons in 1925 by the Minister of the Interior. By this, Canada laid claim to all lands 'discovered or yet to be discovered' between the meridians of 60° and 141° W. This was the first official announcement of the so-called Sector Principle which has been much more widely applied in the Antarctic. At the time of its announcement there was a possibility that further land would be discovered in the Canadian sector. That, by the mid-twentieth century, has now been ruled out. The Canadian right to these lands is now fairly well undisputed. Such sovereignty problems as remain are concerned far more with the establishment of foreign strategic bases on these lands.

SOVIET UNION

For seven years after the revolution, the Soviet Union was too preoccupied to restate any claims to its Arctic territory, but in 1926, shortly after the Canadian Sector claim, the U.S.S.R. issued a similar decree covering the sector from approximately 32° E. longitude (the former Finnish border) to approximately 169° W. longitude, the mid-point of the Bering Strait. Before this date the Franz Joseph archipelago had no claimants and had, in fact, been explored by parties from many nations, none of them Russian, before 1914.

In addition to the sector claim the Soviet Union went a good deal further. She claimed, for example, a twelve-mile nautical limit, and in various theoretical statements by Soviet lawyers much more sweeping claims than merely to the lands of the Soviet sector have been made—rights to the sea, the floating ice and to the air space above the sector.

This raises points which are of greater interest perhaps to lawyers than to geographers. The sea-ice, the Arctic pack, is, as we have now seen, perfectly possible for human occupation by floating stations which can remain encamped for several years. But sea-ice attached to the coast is different from sea-ice when it is floating freely in the so-called High Seas. When, in fact, are the High Seas not the High Seas? In addition to a general territorial limit, Russia, for instance, claims the White Sea as wholly Soviet territory (so incidentally, on no firmer basis, does Canada claim Hudson Bay).

A special case of interest is that of Wrangel Island within the Soviet-claimed sector. This island, it has been stated, was heard of by a Russian in 1824, seen by a British sailor in 1849, landed on by an American in 1881 but had still no effective claim or occupation in 1920. In 1922, the Canadian-American explorer, Stefansson, decided that the polar air-age was imminent, that Wrangel Island was a cross-road point for such potential air-lines and therefore should be claimed by Britain or by Canada. Neither of these two governments, however, were prepared to become involved, despite lengthy attempts by Stefansson after his occupation party, which was all-American except for a youthful Canadian leader, had been landed. In 1923, as a result of no government interest, it was impossible to send a relief party and when one was dispatched, in 1924, all members of the expedition, except for a single Eskimo woman, were dead. Some further Alaskan Eskimo were landed but in 1925 a Russian vessel arrived off Wrangel Island, removed all these Eskimo to Siberia (where they languished for some time before returning to Alaska) and hoisted the Hammer and Sickle which has flown there ever since.

GREENLAND

Greenland is now universally recognized as Danish territory but it was only in 1921 (two hundred years after the first colonizing by Hans Egede) that sovereignty was proclaimed over the whole island (and not, incidentally, over any further polar 'sector'.) Up to this date only the west coast south of Melville

Bay and a region around Angmassalik (1894) had been effectively administered and in fact, when Knud Rasmussen established his trading post at Thule in 1910, it was in a region
that could be described as of no administration, or *terra
nullius*. A large part of northern Greenland had been explored
by citizens of the United States, particularly Admiral Peary,
and in 1916, on Denmark's sale of the Virgin Islands to the
United States, the latter specifically renounced any claims
to northern Greenland based on these discoveries. Much of the
east coast also had been explored by nationals of countries
other than Denmark and, in fact, the 1921 declaration of
sovereignty over the whole island was particularly disputed by
Norway, whose citizens had long used the east coast for hunting
and trapping purposes.

By an agreement at the Hague Convention of 1924, these
hunting rights were confirmed to Norway on the east coast
from latitude 60° to 81° N. with the exception of the Angmassalik and Scoresby Sound regions which were earmarked as
purely Danish enclaves. Great Britain, incidentally, was given
similar rights to those of Norway for no apparent reason except
spite.

The friction between the two Scandinavian countries continued and in 1931 the Norwegians raised their flag and
claimed part of the east coast as Norwegian sovereign territory.
The international court at the Hague, however, disapproved
this in 1933 and awarded the whole country to Denmark with
the reservation of hunting rights as before to Norway.

During the Second World War, the United States built
military air bases in Greenland under treaty with the Danish
ambassador in Washington who, when his country was overrun
by the Germans, had assumed responsibility for Greenland.
These air bases were to be evacuated when 'the emergency is
over', but Denmark and the United States were still arguing
over the interpretation of the word 'emergency' when in 1950 a
new agreement under the North Atlantic Treaty Organization
was signed between Denmark and the United States which left
the latter in control of military bases for some time to come.
As a result of this agreement, the enormous military air base
at Thule, now called Dundas, was built.

ALASKA

Alaska, formerly Russian America, was purchased by the United States in 1867 for the sum of 7,200,000 dollars. The purchase, universally described at the time as 'folly', was one which has paid off many-fold since. The United States has made no official claim to a sector north of Alaska but the Secretary of the Navy, in 1924, stated 'if land in the Arctic to the north of Alaska is discovered, it should be the property of the United States'.

President Truman's declaration of 1945 announced the United States' claim to the continental shelf around its shores (presumably extending to the two-hundred-metre contour).

This claim would have the effect of adding to United States territory a certain proportion of the Alaskan 'sector', curiously enough in an oil-bearing region similar to that of the Gulf of Mexico with which the declaration was primarily concerned.

The continental shelf theory would automatically join all the islands of Canada and of the U.S.S.R. within their claimed sectors to the home territory, with the exception in the latter case of the Franz Josef archipelago. It is now possible to state confidently that no further undiscovered lands exist within the 'sectors'.

SVALBARD

Only one other Arctic territory is still completely insular, surrounded by ocean over two hundred metres deep. This is Svalbard where the northernmost industry and white settlements exist. It was long a *terra nullius*, its coal exploited by private commercial companies from Holland, Scotland, Norway, Sweden, Russia and the United States. The situation with several conflicting mineral claims by so many varied companies was becoming completely chaotic and in 1920 the whole territory was awarded to Norway as sovereign power by the League of Nations. The sovereignty was, to some extent, however, limited. By the treaty, nationals of all signing countries had equal rights with Norwegian citizens. This was in order to protect the coal-mining industry. Furthermore it was laid down that the islands should remain unfortified. On the basis of this provision, Norway was able to decline a Russian proposal in 1947 for joint fortification of Svalbard and later resisted U.S. representations on similar lines. Yet we have seen that Svalbard was important enough in the Second World War to have seen a good deal of fighting on a small scale, and to have changed hands several times. Norway is now back again in sovereign control of the islands and the coal mines today are owned and operated by Norwegian and Russian companies only.

POLITICAL ADMINISTRATION

The mid-twentieth century is characterized by a resurgence of nationalism and the negation of colonialism throughout the world. It is of interest to examine how self-governing, to any extent are the Arctic territories. In Svalbard, although it has been officially proclaimed a part of the kingdom of Norway, there are considerable differences on account of the treaty limitations. It is not, for example, a 'county' (Fylke). Norwegian civil and criminal law hold for Svalbard but laws passed in Oslo do not apply to the territory unless specifically so stated. The central government administers the territory directly and appoints a Governor. By the treaty it is unable to levy more tax than is needed for the administration of the treaty. So there is only a very small export duty on coal paid by the Russian concern and a very low income tax paid by the Norse miners. This, of course, they appreciate, so there is little agitation for self-government here.

Alaska became the forty-ninth state of the United States in 1958–9. After its purchase from Russia, a long period intervened before there was any attempt at administration. For nine years Alaska was run by the War Department in very much a Fifth Cavalry 'boots and saddles' style. For two successive years its administration was transferred to the Department of the Treasury and one man was sent with civil authority to this vast region. Then came five years of naval control. It was not until 1899 that a criminal code and taxes were established. In the Yukon gold-rush of '98, Americans were astonished to find there were laws and law officers when they crossed the frontier into the Canadian Yukon.

In 1912 Alaska became a territory, which meant it had an elected local legislature and a voteless representative in Washington. The Governor was not an elected individual but was

4. Indian trapper with pack-dogs in the Yukon (*see pp.* 147–148)

5. Sled dogs in Antarctica (*see pp.* 148–149)

26. Snocats and sledges of Fuchs' Transantarctic Expedition, at South Pole after 950-mile journey from Weddell Sea coast (*see pp.* 153–155 and *pp.* 268–269)

27. U.S. Icebreaker "Glacier" forcing passage through pack-ice in Ross Sea (*see p.* 158)

appointed directly by the President of the United States. This status continued for forty-six years despite fairly continuous agitation for statehood and covered the period which included the final reason for achievement of statehood—the achievement of a majority within the population by white immigrants.

Alaska has therefore, within the framework of the United States, come the full way to self-government after a most extraordinary lack of government.

Greenland has perhaps seen the happiest experiment in colonialism in world history. It achieved, in 1953, full status as a part of the Danish kingdom and now sends two members to the 180-member Folketing in Copenhagen. Nowadays, Greenlanders have completely similar electoral rights to Danes. The whole situation has altered radically within the last generation. Until then, as Eske Brun says 'the basic principle of Danish rule has been to assist the people of Greenland to achieve the fullest possible life, protected, as far as may be, from the disadvantages which might accrue from connection with the outside world'. This meant paternalism, very gradual education in democracy, a government monopoly of all trade and therefore of the whole economic life of the country, and the exclusion, except for visiting scientists, of all foreigners. But the war of 1939–45 ended all this. The local district councils, which had begun in 1908, were forced for the first time actually to govern the country, and it was obvious at the close of hostilities that this new-found independence must continue. Accordingly, a Royal Commission reported on constitutional reform which has resulted in the present full Danish status. This has been recognized by the United Nations, whereupon Denmark ceased reporting to the U.N. Trusteeship Committee as she had been doing, entirely voluntarily, since 1945. Administration and trading are now separate, and private enterprise has been allowed in where once the government monopoly was the rule.

In the Soviet Union it is probably true to say that there is as much self-government in the Arctic regions as anywhere else within the Union. There has been frequent redrawing of administrative boundaries, now, in every case, linking the Arctic extension with the non-Arctic main body of an administrative province. There is, therefore, little uniformity in the administration of the Soviet Arctic and the monopolistic position of the

N

administration of the northern sea route, which in the thirties
was really an empire of its own, is now finished.

The Canadian Arctic territories include part of the province
of Quebec, part of the province of Newfoundland (Labrador)
and the North-West Territories. These latter are still territories
administered directly from Ottawa. There is one member of
the Canadian House of Commons from the MacKenzie district, one from the Yukon, but none from the truly Arctic
portion of the territories. In addition, there is a North-West
Territories Council of eight members, five appointed and three
elected, but again, from the MacKenzie district with its large
white population, alone. The Canadian Government, since the
Second World War, has been very considerably increasing its
health, education, and other social services in the territories.
But administratively it is still, in effect, a colony of Canada and
the population is so small that it is unlikely that the Arctic
realm will ever be a province of its own. More likely is that it
will be divided eventually among the other provinces and thus,
as with the Soviet Union, will lose its major identity.

STRATEGIC IMPORTANCE OF THE ARCTIC

Since the Second World War two major powers, the U.S.A.
and the U.S.S.R., have emerged as all-powerful and these two
confront each other across the North Polar Sea and the Bering
Strait. Many smaller powers have felt it vital to link themselves
by alliance to one or other and a few, but none with Arctic
interests, have preserved strict neutrality. In effect, the mid-
century set-up consists of, on the one side, the Soviet Union
and on the other, the United States, Canada and Denmark.
In between is Norway in a particularly unenviable position
because she is a member of NATO but the Svalbard treaty
forbids any militarization of the islands and also permits the
Russians to maintain their economic activities there.

From the break-down of allied co-operation after the war,
the emphasis in strategic thinking has been on the nuclear
deterrent and defence against it. It has been the purpose of
both sides to obtain bases near the potential enemy's territory
and to erect, as far as possible, warning screens and airfields
for the operation of defensive fighters. The Soviet Union has so
far kept to its own soil except for the attempt to come to a

fortification arrangement with Norway in Svalbard. The United States has established bases in Greenland and northern Canada and in addition has mainly financed the building of the DEW Line (Distant Early Warning) roughly along the northern edge of the continent on the 70th parallel. This astonishing operation has altered the face of the North American Arctic. Conceived in 1952, it was completed five years later at the cost of six hundred million dollars and some thirty-five lives. Twenty-three thousand men worked on it and it is now manned by about seven hundred at six main stations, thirty auxiliary stations and a few so-called 'I-Sites', the latter manned by a team of three civilians. In essence the DEW Line stations have their vast scanning radars housed in plastic domes resembling orange golf balls of fifty-five feet in diameter. To build these in the sites where an uninterrupted scan could be obtained, astonishing feats such as dropping tractors by parachute were required. Now, on the completion of this chain, it is possible to fly across the North American Arctic without losing sight of the lights of human habitation. Yet it is true to say that almost concurrently with its completion this astonishing enterprise was out of date. Two things have completely altered the picture of strategy in the Arctic—inter-continental ballistic missiles and the nuclear-powered submarine. With warfare's range so extended by these two means, the polar distances cease to matter. They only did for a short period, the period of the manned bomber which was able to travel that particular number of miles. For strategic thinking we can perhaps abandon the polar chart which came in so suddenly in 1945 and return to Mercator again.

It is unlikely that the north can ever see conventional forces operating in any large numbers and it is unlikely that any small wars will develop there. However, the strategy of the 1947 to 1959 period has revolutionized the Arctic lands, has precipitated Greenland and Alaska into self-government and has left Canada at least much more aware of her North-West Territories than she was before. Today the value of the expensive bases is very much diminished but some of them are and will continue to be useful for civilian air transport. Stefansson was a little previous in his polar air-age ideas but we now do see two trans-Arctic air routes of Scandinavian Airlines and Air

France as well as more southerly ones across Greenland and the
Canadian archipelago. The establishment of Great-Circle,
shortest-distance commercial air routes across the North Polar
Sea is now a political rather than a technical problem.

If the international climate begins to thaw and there is less
fist-shaking across the Bering Strait and the North Polar Sea
we can hope to see a considerable extension of commercial
routes with all the benefits they may bring and the concomitant
responsibility of the Arctic Nations to maintain airfields and
the necessary weather service to go with safe flying.

Already we have useful international co-operation on these
lines. ICAO, through 'joint support' assists Denmark financially
in maintaining its important weather stations in Greenland,
and the United States co-operates with Canada in maintaining
joint weather stations north of latitude 74°. Another humani-
tarian international activity is the international ice patrol begun
after the *Titanic* disaster of 1912 and ably operated ever since
by the United States Coast Guard. This patrol studies, reports
on, and gives warnings concerning icebergs in the North
Atlantic shipping lanes, and has conducted iceberg research in
more northern waters. Something similar in the way of an
international rescue service will be required when transpolar
flying develops to a greater degree. Here already, however, the
United States' Tenth Air Rescue Service has a tradition second
to none in operation under conditions of extraordinary difficulty
in the Arctic regions.

It is in this way, by the treating of the North Polar Sea as a
Mediterranean criss-crossed by air routes and used by nuclear-
powered merchant submarines, that one sees a future for the
Arctic lands. It is unlikely that a polar climate can ever support
a much larger population at any reasonable standard of living
than it does at present since the potentialities of wild life are
limited and of agriculture are virtually nil. There will, undoubtedly, be a considerable development in mining with the
world's continual search for minerals going ever further and
further afield into areas previously considered uneconomic to
exploit. And the key to the economics is transport and in the
use in the Arctic lands of people who are suited to the isolated
life whether they are white or non-white.

FURTHER READING

Hanessian, J., 'The Antarctic Treaty, 1959', *Int. and Comp. Law Quarterly*, 1960, pp. 436-80.

La Fay, H., 'Dewline', *Nat. Geog. Mag.*, 114, p. 128 (1958).

Stefansson, V., *The Adventure of Wrangel Island*, New York, 1925.

Svarlien, O., 'The Sector Principle in Law and Practice', *Polar Record*, 10 (1960), pp. 248-63.

Taracouzio, T. A., *Soviets in the Arctic*, New York, 1938.

Chapter 10

REGIONAL DESCRIPTION OF THE CANADIAN ARCTIC

UNDER Canadian sovereignty we have the largest bloc of territory north of the tree line. It is made up of two mainland areas to the west and to the east of Hudson Bay, and the northern group of islands which itself is the second largest archipelago in the world. This in turn can be divided into three sections—the northernmost rank of islands, the Queen Elizabeth group north of the North-West Passage (Lancaster Sound–Melville Sound), and two more southerly groups of islands which can be termed 'eastern' and 'western', depending on their accessibility from the Atlantic or from the Pacific. There is great variety of surface configuration in this nine-hundred-thousand square mile area from low alluvial flats to rugged mountains of over eight thousand feet. It has always sustained a smaller population than most other Arctic lands and has included the most primitive groups, perhaps, of the Eskimo race. White settlement and development on Canadian soil has been of more recent date than throughout the rest of the Arctic circumpolar region.

GEOLOGY

The mainland areas on both sides of Hudson Bay extending as far west as the 120th meridian are underlain by rocks of the Canadian Pre-Cambrian Shield. Several fingers of this exposed basement protrude further north into eastern Devon and Ellesmere islands, up Boothia Peninsula and Somerset Island, with two smaller extensions into Victoria Island. The shield is composed mainly of highly altered acid granite and granite gneiss, but with certain areas of Proterozoic and Archaean sedimentary rocks and smaller areas of volcanic extrusions. The chief among these are as follows:

1. The termination of the Labrador iron-bearing trough at Payne Bay.
2. A belt of volcanic rocks including some greenstones extending from Cape Smith across the Ungava Peninsula to Wakeham Bay.
3. Isolated areas in Baffin Island, especially in the region of Admiralty Inlet.
4. From Baker Lake to Bathurst Inlet and on by the 'Wellington Arch' to Victoria Island.
5. A group of rocks extending from Coppermine to Darnley Bay and thence by the 'Minto Arch' on to north-western Victoria Island.

Upon this original basal complex, worn down by the passage of most of geological time, were deposited Palaeozoic rocks, mainly limestones, which survive today in certain basin areas. Palaeozoic rocks, mainly flat-lying and comparatively undisturbed, also form extensive plateau regions, particularly in two prominent areas just to the north of the exposed shield edge in northern Baffin and Devon island and to the west in Banks and Melville islands, probably resting on the hidden shield edge. Beyond these, and further north again, comes an area of much more complex geology whose investigation has only just commenced. Here are rocks of various geological ages, in places highly folded and faulted, and showing evidence of at least three orogenic movements extending in time through to the Tertiary period. This region fronts the main North Polar Sea basin and appears to provide a folded edge to the continent, corresponding in some detail at least to the Appalachian folding of eastern North America and the Cordillera folding of the west. With its large area of the Pre-Cambrian Shield and the lengthy geological evolution of the northern group, Canadian Arctic rocks are thus potential bearers of mineral resources as are other parts of Canada which have been much more closely investigated. Iron ores are plentifully present in the Proterozoic sediments. There are many occurrences of coal in the archipelago, much of which is also of a formation favourable for oil.

PHYSIOGRAPHY

To describe in detail the physiographic make-up of the Canadian Arctic we have to examine not only the geological base but also the modifications which may have been imposed by the various processes of weathering, and in particular the effects of glaciation. Almost all the region with which we are concerned was heavily glaciated throughout the Pleistocene period. Certain areas in the north-west appear, however, to have escaped most of this glaciation and to the east there are extensive areas still covered with permanent ice today, extending to something of the order of sixty thousand square miles, more than half of it on Ellesmere Island. There has been extensive submergence in the area and certain regions are rising noticeably today, presumably those from which the ice load has been most recently removed. The map (Fig. 59) shows the whole Canadian territory divided into twenty-six generalized physiographic regions and these will now be described in detail.

I. The Pre-Cambrian Shield Area

(a) *The Western Shield Region*. This is essentially an area of rugged granite rock, speckled with rock basin lakes and frequently showing clearly the underlying structure. To the east elevations are of the order of two thousand feet, but the country slopes downwards towards the western margin of the shield which is by no means clearly exposed on the ground and, although marked as a clear line on the geological maps, is in fact very vague and considerably drift-covered. To the west of the Dismal Lakes the glacial deposits show a distinct trend from south to north.

(b) *The Coppermine Region*. This is a distinctive area of Proterozoic sedimentary rocks which include the copper-bearing strata from which the Coppermine is named. The strata have a slight northward dip resulting in steep south-facing scarps and gentle northern dip-slopes, the islands immediately off the coast having, therefore, a 'writing-desk' appearance with southern cliff shores. In the extension of this region on Victoria Island some of the scarps also face south but many face to the north or north-west, in some areas the hill tops reaching 2,500 feet.

(c) *The Keewatin Drift Region*. This large mainland area to the west of Hudson Bay and to the east of Bathurst Inlet is of fairly low relief and monotonous in the extreme though there are more glacial deposits in this area than in the region further west and the most classical examples of lengthy eskers, oriented drumlins and totally disorganized drainage with an infinite number of lakes spilling uncertainly one into the other are found here. Much of the area is between five hundred and a thousand feet with very imperceptible watersheds between the major rivers, and the coasts south of Wager Bay and of Queen Maud Gulf are low. To the north-east of Wager Bay the country is higher and with much more exposed bedrock rising to the order of two thousand feet and here again on Melville Peninsula and Boothia Peninsula the underlying structure of the Pre-Cambrian bedrock imposes a linear pattern on the surface resulting in straight trenches such as Bellot Strait and its companion False Strait immediately to the south.

(d) *Southampton–Melville Region.* The eastern part of South-ampton Island is a smooth Pre-Cambrian plateau rising to between one thousand and two thousand feet with a very prominent scarp towards the lowlands in the west. Melville Peninsula is a very similar rolling plateau area with rather more rock exposure, much more rugged on its western than its eastern side. It is deeply indented by inlets of a fiord-like character whereas the Southampton Island coast is straight but cut by narrow, deeply incised valleys.

(e) *The Ungava Region.* On the east side of Hudson Bay a fairly large area north of the tree line has again a surface typical of the shield. Relief is high on the northern coast between Cape Wolstenholme and Cape Hope's Advance and from here the land on the whole slopes southward. The two-mile-wide New Quebec Crater is an interesting feature of this region, apparently formed by a falling meteor. The Proterozoic rocks along the west coast and adjacent islands, particularly the Belcher Islands, form a most striking orographic type, the summits of the folded ridges appearing as long island festoons. On the east side of Ungava Bay the land rises sharply from a low coast to a high, deeply incised plateau, which in turn merges with the uplifted mountain rim of the Labrador Coast.

(f) *The Baffin Uplands.* This Pre-Cambrian region in a similar way forms a transition between the extremely low coast which is part of a sedimentary basin and the tilted upland mountain eastern rim. The local relief is nowhere very great but

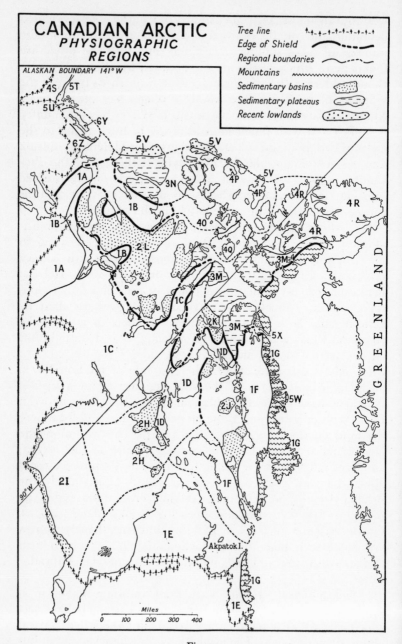

CANADIAN ARCTIC
PHYSIOGRAPHIC
REGIONS

Tree line
Edge of Shield
Regional boundaries
Mountains
Sedimentary basins
Sedimentary plateaus
Recent lowlands

ALASKAN BOUNDARY 141° W

4S   5T
5U
6Y
6Z
5V   5V
1A   3N   5V
1B   4P
1B   4P   4R   4R
40   4R
1A   2L   4Q   4R
1B   4Q   3M
3M
1C   3M
2K 3M
1C   5X
1D   1G
1C   1F
5W
1D   2J
2H 1D   1F
2H
1G
1F
2I
1E
1G
Akpatok I.
1G
1E

G R E E N L A N D

Miles
0   100 200 300 400

Fig. 59.

the altitude rises steadily to reach several thousand feet before merging with the eastern mountains. Foxe Peninsula and the associated small islands to its south-west are rough and rocky with altitudes up to a thousand feet. Further north much glacial material covers the country and a most prominent feature in this region is the Barnes Ice-cap which is located not on a highland area but on the plateau surface which here has an altitude of around 1,500 feet.

(g) *The Eastern Mountain Rim*. From Labrador as far north as central Ellesmere Island the Pre-Cambrian Shield takes on a totally different character. It has been strongly uplifted, probably in Tertiary times, at the same time as the downfaulting of the Baffin Bay depression. It is deeply dissected by fiords, often of a peculiar 'S' shape which may be the result of fracturing of the hard Pre-Cambrian rocks by the great forces involved in the uplift, and which have been over-deepened by the intense glaciation which passed through this tilted coast. Much of the highland is covered today with glacier ice, and this reaches sea-level along considerable fronts in Ellesmere Island, less on Devon and rarely on the Baffinland coast. The altitudes range up to seven thousand feet above sea-level and a remarkable uniformity of mountain tops appears to exist at around the six-thousand-foot level. Here we have some of the most sensational scenery of the Canadian Arctic with the long, deep fiords running between magnificent ice-hung peaks.

Fig. 59. Key to regions:

1. *Pre-Cambrian Shield*
1A Western Shield Region.
1B Coppermine Region.
1C Keewatin Drift Region.
1D Southampton–Melville Region.
1E Ungava Region.
1F Baffin Uplands.
1G Eastern Mountain Rim.

2. *Palaeozoic Sedimentary Basins*
2H Southampton Group.
2I Hudson Bay Lowland.
2J Foxe Basin Group.
2K Boothia Group.
2L Western Artic Group.

3. *Palaeozoic Sedimentary Plateaus*
3M Lancaster Plateau.
3N Banks–Melville Plateau.

4. *Folded Uplands*
4O Parry Island Belt.
4P Sverdrup Belt.
4Q Cornwallis Belt.
4R Ellesmere–Axel Heiberg Belt.
4S Yukon Mountains.

5. *Tertiary and Pleistocene Lowlands*
5T Yukon Coastal Plain.
5U Mackenzie Delta.
5V Arctic Coastal Plain.
5W Baffin Coastal Plain.
5X Pond Inlet Plain.

6. *Great Plains Sediments*
6Y Eskimo Lakes Lowland.
6Z Western Plain.

II. Palaeozoic Sedimentary Basins

Upon the surface of the shield there must at one time have been a uniform deposition of a considerable thickness of Palaeozoic sediments, mostly limestone and sandstones, but these are now preserved only in certain depressed regions and have been almost completely removed elsewhere. Although five basins have been listed they all show very much the same characteristics. Marine submergence during the Pleistocene period of almost all the basin areas has resulted in a uniformity of surface characterized by very prevalent emerged strand-lines with their attendant ponded lagoons. The limestone rock, easily frost-shattered, lends itself particularly well to this type of deposition. Relief is generally low particularly in the large, recently discovered islands in Foxe Basin where an altitude of a hundred feet above sea-level is exceptional. Smoothed, gently sloping coastlines are the rule in the basin areas, yielding few harbours, and where the tide is large, tremendous inter-tidal areas of mud flats appear, strewn with erratic boulders.

III. Palaeozoic Plateaus

In certain areas on the shield edge the Palaeozoic rocks have been much better preserved and stand up as bold, highland areas with a considerable thickness of varied sediments. The most typical development of this is in the lands around Lancaster Sound, in the Brodeur Peninsula of Baffin Island and in neighbouring Somerset Island where a very smooth plateau of the order of two thousand feet in altitude has sheer cliff coasts and very deeply entrenched rivers. On Devon Island the plateau is slightly higher and on its east, where it approaches the mountain rim, is slightly glaciated, thin ice-caps adding to the altitude of the plateau and increasing in thickness towards the mountainous east. The other Palaeozoic plateau area comprising parts of Victoria, Banks and Melville islands is more undulating in character and on Banks Island a good deal of erosion has left the Palaeozoic rocks as isolated, hilly areas. On Melville Island the strata dip gently northward, on Banks gently north-eastward, and here the watershed is located close to Prince of Wales Strait so that the drainage is mainly right across the island to the North Polar Sea coast.

IV. Folded Uplands of Various Ages

The Parry Island Belt (*o*). This region comprising the major part of Melville Island and of Bathurst Island is composed of highly folded rocks of chiefly Palaeozoic time, the eroded synclines and anticlines showing up strongly on the ground and controlling the drainage. Their trend is generally east to west but on the western side of Melville Island more north-west south-east. Both the western shore of this island and the north-eastern part of Bathurst are deeply indented by long inlets which, in the latter case, pass completely through the peninsula cutting it up into a series of islands. Elevations vary from below a thousand feet to over three thousand on Melville Island, which bears on its highest parts three small, permanent snow-fields which are probably very thin. Compared to most of the Canadian tundra considered so far, this region is noticeably lacking in lakes of any size and this, together with other indications seems to show that the area was not glaciated except for extensions of the existing Melville Island snow-fields.

So also was the next region to the north, the Sverdrup Belt. Here such rocks as have been investigated seem to be of Mesozoic age. The rocks are less strongly tilted than in the Parry Island Belt and several Piercement Domes, consisting in part of gypsum, indicating the possible presence of oil, have been found within this region. Little, if any, of the islands exceeds a thousand feet in altitude. There are again almost no lakes and the drainage seems to be controlled by the structure or to be more or less radial. This area has another feature which distinguishes it and that is the semi-permanent character of the sea-ice between its island members. To a great extent this results in the whole area being 'solid land' throughout the year.

The Cornwallis Belt (*q*) is another part of the Innuitian Region but here the trend of the folding is north-south, the folds have been worn down to a smooth surface, and glaciation has certainly had its effect in covering much of the land with surface deposits.

The last of the folded upland areas in the Queen Elizabeth group comprises much of Ellesmere Island and its neighbour Axel Heiberg (*r*). It is a region of highly complex geological folding of various times and, though the general trend of the folds is south-west to north-east, there is much irregularity and local diversification of direction. Altitudes range from seven thousand feet on Axel Heiberg to over eight thousand in northern Ellesmere and a considerable part of both islands is covered today by glacial ice. Immense fiords cut deeply into the islands. Greely Fiord–Nansen Sound can count as one of the longest in the world. Eureka Sound, another fiord, completely divides the two major islands of this group and has around its shores some of the only low-lying ground of the whole region. Another area is at the head of Greely Fiord where Lake Hazen occupies a valley only five hundred feet above sea-level. Many glaciers in Ellesmere Island and at least one on Axel Heiberg reach sea-level but on the whole precipitation is very low in this furthest north Canadian land and the nourishment of the glaciers is small. Rainfall is so low that, in some of the Eureka Sound lowlands salt pans have developed due to evaporation during the comparatively warm summer and in fact, were it not for permafrost, there would be completely desert conditions.

One final small area of folded uplands occurs on the extreme west of the Canadian Arctic inland from the Yukon coastal plain. Here we have the east-west trending British Mountains and the north-south trending Richardson Mountains with an area of plateau in between. Once again this region appears to have escaped glaciation and the mountains which rise to six thousand feet have distinctly V-shaped valleys and sharp ridges and spurs.

V. Tertiary and Pleistocene Lowlands

These areas of recent deposits, the most recent of all being the Mackenzie Delta, which is still building, have only recently emerged from the sea. They tend to be crossed by many parallel braided rivers and to possess offshore shoals and islands and many lakes. Vegetation is extremely rare and there is much fine sand and gravel, giving a distinctive colour to most of the plain. The Mackenzie Delta is the type area for the form known as the 'Pingo' (see Chapter 4). A small area on the central east coast of Baffin Island (w) represents moraine material deposited in recent times by the Baffin Island glaciers and the final region, the Pond Inlet Plain (x), consists of isolated Tertiary sediments with some seams of coal in scattered pockets around Eclipse Sound.

VI. Great Plains Sediments

Two final physiographic regions are located on the mainland between the Mackenzie Delta and the western edge of the Pre-Cambrian Shield and represent an Arctic extension of the sedimentary strata of the Great Plains, Palaeozoic and Meso-zoic in age but tremendously mantled in drift. Some of the rivers are deeply incised and it is only here that bedrock is exposed. Relief is comparatively slight, rising to a thousand feet in the Smoking Mountains on the west coast of Franklin Bay.

From the above descriptions of the different regions of the Canadian Arctic we can see the great variability in surface configuration. Yet to the layman a first glance reveals a striking uniformity in the appearance of the land, conditioned by the tundra vegetation. Even here certain broad, generalized divisions can be drawn from the near rock desert to the more advanced dwarf-shrub heath associations. Where relief is considerable and the surface varied, little pockets of the different divisions of the tundra vegetation will occur close to each other —sedgy plains, moss-lichen slopes and, in the more sheltered and favoured localities, the dwarf-shrub heaths. Yet across the Canadian Arctic as a whole it is possible to draw generalized vegetational divisions as has been done in the vegetation map in the Atlas of Canada. The Queen Elizabeth group extending southwards in a tongue to include most of Prince of Wales and Somerset islands and the exposed fringe of Baffin Island falls within the fell-field rocky desert area where vegetation is extremely sparse and the precipitation so low that, but for the permafrost table, complete desert conditions would reign. The next 'higher' group—the stony, sedge moss, lichen, tundra—occupies the northern halves of Banks and Victoria islands, Boothia and Melville peninsulas, the Hudson Strait coasts and much of the remainder of Baffin Island. The dwarf-shrub heath dominates the more southerly reaches of the Canadian Arctic to the tree line including most of mainland Keewatin and Quebec and an area of interior southern Baffin Island south of Lake Nettilling. Finally, in the western sedimentary area beyond the shield there is a further vegetational type developed, a mature sedge-grass tundra which yields the best grazing for reindeer.

The other great factor of uniformity is the dominance of the landscape by glaciers past and present. Most of the region was not only heavily glacier-covered throughout much of Pleistocene time but was, in effect, in the centre of the North American glaciation; hence marginal features which are prominent in the regions further south are comparatively rare. Large moraines are mainly absent but on the other hand eskers are extremely prolific and particularly in central Keewatin some of the longest eskers in the world exist. Oriented morainal features such as drumlins are again extremely common and many attempts have been made to indicate direction of ice movement and centres of ice sheets from these depositional features. The complexities of the multiple glaciation of the area, the shifting centres of greatest ice depths which undoubtedly occurred make this a rather hopeless exercise. More profitable is the placing of the limits of marine submergence and the margins of ice-age lakes. Many of the latter have yet to be discovered but certain well-defined ones within the Canadian Arctic are:

1. The Kazan Dubawnt Lake with levels up to eight hundred feet above sea-level.
2. The Back River Lake Group which survives vestigially today.
3. Several smaller glacial lakes in the centre of Victoria Island.

As the ice-load gradually lifted, the land has recovered in altitude and is still perhaps doing so, but not nearly so much work has been done here as in the Scandinavian area where a similar ice-load gradually vanished at the close of the Pleistocene. The glacial map of Canada published in 1958 shows, generalized, the extent of marine submergence when the ice had retreated sufficiently to let the sea in over the lands it had previously occupied. On the west of Hudson Bay for instance, Bird has shown that the marine limit was approximately at 360 feet. Today in other parts around the shores of Hudson Bay and elsewhere even greater altitudes are probable up to at least five hundred feet above the existing altitude of the sea, but records, many of which exist, of higher marine limits should be treated with the utmost caution. Some of them may be merely lateral moraine material or the shores of temporary and local ice-dammed lakes.

The tilted eastern mountain rim of the Canadian Arctic has been suggested as the source region for the great Pleistocene ice sheet of North America which, with fluctuations, spread from here over all the region with the exception of the extreme northwest. Most of the existing glaciers and ice-caps are on the highlands with characteristic tongues descending into the valleys or even to sea-level. There are at least two exceptions to this: the Barnes Ice-cap in central Baffin Island and the little ice canopy of Meighen Island. The Barnes Ice-cap, which at present seems to be nourished not by the usual steady accumulation of unmelted winter snowfalls on its higher areas, but in the conversion of this by reason of the great existing cold of the ice to 'superimposed ice' during the summer melt season, is situated on the gently rolling region of the middle of Baffin Island with bedrock at no great altitude above sea-level. It would appear impossible for it to have been re-created after the warm period of several thousand years ago and it is presumed to be a relic (the only one still on low ground) of the vast Pleistocene ice sheet of the whole region. The small ice-cap on Meighen Island and perhaps those on Melville Island are probably similar in their methods of nourishment to that of the Barnes Ice-cap, but are thinner and smaller. The Canadian Arctic glaciers are on the whole receding today, but at a much lesser rate than has been discovered in other parts of the North Atlantic region, such as east Greenland or Svalbard. There appears also to be great variation in the height of Firn Line (the altitude up to which summer melt extends) instead of any uniform poleward decline. It stands, for instance, at only 2,150 feet on the foggy glaciers of Frobisher Bay, but is at about 4,500 feet on Cumberland Peninsula and varies little from this figure on the other Baffin coastal mountains and on much of Ellesmere Island. With the stimulus of the International Geophysical Year, Canadian glaciologists are tackling the problems of the eastern Arctic ice with great vigour at the present time.

All the evidence points to little, if any, glaciation in the north-western group of islands. This must have represented the lee side of the Pleistocene ice sheet, starved of precipitation from the moisture-bearing winds that nourished the areas further south, even as it is starved of precipitation today.

HUMAN GEOGRAPHY

Until the present century this large area of territory was inhabited only by groups of Eskimo with a Stone Age culture and living by a subsistence economy based on the animals of the land and of the sea. There are now some nine thousand to ten thousand of these people and it is unlikely that their population was ever greater than double this. The only non-Eskimo incursion into the Canadian Arctic in the nineteenth century was that of the whalers. These were mainly from Scotland and from the New England whaling ports; they began wintering in the Canadian Arctic at Herschel Island in the west and in Hudson Bay and Cumberland Sound in the east. Their contact with the Eskimo natives was considerable. They used them as boat crews for the actual whaling hunts, they traded with them in fox skins and the meat and skins of caribou and they had considerable promiscuous intercourse with the native women. The result of the whalers' temporary occupation is still seen today in the dances that they taught them and, for example, the use of tea as a popular drink. Scottish reels and American square dances are energetically carried out today to the tunes of early times on the accordion.

In the twentieth century other white settlers arrived. These were the traders interested primarily in white fox skin but to a limited degree in other animal products of the area. There was at first considerable competition in this field but the Hudson's Bay Company has gained and maintained a practical monopoly of the area. In this century, too, came the missionaries and here there is still plenty of competition between those of the Catholic and of the Protestant faith. In the absence of any early Government interest it was the missionaries who established a few hospitals and nursing services to serve this widely scattered population. Posts of the R.C.M.P. began to be built in the twenties. The Mountie in the north was for many years the only government agent, acting not only as policeman but as magistrate, postmaster and later as distributor of Family Allowance and registrar of births, deaths and marriages. Subsequent to the Second World War other settlements have been made by the white peoples in the Canadian Arctic. Weather stations have been widely established and have leapt beyond even Eskimo settlement into the Queen Elizabeth group of islands. Airfields, originally military during the Second World War and subsequently used to service northern weather stations and manned by air force personnel have also come in and in the late fifties there was the 'Crash' programme establishment of the Distant Early Warning radar stations, which obsolete though they may now be, have in fact, completely altered the face of the Canadian Arctic. The Canadian Government is beginning to realize its responsibilities in the north to a greater and greater extent and since 1945 several government schools and nursing stations have been started and a new administrative organization, the Northern Service Officers, have taken over some of the functions previously carried out, albeit efficiently, by the untrained mounted policeman. The white settlements, numbering only thirty or forty in all, vary in size from containing one of the above-mentioned functions to perhaps all of them and recently there has been a considerable concentrating movement of the Eskimo population itself, previously widely scattered as a purely hunting community must be. A trend to urbanization has been suddenly thrust on them. There is some comparison here with the Western Isles of Scotland. A few conservative folk will stay on at the old hunting ground but the younger people will move and, in fact, are being forced by economics to move to the major centres where the pattern is a wage-earning one. The largest settlements are those of the airfields, such as Frobisher Bay, Cambridge Bay and Resolute, the base for transportation in the Queen Elizabeth group of islands, the nickel mine at Rankin Inlet and certain fringe settlements which can almost be described as 'southern ports' of the Canadian Arctic. These latter are Churchill, the centre of sea-borne distribution in Hudson Bay and slowly growing sea route from the prairies to Europe; Old Aklavik, now replaced by the new town of Inuvik at the mouth of the Mackenzie where the sub-Arctic thrusts practically to the coast; Moosonee on James Bay which the province of Ontario would like to see developed as an Arctic port, and Ungava Bay in the province of Quebec where the future may bring large-scale iron ore developments and where again the Arctic and sub-Arctic meet, as do the Eskimo and Indian populations. Frobisher Bay is one of the most peculiar settlements in the Canadian Arctic. At its present site nothing existed prior to 1941, then a military landing field was established and this has grown in the recent decade into a large airfield capable of taking trans-Atlantic airliners and used primarily as a refuelling stop between western North America and Europe. At the present stage of aircraft development this is a very handy refuelling stop—some six airlines have been using it at the rate of 2,500 landings a month and the large amount of aircraft gasoline required is supplied by sea-borne tanker. Frobisher was also the centre of the eastern section of the DEW Line construction and during this period an enormous amount of flying was done. Many of the eastern Arctic Eskimo were attracted to the site and have been working as unskilled or skilled labourers around the airport, living in wooden houses and earning up to $100 a week. Various fantastic schemes have been produced for building a permanent city at Frobisher with a planned population of four to five thousand, looking somewhat like a projected lunar base. It is unlikely that any of these architectural dreams will come to pass. Frobisher is a halt on the world airlines of 1960; by 1970 aircraft development will almost certainly result in its being by-passed and Frobisher may become a ghost town. A more permanent basis must be found for a real population centre in the Canadian Arctic, based on a more permanent resource.

ECONOMIC RESOURCES

The first established economic resource of this area was that of fur, chiefly the white fox of the tundra, but also including the musk rats of the Mackenzie Delta in which up to a thousand Eskimo trappers were involved. The North-West Territories have produced in the past between $300,000 and $2,000,000 per year but in this fur trade not only has the price of fur varied considerably but so has the annual take of the white fox. The fur trade is now only third in economic importance in the North-West Territories as a whole, and the slump in fur prices is liable to last a long time. In the heyday of the trade, particularly during the years of the Second World War, the western Arctic Eskimo trapping the Mackenzie Delta and Banks

Island obtained incomes sufficient to buy schooners. To some extent all the native peoples of the north have invested capital in the fur trade, in their dog teams which have to be maintained and fed.

The disastrous decline of the wild native caribou has already been mentioned in an earlier chapter. This decline has destroyed one of the subsistence bases of the Eskimo's hunting economy and, in fact, has wiped out certain small Eskimo groups which used to live in the interior on caribou and caribou alone. It is a matter for biological argument whether this depleted wild resource can be replaced by domesticated reindeer or other animals and whether the hunting native people can be successfully changed from hunters to herders. To date experience in Arctic Canada is unfortunate in this respect. A herd of reindeer was introduced from Alaska, and after taking from 1929 to 1935 to make the journey, over two thousand deer arrived in the Mackenzie Delta. It was hoped from these to try to build up native herds as had been the case in Alaska and Arctic Siberia; but the herd has grown extremely slowly, has suffered several setbacks, such as the one in 1944 when the chief native trained herders and the white supervisor were drowned in a shipwreck. As recently as 1959 it was likely that the government would scrap the whole programme but it now appears to have received a renewed lease of life. As yet no reindeer have been introduced in any other part of the Canadian north except the Mackenzie Delta. One possible area is that other thrust of the sub-Arctic into the Ungava Bay region. Here, in fact, an experimental agricultural station has been recently established and in 1955 ten sheep made their appearance at Fort Chimo, two of them unfortunately being killed by dogs during the first winter. Geese and poultry have also been introduced here and it seems likely that this area, particularly if a mining economy springs up in the neighbourhood, could be an agricultural base on the Arctic fringe. Commercial fishing has been attempted in Ungava Bay and Frobisher Bay but again without truly economic success. There is no reason to alter the conclusions of two fisheries expeditions to Hudson Bay in 1930 and 1944-5, that commercial fish do not exist here, but almost everywhere in the Arctic there could be better organized subsistence fishing and small local commercial exploitation of white-fish, lake trout, Arctic cod and herring and the Arctic char. The latter is a delicacy which all Arctic inhabitants relish, and which has been recently popularized by tourist fishermen at special luxury camps at Frobisher and Cape Dorset. Two freezing plants have recently been established at George River and Frobisher for export of char to southern markets. An interesting cultural contact has been the Prairie Ice Jigger, a device for net-setting under thick winter ice, which is one contribution that the white man has made to improve Eskimo hunting methods. At Pangnirtung in Baffin Island and Churchill there has been for many years a small commercial white whale industry—the hide being used for boot laces and the oil entering the commercial animal-fat market. For the Canadian Arctic as a whole, though, it is likely that animal resources will continue to be used as in the past, as subsistence for the native population and for perhaps a decreasing proportion of that population.

Undoubtedly the most important natural resource of the Canadian Arctic is that of minerals. In the past flint, soapstone and copper were known and used by the Eskimo, but not coal or iron and there was no knowledge of the use of other mineral supplies. Accessibility is, of course, the key to mineral exploitation—accessibility for export of the products and import of necessary fuel supplies to run a mine. In the Canadian Arctic the shipping season is extremely brief and the transportation problem means that deposits have to be extra rich or in very high demand to be economically workable. Gypsum, for instance, widespread in the Queen Elizabeth Islands is far too cheaply worked in southern Canada to be exploitable here. It is likely that on the spot concentration of ore will be needed particularly in the case of the lower grade Ungava Bay iron ore deposits and another possible future advance to ease the transportation burden is the possibility of using nuclear power with its negligible requirements of fuel. At present there is only one operating mine in the Canadian Arctic, the Rankin Inlet copper-nickel mine. This was opened in 1957 and has been managed in a very enlightened manner, three-quarters of the employees (some eighty in all) are Eskimo who are proving as adaptable to this kind of work as they are to many other white man's activities. A nucleus community of wage earners has thus sprung up around Rankin Inlet, drawing in the old hunters from miles around; but one must remember that the lives of all mines are limited as certain disastrous recent happenings in uranium settlements further south have shown. Miners must always be prepared to move but this should be no great difficulty for the previously migrant Eskimo.

The mineral potential of the Canadian Arctic is considerable. In northern Baffin there are sulphides containing platinum, gold and silver, in the Cape Smith area of the Ungava Peninsula there are nickel-copper sulphides, copper deposits are known in Coppermine and Victoria Island, there is the Firth River gold of the Yukon coast and Richmond Gulf lead to the east. Iron ore is widely distributed: the Belchers, Baffin Island and Ungava Bay and in the latter area four major mining companies have established claims and plan to use beneficiation processes to increase the concentration of the ore, with stockpiling perhaps as far away as Greenland. In the late 1950s, however, the depression in the markets for base metals and iron ore has slowed the tempo of exploitation in the Canadian Arctic. It must always be remembered that the Arctic is a fringe and the first economic cuts come on the fringes. This has not been the case, however, with oil and this bouncing industry has established of recent years many exploration priorities covering a large proportion even of the Queen Elizabeth Islands. It will likely be many years before the oil which has yet to be proved in quantity from these far northern lands can be commercially exploited. New transportation methods, perhaps the commercial nuclear submarine, are required before it will be financially feasible to exploit a bulk product, such as oil, from so far within the Arctic fringe. The Department of Northern Affairs has established a policy for exploration and exploitation of this oil much more analogous to the Middle East fields than to North America. On the permits now held some $600 million must be spent on exploration in the decade of the '60s.

Probably oil and gas represent more than half the mineral potential of the Canadian Arctic. Yet every effort must obviously be made to increase the resource basis of the Canadian north, if only to support the growing native population which it has been proved can be trained in any of the skills required.

A recent Canadian Government estimate has suggested that one-third of the Eskimo working population can continue in the old subsistence economy, one-third can be wage earners in the suggested economic activities and in manning weather and radio stations—what of the remaining third? Migration away from the Arctic or a real campaign for a further development of the resource base; the latter is by far the most desirable and it will be up to the Canadian Government to press it firmly.

FURTHER READING

Blackader, R. G. and J. A. Fraser, 'Precambrian Geology of Arctic Canada', *Geol. Surv. Canada*, Paper 60–7, 1960.

Nicolson, N. L., 'The Northwest Territories', *Can. Geog. J.*, 1960, pp. 2-27.

Glacial Map of Canada, Geol. Assoc. of Canada, 1958.

Chapter 11

ALASKA

In 1959 a new star was added to the United States' flag, representing the new state of Alaska. The truly Arctic portion of this state (about 150,000 square miles) on the northern and western fringes, represents only a quarter of its total area, but it is of considerable importance to the whole. The interior central part of the Alaskan peninsula is thoroughly sub-Arctic in character, considerably wooded and in places with agricultural possibilities, despite the extremely low winter temperatures. The tree line boundary between Arctic and sub-Arctic Alaska is much influenced on the west by the cold waters of the Bering Sea, on the north by the Brooks Range, a high range of mountains trending east-west, and in the extreme south-west against the prevailing fierce storms on the Alaska peninsula and the Aleutian Islands, the trees are advancing only very slowly into an area where climatically one might expect them.

This Arctic portion of Alaska can be divided into four main regions: the northern region, the largest area north of the Brooks Range, the Seward Peninsula, the lowlands comprising the deltas of the Yukon and Kuskokwim rivers, and finally the Bering Sea offshore islands.

The northern region consists of the Brooks Range, named after the former chief of the Geological Survey of Alaska, a rugged mountain region up to nine thousand feet in height, then an abrupt drop to a 2,500-foot plateau about eighty miles wide, eroded into rolling foothills, and then another drop to the northern coastal plain. The Brooks Range appears to be the equivalent in Alaska of the Rocky Mountain Range of North America, consisting chiefly of limestone, quartzite and metamorphic rocks (with some granite intrusions) dating from the Silurian to the Carboniferous in age. Mountain-building movements were strong in Cretaceous times and again in the early Tertiary. Subsequent to each of these movements erosion

deposited great sedimentary thicknesses to the north. The last
and greatest uplift occurred in late Tertiary times when the
present form of the range was established. The highest elevations are found to the east where the Romanzof Mountains rise
above nine thousand feet. In the centre of the Range Mount

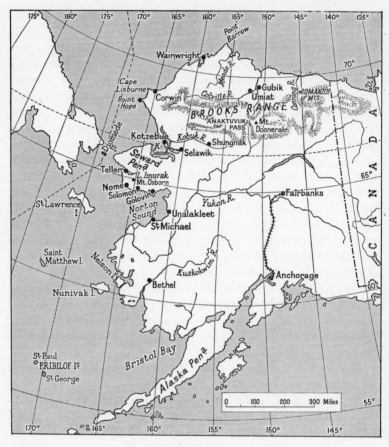

Fig. 60. Alaska.

Doonerak rises to 8,800 but further west the elevations become
progressively lower and the range divides into several smaller
mountain groups with elevations of three thousand to four
thousand feet. This whole mountain area was well glaciated but
now only very small glaciers remain, concentrated in the

larger eastern cirques and around the highest mountains. The
Okpilak glacier here is ten miles in length and many are three
miles or so long. Glacial and fluvial erosion has resulted in
several passes across the range, the best known of which is the
Anaktuvuk lying directly on the line between Fairbanks and
Point Barrow and only 2,200 feet in altitude.

In contrast to the main range the foothills region to its
north was never glaciated in the Pleistocene. It consists again of
Mesozoic rocks, chiefly sandstones and ·shales with simple
folding in the north and more irregular folding with overturning
as the Range itself is approached. The foothills region reaches
the northern coast in Cape Lisburne to the west and approaches
it again near Canning River in the east. Much of it is composed
of sandstones which form mesas and long ridges. To the north
again comes the Arctic slope proper, reaching from sea-level to
five hundred feet, representing a great syncline with twenty-
thousand feet thickness of sediments in the central portion but
only two thousand in the extreme north at Point Barrow. These
rocks are sandstones, shales and coal with a good deal of oil
shale and it is in this favourable region that oil prospecting has
been carried out. A large portion, almost up to 50 per cent. of
the Arctic slope is occupied by water, many of the lakes being
regularly oriented with their longer axes trending slightly west
of north and believed to be parallel to former dominant winds.
With the absence of glaciation deposition has gone on right up
to the present time and some Pleistocene sands and clays are up
to 150 feet thick. This area is typical of permanently frozen
tundra, with much patterned ground, and also contains large
areas of dunes. There is a large stabilized dune area south and
south-east of Barrow, some five thousand square miles in extent,
and much of the northern coast itself consists of sand dunes and
lagoons. On this coast erosion is now considerable and has been
estimated at something of the order of thirty feet per year.
Consisting as it does of unconsolidated recent material with
frequent ice wedges and polygonal ground it is susceptible to
even feeble wave attack. These dunes were probably formed in
a climate slightly warmer than today and in most places have
been stabilized by the permafrost and a light vegetation cover,
but for which, with the very low precipitation of this area, the
Arctic slope would be a desert with shifting sands. Since this

area escaped glaciation there are no erratic boulders as are found on so much of the world's Arctic tundra and winter transportation here has been easy except for the cut banks of the incised rivers flowing across the plain (and in summer the profusion of lakes). Chief of these rivers is the Colville which flows west to east as far as Gubik before turning northwards to the coast. In its middle section the Colville traverses territory where the July temperature is certainly warmer than 50° and along it and many other streams in the neighbourhood willows and alders grow in considerable groves up to fifteen to twenty feet in height.

Kotzebue Sound extending far into the Alaskan Peninsula from the Chukot Sea is ringed at its head by sub-Arctic tree-covered country. To the south of Kotzebue Sound comes the Seward Peninsula, an area of very complex geology. Most of the Peninsula is underlain by Palaeozoic rocks, chiefly slates and schists with granite intrusions (probably of Mesozoic age), which have given rise to considerable mineralization. Across the neck of the Peninsula lies an area of Cretaceous sandstones and there are considerable areas of Tertiary and even Pleistocene volcanic rocks where ropy lava is still preserved uneroded. Near Nome a number of hot springs still exist. The north-west coast consists, like the Arctic slope, of recent sand dunes and around Nome there are considerable loess areas from one to ten feet thick. There must have been a Pleistocene uplift of many hundreds of feet on the Peninsula which is generally an upland with relief around two thousand feet. Mount Osborn, the highest mountain in the Peninsula, is 4,720 feet and a few others are higher than three thousand. But there are lowland basins in the interior and a lava plain surrounds Imurak Lake. This is Alaska's gold area—the gold being originally in quartz veins in the schist bedrock, although only one lode near Solomon was ever workable. The gold was concentrated by frost, rivers and waves and was particularly rich on the beach of Nome itself.

South of Norton Sound comes the third region: the deltas of the Yukon and Kuskokwim rivers, and the intervening territory. Most of this area consists of an extremely featureless swampy plain underlain by permafrost and an ideal breeding ground for birds. One of the birds whose nesting ground was unknown was found breeding here by an Alaskan schoolteacher in 1948—the bristle-thighed curlew. The low relief of the country is indicated by the fact that tides extend something like fifty miles up the two major rivers. Some hilly country does exist, however. North of the Yukon from Mountain Village to St. Michael on Norton Sound is a rolling tundra area underlain by Cretaceous rocks and on the south side of the Yukon are a few isolated Tertiary volcanics rising from the general surface of the plain which is almost everywhere of unconsolidated Pleistocene and recent deposits. South of the Kuskokwim again, is an area of higher ground and this latter area was glaciated during the Pleistocene as an extension of the main mountain belt glaciers to the south, where the Alaska Range swings into the Aleutian arc.

The Bering Sea islands including Nelson Island, which is scarcely separated from the mainland, consist chiefly of bold-cliffed Tertiary basic volcanic rocks with some granites on the Diomede Islands and the south-western portion of St. Lawrence Island. A large part of the latter, however, is a low-lying area underlain by sedimentary and metamorphic rocks of Palaeozoic age. St. Lawrence is therefore the only old island of the group, the remainder being all Tertiary or recent arrivals. Its maximum elevation is of the order of two thousand feet. Nunivak Island has a central volcanic peak of 1,675 feet; the maximum elevations of Nelson Island and the Pribilofs is of the order of a thousand. The Pribilofs and St. Matthew Island are distinct from the remainder of the Bering Sea islands in that they lie in slightly deeper water, but a fall of three hundred feet in the ocean level would unite them all as it would Alaska and Asia itself in the Bering Strait land bridge which existed during much of the Pleistocene. On these volcanic islands, as a result of the weathering of basaltic lava the tundra vegetation is of excellent pasture quality and Nunivak Island has long fed reindeer and in later years musk ox in considerable quantity. The Pribilof Islands, well manured by the enormous seal herds, has also a surprisingly green appearance in the black-and-white landscape of Arctic Alaska.

As was pointed out in Chapter 7, the Bering Sea was the original homeland of the Eskimo and has always been an excellent resource base for these people. Whales, beluga walrus and seal are still numerous and considerably hunted. There was a period of commercial whaling activity from 1889 to 1906 and at Point Hope, Wainwright and Barrow whales are still hunted from skin boats in the spring.

At Bristol Bay south of the Arctic tundra region but still in Eskimo territory is the northern outlier of the great western North American salmon fishing region and there is a seasonal cannery in this area. The fur seal industry of the Pribilof Islands is now a steadily continuing source of revenue and employment for its mainly native population.

These islands were actually uninhabited by man before their Russian discovery in 1786, but the exploitation of the breeding population of fur seals was immediately started by the Russian colonists with Aleut immigrants. As was mentioned in Chapter 6 the herd of fur seals had been greatly reduced by pelagic slaughter up till the signing of the International Convention in 1911. Since then United States' Fish and Wildlife Service has managed the seal herd in such a manner that the numbers have risen to the order of 2 million once more; which is probably the maximum size of the herd. During the annual sealing season from mid-June to the end of July approximately seventy thousand three-year-old males are killed and skinned, the skins subsequently being sent to St. Louis, Missouri where they are processed by the Fouke Fur Company. In addition to the resident Aleut population on the two islands, St. Paul and St. George, white labour is brought in each year from St. Louis and a hundred or more Aleuts from the remainder of the Aleutian Islands. Eighty per cent. of the seal take comes from St. Paul Island and the remaining 20 per cent. from the smaller St. George. On St. Paul oil and meat are also processed in a by-products plant.

Inland, fur, caribou, sheep and later domesticated reindeer have been the staple items in the economy. The caribou numbers suffered a catastrophic decline in the first half of the twentieth century. In 1949 their numbers in all Alaska were estimated at 170,000 but since then, unlike Canada, there has been a recovery perhaps due to good predator control and the latest estimates count three hundred thousand, two-thirds of these north of the Yukon River. In the Brooks Range near Anaktuvuk Pass a small band of some seventy Eskimo continue to maintain themselves as caribou and mountain sheep hunters.

The discovery of gold on Nome beach in 1899 was the first

indication of Alaska's mineral wealth which has since repaid
the criticized purchase of the State many fold.

Nome rapidly drew off the disappointed Klondikers and the
beach has yielded gold to the value of $100 million. Nowadays
placer dredges are still working inland from Nome, the ground
being thawed ahead of them by circulating cold water. On the
Kobuk River there are a few placer gold workings but much of
Alaska's gold production today is in the interior sub-Arctic
province.

At Cape Prince of Wales the granite intrusion is considerably
mineralized and here is located North America's only tin
mine. There has been no production here, however, since 1955.
The Seward Peninsula contains also uranium and tungsten ores,
important to the United States defence production.

North of the Brooks Range considerable deposits of Mesozoic
coal exist. These were formerly worked at Corwin where the
whaling fleets used them for local refuelling—present workings
are at Meade River. Recently drilling for copper has been
started ten miles north of Shugnak on the Kobuk River.

Potentially the most valuable mineral deposit is that of oil
and natural gas in the Arctic slope geosyncline. In 1924 this
area was set aside as the Naval Petroleum Reserve No. 4 and
from 1944 to 1953 considerable test drilling was carried out based
on Barrow. The main proven field is about eighty square miles in
area centred around Umiat, and the reserves there are estimated
at seventy to a hundred million barrels. The best natural-gas
field is at Gubik at the junction of the Anaktuvuk and Colville
rivers but natural gas also occurs close to Barrow itself and many
of the village's houses now have a piped fuel supply. Drilling
operations were suspended by the Navy in 1953 in the absence of
markets but at present a gas pipe-line is being started from Fairbanks via the Anaktuvuk Pass to the Gubik field where not far
short of a thousand billion cubic feet are believed to exist.

The gold-mining industry in Alaska, as with its neighbour the
Yukon, has been typical in its tremendous upsurge and subsequent decline to a present low level but steady output. An even
sorrier story can be told of another major industry of Arctic
Alaska—that of the domesticated reindeer. These were originally introduced from Siberia by Dr. Sheldon Jackson, a missionary, to help the Eskimo who were then in a very depressed

economic state. Some 1,300 deer altogether were imported between 1892 and 1902 and until 1914 only Eskimo and Lapp herders who were brought in to train the natives were allowed to own deer. Introduced at Teller on the Seward Peninsula, the herds spread north and south and during this early period there was an excellent market at the mining community of Nome. By 1914 the herds had risen to a total of fifty-eight thousand. This was despite the reluctance of the mainly coastal-dwelling natives to take up the comparatively boring occupation of herding deer inland, particularly at seasons when his traditional game of the sea was abundant. Already by this date some over-grazing had been noted and predators had increased enormously in the districts occupied by the reindeer. In 1914 commercial operations were started by the Lomen brothers of Nome. They introduced open-range grazing as opposed to the Lapp system of close herding and invested considerable capital in refrigerating plants and shipping of the meat to the United States. Here, however, they ran into considerable marketing difficulties and opposition from western beef interests. Meanwhile, Corporation deer and Eskimo-owned herds were intermingling and breeding, claims and counter-claims were legion, and over-grazing and predator increase were very apparent. In 1939 the Alaskan Government decided to make a clean sweep of a confused operation and bought back from the commercial firm all the reindeer that it owned. Despite the fantastic numbers that had been claimed the actual count of the purchase was only eighty-seven thousand head, fourteen thousand of these belonging to the herd on Nunivak Island. In 1941 it was estimated that the total number of reindeer was still as high as two hundred thousand but the decline continued during the war years and a count in 1949 revealed less than thirty thousand deer. The main herds existing then were three at Barrow, two at Kotzebue, one at Selawik and one at Golovin, which were in a healthy condition; but other herds, including that on Nunivak Island, were in a rather depressed condition. Since 1949 there has been further reduction in the numbers of reindeer on the Arctic slope. Elsewhere a slow recovery has set in. There is now plenty of local market for reindeer meat and if grazing and predators are efficiently controlled it is probable that a small steady industry will continue to provide income for a reasonable number of Eskimo families. Herds of two thousand deer are probably ideal in that this means full-time occupation whereas lesser numbers tempt the owner to find other work and neglect the herding. But many years of chaos remain to be made up and no one is now likely to predict a very important future for the reindeer in north-western Alaska.

Other industries in Arctic Alaska comprise a considerable tourist industry and the production in native homes of purely Alaskan goods, such as ivory and skin products. The Alaskan native is now fully wedded to a money economy and is benefiting from the rapid expansion of Alaska's population and economy. This expansion, though, is liable to take place more in the interior and south-east and this represents a drain on the population of the Arctic north-west who can find employment more easily by moving. Already by no means all the Eskimo are concentrated in the Arctic area but at least twelve thousand of them live here together with two or three thousand white civilian permanent residents. As with other Arctic areas the people are becoming more and more concentrated in a few major settlements.

The largest of these is the town of Nome which once had a population of twelve thousand but now numbers something like two thousand, half of them Eskimo. In addition there is a summer influx of the people from near-by King Island—the famous ivory carvers who come to Nome to trade in summer and live a hunting life in stilt houses on their high rocky island during the remainder of the year. The Nome Skin Sewers, producing seal and reindeer garments, do an annual business of something like $50,000. Nome also counts a radio broadcasting station and an airfield and is the base of operations for the gold-mining industry inland. Port facilities are very poor, however. It is not until June that the sea is ice free enough for navigation and all cargoes of any size have to be lightered ashore from the open roadstead. Further north Kotzebue is a town of over a thousand people. It is still the centre of considerable local hunting economy of white whale and seal and is a popular tourist resort of modern times. This tourist industry depends on air transport and at least one local pilot in 1955 was an Eskimo.

P

Barrow on the extreme north tip of Alaska counts a population of about a thousand. This was the base of operations of the
oil prospecting that has now closed down, as a result of which
Barrow is in an economically depressed condition. Here, however, we have a native-run hotel, restaurant and co-operative
store and there is still a considerable local whaling industry.

Other settlements in Arctic Alaska include Point Hope,
Wainwright, Bethel and Unalakleet and at all of these co-
operative stores and schools are established. There are, in fact,
over fifty Eskimo schools in the territory and schooling is compulsory to the age of sixteen or to grade eight. Hospitals have
been built at Barrow, Kotzebue, Nome and on St. Paul Island
in the Pribilofs, and with the coming of statehood to Alaska
the natives are taking an increasing part in the management of
their own affairs. In the State legislature four members of the
Eskimo race hold seats in the House and the Senate. A colour bar
has scarcely ever existed in Alaska and native and white populations alike are thoroughly integrated into the modern economy.

As with other Arctic territories, communications are the key
to existence and Alaska is perhaps the most air-minded region
of the world. It has been stated that there are more
private aircraft in the state of Alaska than in the whole of
western Europe. The major commercial local airline, Wien-
Alaska, which started in 1929 experienced a tremendous boom
during the construction of DEW Line posts in the north and
has now established a steady and profitable tourist industry.
Two factors ensure that the Alaskan economy will be reasonably healthy for many years to come. First, its strategic position
as an outlier of United States territory, close to Russian Siberia;
and secondly its position as a crossroads in the world's airlines—
as yet the latter affects north-western Arctic Alaska comparatively little, the main base being at Anchorage in the south, but
alternate landing fields and weather installations are necessary
to serve the growing air traffic over what was described in the
American Congress shortly after its purchase as 'Walrussia'.

FURTHER READING

Gruening, E., The State of Alaska, Random House, 1954.
Lantis, M., 'Reindeer in Alaska', Arctic, 3, pp. 27-44 (1950).
Kyllingstad, H., 'The Bristle-thighed Curlew', Arctic, 1, p. 113.
U.S. Geol. Survey: Landscapes of Alaska, Univ. California Press, 1958.

Chapter 12

THE SOVIET ARCTIC

THE Soviet Arctic territory, not far short of the areal extent of the Canadian Arctic, consists of a tundra strip extending along the whole northern coast-line of the U.S.S.R. together with offshore islands of a somewhat different character since many of them are considerably glacierized. The Soviet tundra merges rather indefinitely into forested Russia and Siberia to the south. It reaches its widest extent in the central portion where Asia attains its northernmost latitude and another wide stretch in the far east where the latitudinal and altitudinal effects combine to provide a large area of treeless land. The chief geographical feature of this territory is the sea front, the former North-East Passage, the main street of the Soviet Arctic; but adjoining this are many side streets, large navigable rivers flowing from south to north, such as the Yenisey which has a depth of nine feet as far inland as the trans-Siberian railway. These rivers connect with areas of greater population, resources and industry, so there are trading routes through the Arctic into its main street, just as there is a coming and going of the native inhabitants across the *Lyesotundra* from the forest to the coastal plains.

The Soviet Arctic has been much explored and exploited since the revolution, more so than up to very recent times was Arctic North America. The main reasons for this are:

1. That the North-East Passage, though difficult, is easier to navigate than the North-West Passage and the big rivers can be exploited by moving their products downstream.

2. The Russian people are more used to the northern climate and many of their leaders, in fact, have 'done time' in Siberia, e.g. the imprisonment in Tsarist days of Stalin at Kureika on the Yenisey.

3. The profit motive being more or less absent from Marxist economics, comparatively unprofitable ventures can be carried

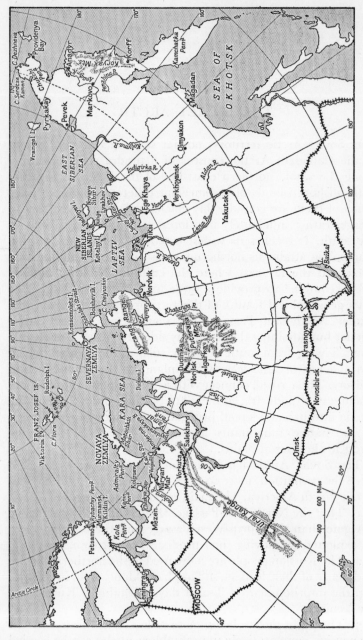

Fig. 61. Northern Territories of the U.S.S.R.

out in the far north if they have a part in the overall plan of development of the country.

4. The establishment of northern bases and the dedicated scientific life at them represents to some extent the mission sense of the communist philosophy.

Covering many thousands of miles in length, the Soviet Arctic as might be expected has a very varied geological make-up. In the far west, the Kola Peninsula is part of the Pre-Cambrian Fenno-Scandian Shield, composed of granites, gneisses and schists, the oldest rocks of Europe. The northern third of this peninsula is tundra. It is a heavily glaciated dissected plateau of moderate relief with many moraines, eskers and rock basin lakes, an area essentially of glacial erosion. Two small exceptions to the general geological picture are presented by the Rybachiy Peninsula and Kildin Island to the west and to the east of Murmansk respectively, where Palaeozoic sediments occur. The average height of the plateau is of the order of seven hundred feet dropping quite sharply to the sea with a fiord-indented coast. This coast is washed by a warm current extension of the North Atlantic drift and at the head of the only long fiord the port of Murmansk is ice free all the year. Permafrost is absent from the region except for a few places in peat bogs and here as with Scandinavia in general the last outlier of the tree line is the birch.

EUROPEAN RUSSIAN MAINLAND

East of the White Sea tundra begins on the Arctic Circle north of Mezen and includes the Kanin Peninsula, Kolguev Island and the areas west and east of the mouth of the Pechora River, which are named the Malozemel'sk and the Bol'she-zemel'sk tundras. This area corresponds roughly with the Nenets National Okrug and is the classical tundra area described by nineteenth-century observers. Geologically the area is composed of Pleistocene deposits on the old Russian Palaeozoic platform. An exception is the Timan Ridge which divides the western tundra. This is a worn-down ridge of Palaeozoic rocks folded in Caledonian times. It forms the rocky horns of Cheshkya Bay on the northern tip of Kanin Peninsula (Kanin Nos). This gives a relief of several hundred feet (seven hundred at Kanin Nos), otherwise relief is only provided by glacial depositional features, such as eskers and moraine ridges. The whole area was subject to multiple glaciation and was at times a boundary area between the European ice from the Scandinavian highland and the separate glaciation from Novaya Zemlya.

The Pechora River has a complex delta system with many offshore islets. To the east and to the west of it are low shores and small rivers of no importance. Kolguev Island is composed of recently emerged Pleistocene sands and silts and rises to a maximum elevation of five hundred feet. With its comparative isolation it is a great breeding ground for geese, ducks and swans. On the southern margin of this area of tundra spruce trees are dominant, but long human occupation and felling has caused a retreat southwards of the tree line. Permafrost occupies most but not all of the tundra, thickening and extending further south as the Ural Range is approached.

THE URAL NOVAYA ZEMLYA RIDGE

Next, to the east comes the bounding ridge of Europe represented by Hercynian folding of Palaeozoic rocks of many kinds including slates and limestones, often with vertical strata. In the Ural system the crystalline rock core appears occasionally with many small patches of gabbro intrusions. To the northeast of Vorkuta, the coal rail terminal, the Ural Mountains strike north-eastward towards the head of Baydarskaya Bay, the Pai-Khoi Mountains strike north-west to be continued in Vaigach Island and Novaya Zemlya. Between them is the Kara River basin and a small strip of coast including the sea-port of Amderma. The Pai-Khoi Mountains attain elevations of 1,500 feet. Vaigach Island although composed of similar rocks with vertical strata controlling its straight coastlines is much lower, only five hundred feet at maximum, and shows signs of very recent uplift. The island has a winter ice connection to the mainland, whereas to the north of it the wider Kara Strait is open. Permafrost is widespread throughout this region and at Amderma is extremely deep. This depth so comparatively close to the permafrost boundary is difficult to explain.

Novaya Zemlya, the continuation of the same mountain-building system, is an island composed almost entirely of the same folded Palaeozoic rocks and is of the order of sixty to seventy miles wide. It can be divided into three main sections: the southern part, up to latitude 72° N., is composed of low ground below five hundred feet in altitude, with a highly indented western coast and many marshes (another excellent wildfowl breeding area), and here there has been a small settled population for centuries. The vegetation and wild life are much richer on the whole of the west coast of the island, since the east coast is colder and bleaker at all seasons of the year. From latitudes 72° to 74° Novaya Zemlya is mountainous with elevations up to three thousand feet, and deep transverse valleys and fiords along apparent fault lines cut into both coasts. At Matochkin Shar these fiords actually meet to provide a deep, narrow strait across the width of Novaya Zemlya dividing the island into two. Hereabouts mountain glaciers begin. From 74° N. there is a continuous ice-cap inland, about three thousand feet in elevation with outflowing glaciers reaching the sea often on wide fronts. The glaciers here, however, follow the North Atlantic pattern in their recent retreat and there are ice free coasts on both sides of the ice-cap and a sizeable area of much lower ground in the extreme north-east of the island where several fifteen-mile-long rivers flow over a Silurian basement. Novaya Zemlya is believed to have been a radiating ground for certain stages of the Pleistocene glaciation. At present the land is still rising and an example of this in historical times is shown by the Admiralty Peninsula which was an island at the time of its exploration by Litke (1820).

THE WEST SIBERIAN PLAIN

To the east of the Urals the belt of tundra becomes gradually wider. In this area the exposed rocks are entirely of Pleistocene date, many of them laid down as silts in a glacial lake which must have been perhaps the largest in the world. This occurred when the two major rivers, the Ob' and the Yenisey were blocked by ice to the north and drainage went south into the Caspian through the Turgay Gap. This former southward drainage has inspired modern Soviet technicians to consider reapplying it artificially but the engineering problems are still very considerable. The incredible flatness and hence marshy character of this plain is instanced by the slope of the River Ob' which is probably the slightest of any of the major rivers of the world. The town of Omsk, 1,500 kilometres (900 miles) from its mouth is only 80 metres (269 feet) above sea-level. During the multiple Pleistocene glaciation there have been up and down crustal movements, for example, the estuaries of the Ob', the Taz, the Yenisey, suggest drowning, yet the land is now rising and deltas are forming at the heads of these deep bays. To the west of the River Ob' is the Yamal Peninsula, a low divide less than 250 feet in elevation with many shallow lakes and swamps. On this comparatively featureless peninsula a fine gradation from the tundra to the lyesotundra to the forest can be seen and in the extreme south alders and spruce are dominant. The peninsula is inhabited by about a thousand Samoyed herders who move north in summer and south in winter. Between the Taz and the Yenisey there is slightly greater elevation—up to six hundred feet maximum, but once again there is particularly low ground on the western banks of the Yenisey which floods in the spring giving a fertile silt and a strong growth of grasses. East of the Yenisey the tundra limit continues to slope northward until the most northerly trees in the world appear near the mouth of the Khatanga River. This is another highly glaciated area of Pleistocene deposits to the north of the abrupt edge of the central Siberian platform where the Putorana Range rises to five thousand to six thousand feet. The tundra here is much drier than in the other portions of the west Siberian plain since there is less precipitation and better drainage. Noril'sk, the recent large mining town, is on the boundary between the mountains and the tundra.

The northern part of the Taimyr Peninsula forms a different physiographical province to be grouped with the Ural–Novaya Zemlya province. From latitude $72\frac{1}{2}°$ on the east shore of the Yenisey Gulf Palaeozoic rocks, folded in the Hercynian period, once more occur, and these form a steep but comparatively narrow ridge, the Byrranga Ridge, which cuts right across the peninsula to latitude $75\frac{1}{2}°$ on the Laptev Sea. These mountains rise to a height of five thousand feet, and as with the Urals and Novaya Zemlya, Silurian and Permian rocks are intruded by gabbros and granites. The Taimyr River beginning in Lake Taimyr to the south of the range cuts completely through the ridge to the northern coast. To the north of the Byrranga Ridge a stony tundra slopes northward to the sea and here are exposed metamorphic rocks of Proterozoic age with considerable granite intrusions. As a result there is a coast-line which is mostly rocky and steep with many offshore rocky skerries. Strong uplift has taken place here in recent times and terraces can be seen up to 350 feet with contemporary driftwood five to ten metres above the present sea-level.

Also belonging to this physiographic province is Severnaya Zemlya, a group of four large main islands off the coast only discovered in 1915 and explored from 1930 onwards. The southern island, Bol'shevik, is composed of Proterozoic rocks, the central two of folded Palaeozoics, but the northernmost island, Komsomolets, shows only Pleistocene deposits where it is not covered with ice. Glaciation is very considerable and ice covers some 40 per cent. of the total area of the islands, rising to over two thousand feet. The Shokal'ski Strait between the southernmost and central island has some extremely deep areas—a sounding of three hundred metres (nearly a thousand feet) has been made close inshore, and it is uncertain whether this is due to glacial erosion or to block faulting of which there is considerable evidence throughout the islands. Glaciers reach the sea in many parts of Severnaya Zemlya and small icebergs are continually discharged. The year 1939 appears to have been one of very significant iceberg discharge, apparently due to the high summer temperatures recorded when Shokal'ski Strait became free of pack ice. As with all the Arctic peninsulas or archipelago groups the current on the east coast is southward flowing and on the west coast north flowing, therefore the icebergs discharged on the western shores drift northward towards the polar basin where they merge with the general ice drift.

EASTERN SIBERIA

Beyond the Khatanga River mouth a different physiographic province is encountered. Here the basal rocks are Mesozoic in age and to the east of the mouth of the Lena the northern extensions of folded mountain ranges reach the tundra until the Kolyma River is passed. Between the Khatanga and the Lena the coast is steeper, rising to a hundred metres in altitude and many salt domes are present in this area together with oil deposits. The complex delta of the Lena is a large area of recent sediments brought down by the river between two hilly ridges 1,500 feet high on the western bank and three thousand feet on the right or eastern. The Olenek River also has a small delta in the middle portion of its gulf, the western shores of which are also composed of Pleistocene sediments. From the Lena to the Kolyma River the coast-line is composed almost entirely of Pleistocene sands, very low in elevation, backed by a lake-studded tundra. Precipitation here, however, is low so the major portion of the tundra is comparatively dry, permafrost is very powerfully developed, and apart from the mountain ridge ends, most of this area was unglaciated during at least the latter part of the Pleistocene. The only part of this area having great relief is at Cape Svatoi Nos where intrusive rocks and basalts rise to 1,300 feet elevation. Three large and navigable rivers traverse the tundra here, the Yana, the Indigirka and the Kolyma, all rising in the forested south in the region of the extreme low winter temperatures of dry eastern Siberia.

THE NEW SIBERIAN ISLANDS

This group of islands lies to the north of Cape Svatoi Nos and is separated from it by the Laptev Strait. There are four main islands and a large number of smaller islets. The westernmost, Kotel'nyi, is the highest and consists of faulted Palaeozoic slates and limestones with some basalts and Pleistocene sediments. Its maximum elevation is about a thousand feet. The easternmost island, Novaya Sibir' is composed of Tertiary folded sediments with a few coal seams. The southernmost, Liakhov Island, has a granite core up to nine hundred feet in elevation but around this and comprising also all the central island, Faddeev Island, are Pleistocene silts and sands with large quantities of fossil ice up to seventy feet in thickness. The islands are rising from the sea and between Kotel'nyi and Faddeev, Bunge Land, now counted as an island, was only considered as tidal sand on maps published ten to twenty years ago. A rise in temperature also seems to be a feature of the New Siberian Islands and a great deal of the fossil ice is now being thawed revealing within its mass and within some of the Pleistocene mucks tremendous deposits of fossil mammoth remains, the ivory of which has been exploited for several hundred years.

Kettle holes can thus be seen in actual process of formation in this thawing land.

FAR EAST SIBERIA

East of the Kolyma River Siberia becomes a mountain complex and it is difficult and impractical to separate the mountain from the low-lying tundra. Although much geological work has been done in this area recently by Soviet expeditions, much remains to be learnt about its geological make-up. The area seems to be essentially a folded mountain area of Mesozoic rocks with considerable basalt outpourings. The Arctic coast has a low sandy shore as far as Cape Serdtse-Kamen' with many offshore bars. The tundra rises inland to hills and mountains of over seven thousand feet in height with a well-developed river and valley system, the most important of which is the Anadyr' valley flowing into the Bering Sea south of the straits. Much of the Anadyr' basin has a sub-Arctic character. From Cape Serdtse-Kamen' east to the Bering Strait and southwards the coast is steep-to. South of the Anadyr' basin the Koryak Mountains flank the coast. Here the short consequent rivers have cut deep valleys in which scattered trees grow. The Anadyr' basin appears to be another unglaciated area where there are considerable recent and Pleistocene formations and a peculiar and rather rich endemic flora is present. It is an area of particularly good grazing and reindeer culture has been well developed here. In the extreme south of the Arctic area the mountains around the Penzhina River basin and the Koryak Mountains are the result of Tertiary folding, part of the big Pacific province of this orogeny. There was active glaciation south-eastwards from the Koryak Mountains but very little inland. As with the opposing coast of Alaska the extreme tip of the Chukchi Peninsula has several areas of intrusive granite resulting in bold capes such as Serdtse-Kamen'. Cape Dezhnev on Bering Strait is a 2,500-foot limestone 'Gibraltar'. Similar granitic rocks are present on Vrangel' (Wrangel) Island to the north in the Chukchi Sea. This comparatively large island reaches about three thousand feet in altitude but despite this glaciers are no longer present though evidence of past glaciation is plain to see. Vrangel' Island today is extremely barren with a very low precipitation.

FRANZ JOSEF ISLANDS

The final province of the Siberian Arctic is the Archipelago of Franz Josef, separated far from the remainder of Soviet territory and the northernmost land on the Asiatic side of the Pole. This consists of a group of a dozen large and many smaller islands. Such sedimentary rocks as are present are of Mesozoic age but the main rock mass of the island consists of basalts, chiefly of Tertiary age, up to five hundred feet in thickness. The island group seems to have been subjected to powerful Pleistocene faulting, dissecting what was perhaps a fairly continuous basalt plateau into its island components, with deep rift straits. A large portion of the archipelago is glacier-covered with the firn line only three hundred feet above sea-level. One of the few low-lying areas is Cape Flora on Northbrook Island where bird liming has resulted in a tiny green flower-covered plain. The ice free areas are generally on the southern or western shores of the islands.

The Soviet Arctic has, when compared with the North American Arctic, a considerably greater native population and more frequent and larger settlements of non-natives (Russians). The general economy, moreover, is more highly developed, but nevertheless the Arctic fringe of Siberia is still a 'poor relation' of the more southerly parts. The most recently drawn administrative boundaries run north and south, dividing the Arctic region up therefore into areas each attached to its much more important southerly component. A recently published Economic Geography of the U.S.S.R., for instance, follows this division, the Arctic section of each region being very slightly treated. The basic economy is that of most Arctic lands—hunting and fishing, reindeer herding and the exploitation of minerals. Fishing stations are scattered along the length of the Siberian coast-line but the chief areas are the Barents Sea, exploited particularly by the fleet from Murmansk, where there are fish canneries, and from other settlements on the Kola Peninsula, the mouths of the Ob' and the Yenisey and the Bering Sea coast. The chief catch is of whitefish and sturgeon with some whaling in the Bering Sea and pursuit of the beluga in the west. Walrus and seal are present all along the coast except for that of the Taimyr Peninsula. The Arctic fox is trapped on the tundra but there are also blue and red foxes farmed in captivity in the far north as well as mink. A small eiderdown-collecting industry exists in the European Arctic and Novaya Zemlya.

A large proportion of the native population is engaged in reindeer herding. There are estimates of between 2 and 3 million reindeer in the whole of the northern Soviet Union, but it is difficult to say how many of these are herded in the tundra zone proper, though many of them move there in the summer and the northern pastures are probably fully utilized. Any expansion of the herding can probably only take place further south. Many of the deer are in 'collective' herds, but there are still a good many herds owned by individuals. A considerable veterinary service exists and the Russians claim that the warblefly menace has been successfully controlled by spraying, and as in Alaska, wolf hunting has been carried out by light aircraft and shotgun. In the west it is the Samoyed (Nentsi) people who are the chief deer herders, in the east the interior or reindeer Chuckchi, who are in possession of the best reindeer grazing area of all, in the basin of the Anadyr'. There are estimates of three-quarters of a million deer in this area. There was a considerable setback to the reindeer herding during the war but recovery is believed to have been rapid, thus deer herding occupies a far greater proportion of the Asian natives' economy than is the case elsewhere in the Arctic regions of the world.

Considerable experiments have been made with far northern agriculture, the Soviet philosophy being that the northern agricultural limit depends not on physical but on economic considerations. At most of the Russian settlements and polar stations a good deal of vegetable-growing under glass is carried out. Further south, in the sub-Arctic regions, field growing is the case. During 1953 several hectares were actually ploughed at Tiksi, on the Lena delta (latitude 72°), where a State Research Farm exists with as many as 150 dairy cattle. Attempts have been made to grow field crops here in the open with the use of large amounts of organic fertilizer. The expense of bringing fresh foodstuffs in from the south is perhaps even greater than expensive methods of local produce, but agriculture is not likely to be a great occupation in the tundra regions anywhere.

Mineral exploitation has been the most important economic influence in the development of the Soviet Arctic, and here the drive for self-sufficiency and avoidance of dependence on any world trading has increased the Soviet potential. The most recently explored (geologically) part of the Siberian Arctic is the far east and the Chukchi Peninsula which is perhaps the most promising. Deposits of lead, zinc and copper have been discovered here but as yet are not much exploited. There is gold in the Anadyr' basin at Markovo but the most important mineral in this area is tin. The Soviet Union, like the United States, is very short of this important material and it is significant that the Arctic yields most of the native tin in each of the world's major powers. The two most important mines are at Ege-Khaya on the Yana and at Pyrkakay on the north coast of the Chukchi Peninsula, the latter deposits being associated also with tungsten. The tin ores are concentrated on the spot and shipped to southern Siberia for smelting.

Eastern Siberia is also the major source of Soviet gold. The exploitation of this dates back over a hundred years when a British company was formed for mining gold in the Lena basin. Now the emphasis has shifted to the upper Kolyma where the Dalstroy Combine produces probably half the Soviet total of gold. This region is, however, south of the Arctic boundary and its communications are southward also. Uranium has been noted from Komsomolets Island in Severnaya Zemlya but as yet is probably unexploited and the mineral often associated with uranium, columbium, occurs on the Kola Peninsula at Lovozero in probably the world's largest deposit of this mineral. Lead, zinc and copper also occur in the Ural belt and its continuation in Novaya Zemlya where they are believed to be worked. At Amderma just east of the Ural Range fluorspar has been worked since 1935 but it is now believed to be discontinued.

By far the most important metallic mine in the Soviet Arctic is at Noril'sk east of the Yenisey on the tundra fringe. A very large sulphide ore deposit here provides nickel, copper, cobalt and platinum and in addition there are well-worked coal deposits in the neighbourhood. Nickel production began here in 1940. A narrow gauge railway, recently converted to standard, was built to Dudinka on the Yenisey and political and war prisoners were used to rush the mine to completion. The growth of the settlement has been phenomenal and the town has a population now of over a hundred thousand people with not only primary production but smelting carried out as well. When the mine was initiated it was practically the only source of nickel in the Soviet Union but now other deposits are being worked in the southern Urals and at the Finnish mine at Petsamo which was taken over in the territorial adjustment after the Second World War. Nevertheless, the position of Noril'sk seems assured as the world's furthest north city of this size.

The Soviet Arctic is also a provider of the non-metallic minerals, coal and oil. The main coal producer of the north, Vorkuta, is south of the territory we are considering and many other vast deposits as yet practically unworked exist in the Siberian taiga, nevertheless, the difficulty of transportation has meant that several smaller deposits near the Arctic coast have been worked for local use. At an earlier date the northern sea route depended largely on Spitsbergen coal for fuelling but with increased local production and probable conversion to oil the need for this import has dwindled. On the Bering Sea coast small coal mines are worked at Anadyr' and Korff, and at the mouth of the Lena, at Tiksi, a small mine is in production. The Pechora basin in addition to its vast yield of coal is also now an important oil or at least natural gas producer, from Ukhta. But in the Arctic region oil production has so far been negligible. At Nordvik at the mouth of the Khatanga salt domes containing gypsum and salt were mined in the five years just prior to the Second World War and the produce shipped to the Bering Sea coast fisheries. During the war, however, concentration here was on oil drilling, and oil was brought in from the permafrost region at 120 metres depth. It is believed, however, that there is yet no significant production from here, or from the other area where drillers have been active, as at Ustport on the Yenisey, where natural gas is also present. With other large oil supplies available in the Soviet Union it is unlikely that much exploitation will be made of the far northern deposits for a long time to come; moreover, Soviet economics do not allow the fantastic fortunes that are made in North American oil.

As can be seen from the above paragraphs the Soviet Union resembles Canada in many mineral respects in that the large mines and major deposits at present worked lie south of the tree line and moreover face southwards. Only the tin has to move northwards before entering the main stream of the Russian economy. Another northward movement, however, is a considerable export trade in lumber, mainly from the Yenisey, but also from Naryan Mar on the north European Russian fringe. The Yenisey lumber trade was initiated considerably before the revolution when a Norwegian company with some British shareholding started in 1912 to trade in the softwood lumber from upstream. The Soviet Government took over this export trade and the river port of Igarka, where with large sawmills, twenty thousand people now live, was established as the entrepôt. The record export year before the war was 1939 when about fifty shiploads of lumber were exported. Subsequent to the Second World War the export trade was much diminished but by 1956 had climbed to practically the same proportions and the last ships left the Yenisey in the second half of October.

THE NORTHERN SEA ROUTE

Though it was due to the initiative of the Norwegians and British that the Kara Sea route was first established, the whole concept of transportation along the Siberian coast was taken up enthusiastically by the Soviet Government after the revolution for strategic as well as economic reasons. In the early 1930s, when North America, in the grip of the depression, was cutting down all its northern activities, the Russians went ahead with tremendous energy to develop Siberia. In 1929 aerial reconnaissance began in an attempt to survey the ice situation. There has since then been a steady increase in the number of meteorological and hydrographic stations at many of which aircraft can be based and ice reconnaissance and forecasting made rapidly and successfully. The year 1932 saw the foundation of the organization known as Glavsevmorput which in the period up till 1938 created for itself a northern empire, controlling not only the scientific exploration of the northern sea route but a tremendous part of northern Siberia including the river waterways and mines and settlements far removed from the

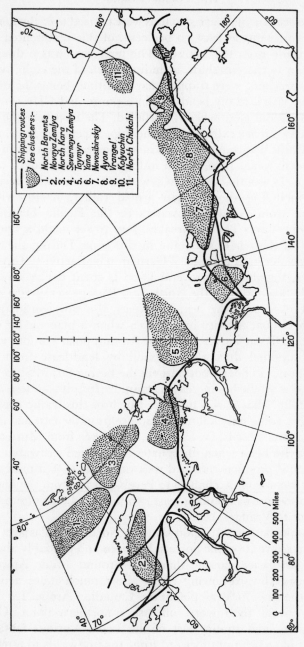

Fig. 62. Ice Clusters and Shipping Routes.

northern sea. In 1936, 270,000 tons were carried over the northern sea route but at least 50 per cent. of this represented the
timber trade from the Yenisey. The next year was a disaster
year when twenty-six ships, including seven of the eight available ice-breakers, were trapped, ice conditions being the worst
for many years. Many heads fell in a purge and Glavsevmorput's operations were severely curtailed. The next year the old
ice-breaker *Yermak* extricated all the ships except the *Sedov*, and
freight traffic was resumed on an increasing scale, so that in the
last pre-war year, 1940, half a million tons were moved over
the route. It was this year that saw the through trip of several
vessels including the German armed raider, *Komet*, which
traversed from Norwegian waters to the Pacific Ocean in
twenty-one days. The ice-breaker *Josef Stalin* made a double
traverse of the whole sea route in this year. During the war
there was a certain amount of German naval activity. In 1942
a cruiser, together with several U-boats spent twelve days in
the Kara Sea and sank the North-East Passage vessel *Sibiriakov*
and a tanker, and the next two years also saw considerable
German U-boat activity in this area when a place as far east
as Ostrov Dikson was shelled. The Russian polar stations were
mainly supplied during this period by lend-lease from the
United States in Soviet bottoms via the Bering Strait. Since the
war general traffic has increased again. In 1954 it was described
as 'fourfold' what it was in 1940. Much of this traffic consists
of supplies going only a limited distance from the east and from
the west, but there is, for example, commerce from Murmansk
as far as the Lena when phosphates are carried eastwards and
agricultural products returned westwards. In 1956 a passenger
steamer went from Archangel to Pevek, not far from the Bering
Strait, and returned, and at least two thousand tons of supplies
were sent to Vrangel' Island.

It should be stressed again that the North-East Passage, the
northern sea route of the Soviets, has been and probably always
will be an easier passage than that around Arctic America
and the northward-flowing rivers allow much more activity
than is the case, for example, in the Canadian Arctic. Ice conditions are at their worst off Asia's northern point, Cape
Chelyuskin, and to the east of the Lena. Various fantastic
schemes have been put forward from 1955 onwards to attempt

to by-pass these ice-restricted areas by a canal system across the Taimyr Peninsula and by utilizing the Lena River and its tributary the Aldan with a further canal to break through to the Sea of Okhotsk. Fantastic though these ideas seem one should not underestimate the capacity of the communist world for large-scale engineering projects if there is an economic or political advantage to be gained. Even without these embellishments, however, the northern sea route is now carrying a fair amount of traffic and playing quite an important part in the development of Siberia as a whole. As Armstrong has said, it is no longer 'an expedition' to take a ship through the North-East Passage; nor, however, is it in any sense a normal international waterway.

Along the route and on the offshore islands the Soviet Union has established more than a hundred polar stations. These are basically meteorological and hydrographical stations for weather reporting and ice forecasting on the route, but some of them are on a larger scale and are fully-fledged scientific observatories. The furthest north is on Rudolph Island, the most northerly of the Franz Josef group. Another was established in 1959 on Ostrov Victoria between the Franz Josef group and Svalbard and in the same summer a new station was built on the north side of Bol'shevik Island to study conditions in Proliv Shokalskogo to the north of the island which could be an alternative shipping route when the strait to the south is blocked by ice. The most important of the northern settlements, where activities other than purely scientific go on, are mainly inhabited by Russians, the native population on the whole being still semi-nomadic. On the Kola Peninsula Murmansk is now a large city with 160,000 people, having grown to this size from a small fishing port of three thousand in 1916, the year when the railway was built. Murmansk, however, with its open water season and export trade from the mines to the south is more or less non-Arctic in character. Naryan Mar, the capital of the Nenets National Okrug, whose total population is something like thirty thousand, is a centre of sawmilling and tanning. The railway from Vorkuta has now been continued across the Urals to the mouth of the Ob', where the town of Salekhard now numbers some fifteen thousand people, and here again are sawmills and fish canneries. Near the mouth of the

Yenisey the two main settlements are Dudinka, the terminus of the railway from Noril'sk, and Ostrov Dikson which has long been used as a refuelling point on the northern sea route. Further east Nordvik at the mouth of the Khatanga and Tiksi on the Lena delta are important settlements. The latter now numbers several thousand people with an airfield, heated main water supply, streets, shops, restaurants, a hospital and short-wave radio station. Some agriculture is being practised here and crops are grown in the open on a heavily fertilized State farm. A similar settlement Anadyr' on the Chukchi Peninsula also has a population now numbered in the thousands and on this Bering Sea coast Providenya Bay has been developed as a considerable harbour and fishing station.

As will be seen from the foregoing description the Siberian Arctic's development is considerably ahead of that of northern North America, with greater exploitation, financial resources and a much firmer population base with some hundreds of scientists, some thousands of Russian settlers and some tens of thousands of native inhabitants, mostly still engaged in their old time practices of hunting, fishing and extensive reindeer herding. It is a long time, however, too long, since a western geographer was able to visit the area in person and produce a description equivalent to that provided by Nordenskiöld some eighty years ago. Siberia remains a land of considerable mystery, a mystery deliberately fostered by the Soviet Government itself.

FURTHER READING

Armstrong, T. E., *The Russians in the Arctic*, London (Methuen), 1958.
Armstrong, T. E., *The Northern Sea Route*, Sp. Pub. S.P.R.I., Cambridge, 1952.
Baransky, N. N., *Economic Geography of the U.S.S.R.*, (English), Moscow, 1956.
Berg, L. S., *Natural Regions of the U.S.S.R.* (English), New York, 1950.

Chapter 13

SVALBARD

NORWAY's Arctic islands, over which her sovereignty has been exercised since the 1920s, go by the general name of Svalbard. This is the medieval name recorded in the Landnamabok as the cold northern coast allegedly discovered in 1194, but it was more than four hundred years before any of the territory was re-discovered. Since 1600 the islands have been well known to European civilization and have become, in fact, the best known and most visited parts of the whole Arctic. The Atlantic warm current flowing into the North Polar Sea past its shore makes Svalbard accessible by sea in summer to beyond latitude 80° and many shipping companies have run midnight-sun cruises to this area. It has also been a most popular ground for small-scale scientific expeditions from European universities, particularly those of Oxford and Cambridge, and scientifically, therefore, a great deal has been learned of this region. Svalbard has never had native inhabitants yet it has been exploited by northern Europeans for 350 years. The so-called renewable resources, the land animals and sea animals, have been nearly exterminated; now the non-renewable resources are being worked in the coal mines of Vest Spitsbergen and attract the existing permanent population.

The Svalbard realm consists of two separate and isolated islands, Jan Mayen and Bjornøya, and the Spitsbergen group, the latter consisting of a main island, Vest Spitsbergen, 15,200 square miles; Nordaustland, 5,800 square miles, and a series of smaller islands including Edgeöya, Barentsöya, Prins Karls Forland, Hopen and many smaller islands whose total area is slightly under three thousand square miles. Thus the Spitsbergen group as a whole has an area approximately that of Nova Scotia, considerably ice-covered, mountainous and deeply indented by long and branching fiords.

The geology of Spitsbergen is extremely complicated. It has

long been considered that the comparatively shallow Barents
Sea is an outlier of the Fenno-Scandian Pre-Cambrian Shield.
No Pre-Cambrian rocks appear in Vest Spitsbergen but a small
area of crystalline rocks in the extreme north-west of Nordaustland are almost certainly of this age. The next earliest group of
rocks is a complex series of metamorphics, dating from the early

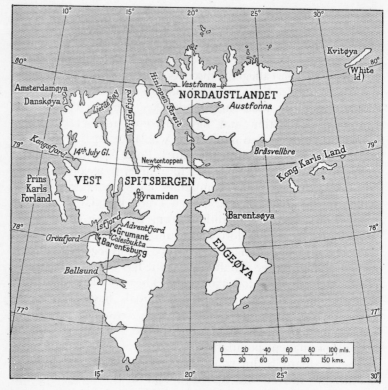

Fig. 63. Svalbard.

Palaeozoic to which the name Hekla Hoek series has been
given. This together with some granite intrusions was subject
to folding in Caledonian times. The Hekla Hoek series forms a
comparatively narrow belt along the western coast of Spitsbergen and the serrated mountains of these folded metamorphic rocks resulted in the Dutch name 'Pointed Mountains'
being given to the whole island. To the east, separated by a

north-south fault, the basement rocks are entirely overlain by nearly horizontal sediments of Devonian, Permo-Carboniferous, Mesozoic and Tertiary rocks, forming a temple-like landscape: a well dissected plateau with steep slopes and U-shaped valleys either ice-filled or bare with short braided streams. Isfjord, the main inlet in the centre of Vest Spitsbergen separates the Devonian old red sandstone area to the north, with gentler slopes, from the castellated plateaus of the later rocks to the south. East of Wijdefjord (the long inlet breaching the northern coast of Vest Spitsbergen), come Hekla Hoek rocks again, this eastern portion of Vest Spitsbergen being much more heavily glaciated and rising higher than the remainder of the island; here, in fact, is located the highest mountain, Newtontoppen, over 5,600 feet (1,700 metres) in height. Hekla Hoek rocks again form the northern two-thirds of Nordaustland; the southern part of this island is composed of Carboniferous and Mesozoic rocks, but a very great proportion of Nordaustland is covered by ice-cap, including the whole of the eastern and part of the southern coasts. Nordaustland was probably separated from Vest Spitsbergen in Tertiary times when large-scale faulting depressed Hinlopen Strait and basalt lavas were poured out in this area and on Kong Karls Land (the group of islands to the south-east of Nordaustland). Volcanic activity persisted even longer in the extreme north-west. In Liefde Bay there are Pleistocene volcanic cones of slag and ashes up to two thousand feet in height, and a hot spring here, discovered as recently as 1910, has a temperature of 27° C. and is surrounded with calcareous sinter pools. Coal seams are present in the rocks laid down from the Carboniferous period onward.

More than half the area of Svalbard is covered with ice and here have been located some of the classical studies in glaciology begun by H. W. Ahlmann and continued by many parties of different nationalities. Generally speaking, glaciation increases from south-west to north-east across the archipelago. This shows the importance of summer temperature since the two main contributing factors to glaciation, precipitation and summer temperature, both diminish from south-west to north-east. An exception is provided by Prins Karls Forland where the cloudier summer keeps down summer ablation and leads to greater snow and ice cover than on the neighbouring Vest

Spitsbergen coast. On this main island the firn line trends from
about two thousand feet above sea-level in the south-west to
1,300 in the north-east where a nearly continuous region of
highland ice reaches the sea in many places. Elsewhere the ice,
though continuous on the higher plateau, through which only
nunatak mountains are seen, flows down as valley glaciers. The
largest areas of ice free land are around Bellsund, Isfjord and
the wide strip of land to the west of Wijdefjord. On Barentsöya
and Edgeöya ice-caps are again present, particularly on the
colder east sides of these islands where glaciers reach the sea.
Nordaustland is almost completely ice-capped but a central
ice free valley divides the smaller Vestfonna from the larger
Austfonna. The latter reaches the eastern and southern coasts
of the island in a broad front forming one of the major 'Antarctic' type coast-lines in northern lands. The firn line falls from
1,500 feet on Hinlopen Strait to three hundred feet on the
north-east and is as low or even lower, on Kvitöya, a small
island stretching out towards Frans Josef Land. Only the south-
western cape of this island is ice free. On Nordaustland the ice
has been classified as 'sub-polar', that is with negative temperatures in the ice below a certain depth; however, much of the
Vestfonna is perhaps not far below freezing-point and the same
is true for many of the glacial bodies in Vest Spitsbergen. The
14th of July Glacier, for instance, is at the pressure melting-
point of ice throughout its depth and therefore can be classified
as temperate.

Ice motion on the whole is very slight throughout the archipelago. The 14th of July Glacier moves at only six inches a day
and almost everywhere signs of retreat are very evident since
the ice margins have often been known from well back in the
nineteenth century. Recession has been particularly pronounced
since about 1920, but has slowed down again in the last two
decades.

One great exception to this general picture is on the southern
coast of Nordaustland where the Brasvellbre sometime between
1936–8 made a great surge forward adding an area of over 150
square miles to the island. The reason for this sudden surge is
hard to determine. Robin cites it as a possible case of cyclic
temperature change at the beds of polar glaciers. A greater
shear stress is required to produce ice flow when the basal

temperature is well below freezing. If this temperature is raised to the freezing-point by some mechanism friction, volcanism or climatic change, a sudden surge forward will perhaps take place. On the surface of the Nordaustland ice-cap in the direction of Brasvellbreen, Nordenskiöld, the first man to cross this ice-cap, found features which have never been observed since. These were long vertical-sided rifts up to twenty feet deep and a hundred feet wide, forming excellent camp sites as he illustrates in his account of his journey. Hobbs believed that these were caused by trough faulting in the basement rock. Such a trough fault could cause a surge forward of the ice by removal of a previously existing rock barrier but there is no known report of what must have been a violent earthquake in the 1930s in this region.

The general retreat of glaciers in Svalbard recorded up to the 1930s seems in some respects to have been halted. The 14th of July Glacier, so closely investigated by Ahlmann in 1934 when he showed a retreat of the snout of one thousand metres since 1906 had, up to 1955, recovered some seven hundred metres of that distance. The accumulation surface seems to have increased in recent years and the glaciers in the Kongsfjord area in north-west Spitsbergen are now in a much more strongly active state. Recently the Norsk Polar Institute has established a major study area on the Finsterwalderbre in Bellsund in the central south-west coast. This glacier was fairly constant in volume between 1920 and 1936 but decreased between 1936 and 1950 and was strongly negative in 1950–2 mainly because of scanty accumulation of snow. The general precipitation seems, therefore, to have moved northwards along the coast, a matter of some $1\frac{1}{2}°$ of latitude. The glaciation of Svalbard has been described in some detail because it has been a noteworthy area in the warming up of the climate in recent years but, as the activity of the glaciers show, this warming may have now at least temporarily ceased. The winter temperature of Isfjord where records have been kept for a considerable time has increased 9° C. (16° F.) and the whole year by 3° C. (5° F. +) since 1900. At the same time the shipping season on this coast has increased from three to six months.

The wild life resources of the Svalbard group were in the past as rich as or richer than any other Arctic region and were fiercely exploited from the beginning of the seventeenth century. The oil from walruses and the Right whale was the chief product of the islands during this time but with the usual result of over-exploitation—the whales vanished from Svalbard waters. Dutch, Danish and English fleets competed in the area and each of them had their shore station as is evidenced by present-day names: Amsterdamöya, Dansköya and Engelsk-bukta. As early as 1613 there were thirty vessels whaling in the Spitsbergen waters and four years later the Dutch founded Smeerenburg where during the 1630s at least 1,200 people spent the summer, and the town contained a church, some shops and a bakery. Some sixty-thousand whales were caught by the Dutch in the seventeenth century and around 1700 their fleet consisted of about a hundred ships with a hundred from other nations competing for the diminishing number of whales. In 1905 there was a brief period of renewal of whaling (this time a Norwegian venture) which lasted only seven years and included one shore station on Grönfjorden.

For most of the eighteenth and nineteenth centuries Svalbard was abandoned except for a small population of hunters and trappers. These initially were Russians who established them-selves in groups of up to twenty in numbers, exploiting the white fox, polar bears, reindeer and walrus and seal. These Russian trappers wintered not only on the west but also on the east coast of Vest Spitsbergen including Edgeöya. One famous Russian trapper, Stratchlu, spent thirty-nine years on Grönfjord and graves of Russian trappers can be found almost everywhere. From 1800 onwards a few Norwegians joined the Russian trappers and one of these, H. Nøis, had spent at least thirty winters up to 1950. One of the prime activities of the modern Norwegian trapper is the the taking of polar bears and between two hundred and three hundred bears per year are taken including a lucrative trade in live polar-bear cubs for zoos. One Norwegian trapper is said to have killed six hundred polar bears in his time. Since 1939 a bear sanctuary has been estab-lished on Kong Karls Land in an attempt to maintain this resource. Before the last war about thirty trappers were wintering on Svalbard and this was believed to be the 'right' number for the resources, but since the war with the decline in fur prices, especially that of the Arctic fox, trappers have been very rare indeed. The reindeer on the islands, once fairly numerous, and coming apparently from Siberia, were nearly exterminated at the end of the nineteenth century, chiefly by sporting hunters, and have been protected since 1925. A few musk ox were introduced in 1929 and appear to be maintaining reasonable numbers. Other natural resources which have been exploited include a small eiderdown industry and in the waters around Svalbard cod and halibut fishing at times is very lucrative, but this is a pelagic industry and bears very little relationship to the country itself.

By far the most important economic resource of Svalbard has been its mineral industry and in particular coal. Coal seams are found in several of the sedimentary geological formations throughout Vest Spitsbergen, in the Carboniferous, in the Cretaceous and in Tertiary beds, with seams up to several yards in thickness. Deep indentations of the coast mean that mining operations can take place close to the shore and with a thickness of permafrost of many hundreds of feet mining conditions are fairly simple with little difficulty from water or gas formation. Some sealing vessels drew coal from the easily accessible surface deposits in the nineteenth century and a shipment of coal was, in fact, made to Norway in 1894. But the first mine to go into real production was started in 1904 by John Longyear of Boston, Mass. in Adventfjord. This mine was worked up till 1915 when wartime difficulties forced Longyear to sell to neutral Norway. Many other small companies of diverse nations staked claims, and when the sovereignty of Svalbard was awarded to Norway, a difficult task of sorting and establishing title to these claims had to be carried out. Forty of them were recognized in 1927; 14 Norwegian, 2 Swedish, 20 British, 2 Dutch and 2 Russian, but by 1938 Norwegian companies had taken over the Swedish and all except four of the British claims, none of which was actually working, and the Russian interests had bought out the Dutch claims. The Russian workings are near the mouth of Isfjord at Grumant, Barentsberg, Colesbukta and Pyramiden, the latter in Carboniferous coal. Norwegian mines, operated by the Store Norske Spitsbergen Kulkompani are located around the Adventfjord area with workings now opened up again at Kongsfjord further north. During the Second World War the Norwegian settlements and mining installations were completely destroyed but have re-opened again since the war. In 1939 the annual output from all the coal mines was approximately seven hundred thousand tons, three hundred thousand of which went to Norway and supplied about one-tenth of their country's coal needs. The remainder was exported to the U.S.S.R. where it served to fuel the fleet of vessels operating on the northern sea route. Since the war with the use of more easily available local coal supplies the Russian needs seem to have diminished; however, Russian mining is still continuing and approximately two thousand Soviet workers with their families are present in Svalbard. The Norwegian mines account for a roughly similar population and, with the reopening of the Kongsfjord mine, output is expected to run at about six hundred thousand tons a year. The mines are operated very economically, the average daily output per man being three tons, far exceeding other European outputs, and since the shipping season now lasts for at least five months, export has become a fairly simple operation.

Other minerals have been found in Svalbard but few attempts at exploitation have been made. Asbestos and marble are present at Kongsfjord but an attempt to work the latter broke down as the marble was found to be too frost-riven. There are vast deposits of high-quality gypsum present, which were worked spasmodically until 1930, and there are considerable deposits of high-grade iron ore in Prins Karls Forland and around Bellsund, as yet untapped economically.

The tourist industry has for a long time been an active one in this extremely scenic and interesting land. It is far enough north for mosquitoes to be rather rare and the accessible west coast has magnificent scenery, where tourists can see glaciers, the midnight sun, interesting Arctic breeding birds, historic sites and, if a lengthier stay is possible, indulge in magnificent mountaineering. From 1896–1905 a hotel for tourists actually existed in Advent Bay and in the three years before the Second World War another hotel at Kongsfjord was opened with a fortnightly service to and from Norway. Subsequent to the war tourist vessels are again sailing to Vest Spitsbergen chiefly from northern Norwegian ports, but tourist liners of other countries are also beginning to realize the possibilities of this magnificent land.

ISLAND OUTPOSTS

In addition to the main archipelago of Svalbard two other small islands pertain to the Norwegian Arctic realm. Bjornøya (otherwise known as Bear Island or Cherie Island) is located practically half-way between the northern tip of Norway and Spitsbergen group. It is similar geologically to the latter, its seventy square miles containing Hekla Hoek series and later horizontal sedimentary rocks. A small deposit of Devonian coal was worked on the island from 1915–25 but loading was extremely difficult and the mine has now closed down. Now a weather station represents the only human occupation of Bjornøya. The seas surrounding it are now its wealth, in the Barents Sea fishing area. The island itself has a most miserable climate, the maximum recorded temperature is 61° F. and its average number of fine days in the year is only seven. The highest peak of the island (1,750 feet) is aptly named Misery Fjell.

Even more implacable in its polar maritime climate is the island of Jan Mayen, situated about 300 miles from Greenland, 350 from Iceland and 600 from Spitsbergen. This is the most isolated of Arctic islands, entirely polar maritime, windswept and cloudy with more than eight-tenths average cloud cover and a maximum temperature ever recorded of 59° F. Although it is 140 square miles in extent it consists essentially of a vast volcanic cone, the mountain of Beerenberg, which rises on the north-east end of the island to 7,700 feet with glaciers reaching the sea and occupying the crater and shallow valleys on the mountainside. Beerenberg was certainly active in 1818 and earthquakes are still recorded. It is an uncomfortable site for the weather station which was set up by Norway in 1921. This weather station was maintained throughout the Second World War and Jan Mayen was guarded by a platoon of the Norwegian army. Despite this the Germans managed to land an automatic weather station on the coast which was undiscovered for the best part of a year. The whole island consists of Pleistocene volcanic deposits of lava and ash and vegetation has a difficult time obtaining a footing on the loose volcanic deposits. Jan

Mayen Island isolated as it is on the edge of the pack ice belt has the closest correspondence in the North Polar regions to some of the islands of the Antarctic Sea, and apart from its mountaineering possibilities little use seems possible for such an island except as a weather station.

FURTHER READING

Mathisen, T., *Svalbard in the Changing Arctic*, Oslo, 1954.
O'Dell, A. C., Chapter 11 in *The Scandinavian World*, London, 1956.
Rudmose-Brown, R. N., *Spitsbergen*, London, 1920.
Adams, P., *Arctic Island Hunter* (H. Nøis), London, 1961.

Chapter 14

GREENLAND

GREENLAND is the world's largest island next to the continents of Australia and Antarctica. Its size is some 840,000 square miles, about two-thirds that of India and its shape is not dissimilar—broad in the north and narrowing to a wedge in the south. The northern part is the land nearest to the North Pole, reaching at Kap Morris Jesup latitude 83° 40′. The southern tip, Kap Farvel, is situated at 59° 45′, about the latitude of the Scandinavian capitals. Among the Arctic lands which have been treated in earlier chapters Greenland is similar to Svalbard and to the big Canadian Arctic islands in that it is separated from the forest by sea. There is no graduation from forest to tundra as there is in Siberia or on the Canadian mainland.

Greenland has several unique geographical features which will be developed during this chapter. First, it is composed mainly of an ice-cap; but an ice-cap that on the whole does not reach the sea as does that of the Antarctic continent. Scientifically, therefore, it is of vital geographical importance in that we can study here the edge of an existing ice-cap, such as existed in Europe and North America during the Pleistocene.

Secondly, Greenland is unique in that its extreme southwestern corner is non-Arctic in character and here was located the colony that failed—the Scandinavian settlement of the tenth to fifteenth centuries, one of the most fascinating stories in historical geography.

Thirdly, for study and comparison with less happy results in other Arctic territories, there is the extremely successful social experiment of Danish colonial methods. Greenland is now an integral part of Denmark although structurally and ethnographically it belongs to America. This island, fifty times the size of Denmark, carries, however, less than 1 per cent. of the population of the motherland.

Fourthly, although Greenland has been administratively a colony of Denmark, during the last hundred years its scientific exploration has been carried out by peoples of all countries and of the most recent years by actual international expeditions.

Although as we have seen in Chapter 5, Baffin Bay is deep and wide, Greenland appears to be structurally a part of North America, an outlier of the Canadian Pre-Cambrian Shield. At least one-half of the ice free area is composed of Pre-Cambrian rocks, chiefly gneiss and granite, and there is no great reason to believe that these rocks do not extend under a large portion of the inland ice-cap. The Pre-Cambrian plateau is, however, apparently divided into two sections: north and south, by a belt of Tertiary sediments and volcanics. The eastern coast of Greenland north of the major inlet of Scoresby Sound is composed of a variety of sedimentary rocks from Pre-Cambrian to Mesozoic age, often highly metamorphosed, faulted and folded. Similar rocks occur in a narrower belt on the north coast and it appears that these two margins of the shield have been subjected to geosynclinal processes through a very long period of time and have undergone several periods of folding, particularly in the period of the Caledonian orogeny. As a result of this folding and the varied types of rocks accumulated in the geosyncline, north-east Greenland is the most alpine part of the country with deep valleys and serrated mountain peaks. During the Tertiary period much outpouring of basalt lavas occurred; these are now visible on both the eastern and western coasts and are presumed to form a belt, in fact, across the somewhat depressed central section of the island. At this period of geological history Greenland was warm, if not sub-tropical, as is shown from the fossil flora and deposits of Tertiary and Cretaceous coal. A few hot springs can still be found in the basalt areas and even elsewhere in Greenland, but their development is on a very minor scale. In these basalt areas the typical landforms are well dissected plateaus, such as on Disko Island, the Nugsuak Peninsula and in the Scoresby Sound area to the east. Another area of plateau type with prominent butte-like hills is found in the north-west in the area of deposition of the Thule sandstone. This is a presumed late Pre-Cambrian deposit of an easily distinguished reddish-maroon coloured sandstone, erratics of which can be found in

widely scattered localities and even across Baffin Bay on the
Canadian Arctic islands. Much of the western coast of Greenland consists of a strongly ice-eroded Archean landscape, deeply

Fig. 64. Greenland: the Ice-cap and Ice Free Zones.

dissected by long fiords with much bare rock showing on their
sides and on the rounded summits of moderate relief. In the
extreme south of the island some of the most savage scenery in

the world exists. Here the fiords are extremely steep-sided, the mountains rising rapidly to the order of six thousand or seven thousand feet from sea-level and in addition, since this is a stormy and foggy area the old name, Cape Desolation, was an extremely apposite one. North of latitude 69° on the west coast wider bays take the place of the long narrow fiords and beyond these the coast breaks down into a maze of small steep islands or skerries until in Melville Bay the inland ice itself forms a coast-line.

In the extreme north deep fiords again dissect the country. The glaciation here is much more feeble as precipitation is becoming increasingly low but in some of the fiords shelf ice has formed and persisted.

The eastern coast represents a reversal from the west in that the wider stretch of ice free land, deeply fiord riven, lies to the north of latitude 70° (Scoresby Sound).

Everywhere in the ice-free zones solifluction and other forms of mass wastage are prominent. Old moraines and pingos are also widespread but river development is slight, such streams as do exist being short and steep in gradient.

The main physical feature of Greenland, however, is undoubtedly the inland ice-cap, known generally today by the Danish term, Inlandsis. This covers 80–85 per cent. of the total area of Greenland leaving the only extensive ice free areas in a broad belt on the south-western coast and with smaller scattered areas in the north and central eastern coasts. The surface shape of the ice-cap is roughly semi-elliptical, rising steeply at first and then more imperceptibly to a central culminating point. But as more exploration is done on this immense carapace of ice more irregularities have been discovered. The culminating ridge of the ice-cap is off-centre to the east and this consists, in fact, of a northern and a southern ice-dome, the former rising to over and the latter to slightly under ten thousand feet in height. Recent expeditions, particularly those of the French and American ice-cap travelling parties have made many soundings through the ice and we are now beginning to know better not only the surface elevations but the elevations of the ice-rock interface below. The old idea that Greenland is saucer-shaped begins to be revived, with two mountain rims and a central depression heaped high with the ice. But there is a considerable tilt to the bedrock. The eastern rim of the saucer is much higher, representing the folded mountain belt of the east, and in the extreme south the rock lies at several thousand feet elevation. The western rim and much of the floor of the saucer appears to consist of the Archean shield like Canada and it is towards the central part of this western edge that the main depression occurs and it is in this direction that the main drainage of ice tends. Here are situated some of the largest outflowing glacial streams in the world.

In the eighteenth and early nineteenth centuries the main point of scientific and exploratory interest was to discover how extensive was this inland ice—was there ice free country in which game could abound inland? Today, the chief interest is how much of this ice there is and is it increasing or decreasing in volume? Because of its elliptical shape, a continental ice-cap such as that of Greenland, has by far the greatest proportion of its area in the accumulation zone, the zone where more precipitation falls than is melted off in the subsequent summer. Small changes, therefore, in the accumulated precipitation are of great importance, much more than quite large changes in the amount of melting which can go on around the edge. The latest estimate of mean annual accumulated precipitation on the Greenland ice-cap is twenty-nine grammes of water per square centimetre of area per year and over the immense area of the Greenland ice-cap this represents something like five hundred cubic kilometres of water. The maximum precipitation is concentrated west of the centre of the ice-cap, as shown in the map (Fig. 65). This occurs, therefore, on the western slope and not on the highest part, again contributing to the more powerful drainage of ice towards the central west coast.

The shape of the inland ice of Greenland is ideal for the development of katabatic winds—winds flowing outwards and down slope in all directions, caused by the dense layer of air cooled by radiation. At the British North Greenland Expedition's base at Northice the winds were mostly west between ten and twenty knots. Other directions of wind were very rare, indicating the dominance of this katabatic effect, although the slope of the ice-cap in this locality is only 1/350. On the western side of the culminating ridge the prevailing south-west wind is blowing against the katabatic wind thus causing greater accumulation, on the eastern side the two winds combine to

give a scouring effect with much *removal* of snow. The outward
blowing winds on the coasts of Greenland suggested that it was
covered by an anticyclone and this theory was powerfully

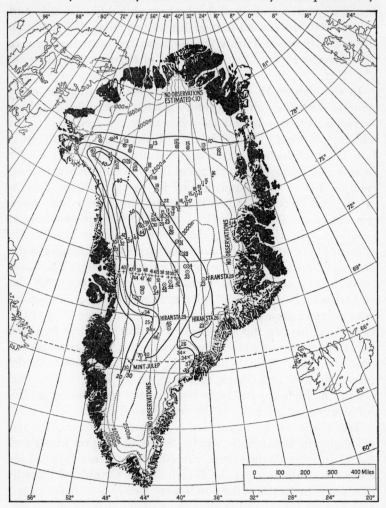

Fig. 65. Mean Annual Accumulation on Greenland Ice-cap in Centimetres
of Water Equivalent.

developed by W. H. Hobbs; but most of the air space, up to
ten thousand feet, is occupied not by air but by the mass of
Greenland itself. The seven-hundred-millibar chart is therefore

the lowest which can be reasonably drawn for the country as a whole and then the anticyclonic configuration is seen to vanish. Everywhere on the ice-cap, however, wind and temperature changes are distorted by a layer of air something of the order of a hundred metres thick which is cooled by the intense radiation from the snow surface and moves katabatically downslope.

The firn line, the line dividing the area on a glacier or on the inland ice of net accumulation from net ablation or wastage, varies from about four to five thousand feet in altitude. Considering the immense latitudinal change from north to south Greenland, it is at first surprising that there is so little variation in this altitude. It is lower than average, perhaps, on Robeson Channel opposite Ellesmere Island, but it is considerably higher around the very dry area of Scoresby Sound in the east. Its altitude is balanced by the much heavier precipitation in the south compared with the snow-starved north. The edge of the ice-cap in summer is the scene of intense melting. Large areas of snow morasses with deeply engorged ice rivers form, and result in an extremely difficult zone for travellers to cross. It is with relief that most of the ice-cap expeditions have come on to the colder higher ground where the thaw ceases. The ablation around the edge of the ice-cap has been studied much less than the accumulation and it is hard to make an estimate of the total amount but it is somewhere between the order of three and four hundred cubic kilometres of water. But the Greenland ice-cap loses in another way than melting, and that is by the discharge of outflowing glacier streams into the sea and the formation of icebergs. West Greenland in particular is the home port of much of the North Atlantic iceberg fleet. There are certain areas, e.g. around Melville Bay, and further north at the Humbolt Glacier, where the inland ice reaches the sea on a broad front but on the whole it is not strongly active at these points. Much more active are the ice streams further south of which Bauer lists the following:

West Coast   Jakobshavn
                  Torsukatak
                  Karajak
                  Umiamako
                  Rink
                  Upernavik

East Coast   Sermilik
               Kangerdlugssuak
               Several glaciers draining into Scoresby Sound.

Some of these ice streams travel at great speeds, up to a hundred
feet per day and each contributes several cubic kilometres of
ice per year. Many minor but active glaciers also reach the
sea and contribute their quota of icebergs. For example that of
Eqe has a mean velocity of 3 metres per day, is 4 kilometres
wide and 180 metres thick at its discharge edge. A recent
expedition has made attempts to study not only the speed at
which these ice streams reach the sea but the time that an
individual crystal of ice has taken to arrive at the sea from its
initiation as a snowflake inland. This has been done by analys-
ing the $C14$ content of the CO_2 of enclosed gas bubbles in the
icebergs. So far much younger ages, of the order of three thous-
and years, have been found than were expected; earlier estimates being that a snowflake would take twenty thousand years
from falling in the centre of the ice-cap to appearing on the
coast of Greenland as ice.

The most important ice free area is in the south-west of
Greenland. Here the inland ice tends to be a hundred or more
miles from the coast, and although the high areas carry their
own smaller glaciers, the longer fiords which reach right across
this belt of ice free land have a milder and really non-Arctic
climate in their central sections. Bocher has distinguished
five climatic types in this area as shown in the following
table:

			Examples
A.	Low-Arctic-oceanic	Precip. 500–1,000 mm. Annual temp. range 10° to 18° C. Warmest month 6°–8° C.	Nanortalik Godthaab
B.	Arctic-sub-oceanic	Intermediate between A and C	Qornoq
C.	Low Arctic-sub-Arctic continental	Precip. 100–250 mm. Annual temp. range 20° to 30° C. Warmest month above 10° C.	Head of Söndre Strömfiord

Examples

D. Low Arctic   Precip. 200–500 mm.
   subcontin-   Annual temp. range
   ental   20° to 30° C.
                 Warmest month 6°–8° C.
E. Sub-Arctic   Precip. 700–1,400 mm.   Ivigtut
   oceanic   Annual temp. range   Igaliko
   suboceanic   15° to 20° C.
                 Warmest month 9°–11° C.

At Godthaab we pass from A through B to C at the head of the fiord, and at Julianehaab through all five types. It was around these two areas in particular that the Norse colonists arrived in the tenth century to found a settlement which lasted for about as long as has any white settlement in the Americas. These settlers came mainly from Iceland and at this period of history, found in south-west Greenland a climate undoubtedly better than that of the present day, yet still marginal for agricultural pursuits. There were probably never more than a few thousand of them settled on the few hundreds of farms and organized into a score of churches and a Bishopric. At first the colony flourished; trading with Europe in skins, falcons and polar bears, receiving in exchange beer, grain and iron goods. But after some four hundred years the colony vanished due to a combination of circumstances too unfavourable for its survival. There was evidence of over-grazing and erosion. Today, now that sheep and cattle are being once more kept in Greenland there is considerable difficulty in obtaining enough hay for winter feed. There were probably hydrographic changes—the waters became cooler and the fish left and seals replaced them. Pollen analysis shows an undoubted deterioration in climate in the fourteenth and fifteenth centuries and in places permafrost has invaded earlier pre-permafrost burials. This deterioration of climate is known from as early as the thirteenth century in Iceland and the marginal situation of the Greenland settlement was even more sensitive to small changes in climate. There was a deterioration of physique of the settlers, as shown by skeletons, with small size and bone deformation showing a gradual increase in malnutrition as the trade with Norway and Denmark languished. From 1262 this became a Crown monopoly with a

ship only every five years or so and the rise of the Hanseatic
League in the Baltic eventually killed even this trade. The
medieval plague, the Black Death, certainly hit Norway and
the traders and may well have been transmitted to Greenland
as well. As the climate deteriorated and the seals moved south,
the Eskimo peoples already in north-west Greenland moved
southwards also and clashes have been recorded with the
Scandinavian settlements. There is in the sagas the story of
the actual destruction of the 'western' settlement, that around
Godthaab Fiord, but it is probable that the last survivors were
actually assimilated with the Eskimo invading wave. During
the great days of Scandinavian expansion their settlers seemed
to assimilate readily with the native populations of Britain,
France and other parts of Europe, giving new vigour to the
population. But it is certainly true that when Greenland was
re-visited in the late sixteenth century only Eskimo-seeming
people were left, but perhaps among them lingered some traces
of the Scandinavian blood.

The Scandinavian tradition, however, was remembered, and
in the eighteenth century Hans Egede, a citizen of the combined kingdom of Norway and Denmark went out to re-colon-
ize this country and 'bring back our poor brothers into the
Christian fold'. Egede found probably six thousand or seven
thousand inhabitants and from these numbers the population
has quadrupled by the present time. Now some thirty thousand
people, an admixture of Eskimo and Danish strains, calling
themselves Greenlanders, form a comparatively thriving community in the land where the Scandinavian settlement failed.
Yet their resource base is still a pretty slim one and Greenland
will long remain on the fringe of human settlement possibility.

Dunbar has called the present-day Greenland position 'an
experiment in human ecology' and lists twelve factors in con-
sideration of the problem.

1. Population: its rapid growth and change in distribution
with ever-increasing concentration in larger settlements.

2. Hydrographic changes in west Greenland which have
brought in a flourishing fish population but might at any time
swing back to colder and less productive waters.

3. Decline of importance of sea mammals, particularly the
seals.

4. The growth of the fishing industry.

5. The redevelopment of sheep farming with an addition today in the introduction of cows and reindeer.

6. The mineral resources: particularly the cryolite mine at Ivigtut in the south-west. This in the past has made up the economic deficit of Greenland but is an exhaustible resource.

7. Miscellaneous resources. There has been a drive to replace the dependence on cryolite with search for other minerals and an attempt for Greenland to be self-sufficient in coal.

8. The native mind and its education.

9. Health policy: with particular emphasis on the drive for elimination of tuberculosis.

10. The policy of the Danish administration.

11. The scientific exploration of the country.

12. Greenland's strategic position as an outlier of the North American continent.

To date the mineral resources discovered in this large island have been very slight. This is in spite of an intense programme of geological investigation carried out on the west coast by the Danish Geological Survey and on the east coast from Scoresby Sound northward by a long succession of expeditions under the leadership of Lauge Koch interrupted only by the war from 1939–47. These latter expeditions have been perhaps the most outstanding in Arctic scientific survey. Since the large number of geologists employed by Dr. Koch had to be mountaineers as well as scientists, Swiss geologists have played a major part in these operations.

The longest existing mine in Greenland has been the cryolite mine at Ivigtut in the extreme south-west. Apart from the U.S.S.R. this is the only place in the world where a large deposit of this mineral has been found. Cryolite (Na_3AlF_6) had originally a commercial use in the enamelling of iron, later in the manufacture of soda and insecticides, but its main use today is as a flux in the electrolysis process of aluminum smelting. The first shipment was made from Ivigtut in 1856; nine years later the present Crown Mining Corporation was set up. Royalties on the sale of this product have gone a long way to balancing the Greenland budget during a hundred years. Production is of the order of thirty to forty thousand tons per year, but rose to over double this during the war when it was stockpiled in the United States. The open pit is two hundred feet deep and only a similar distance from the sea and the deposit is nearly worked out. Estimates have been made that it will last only until about 1972. The natural product is still better than various synthetics which are known. Between one hundred and two hundred men are employed, originally all Danes, but since 1945 Greenlanders have taken an increasing part in the mining operations.

At Qutdligssat on Disko Island deposits of Cretaceous and Tertiary coal, somewhat mixed with the basalt flows, have been mined in a small way since 1775 and originally whaling vessels called here for renewal of their fuel supplies. A regular mine has been operated by the government since 1905. This coal is some 20 per cent. non-inflammable but has a low sulphur content. At Atanikertluk on Nugssuaq Peninsula opposite Disko Island even better coal is available and will probably soon be brought into production. There are considerable difficulties at the moment in loading the coal from this area, but it is hoped that all future local Greenland requirements (about forty thousand tons per year) can be met from this source.

In 1948 Koch's expedition of geologists discovered a deposit of galena and sphalerite at Mestersvig on Kong Oscar Fiord in east Greenland. A company was floated in which Swedish and Canadian interests as well as Danish are represented and an airstrip and mining camp were built in 1952. The ore is concentrated on the spot, since the shortness of the shipping season (four to six weeks) hampers export. Production figures for the first years of operation were:

	Lead 80% concd.	*Zinc* 60% concd.
1956	3,700 tons	4,900 tons
1957	8,750 ,,	13,650 ,,
1958	9,600 ,,	8,650 ,,
1959	11,000 ,,	9,950 ,,
1960	8,300 ,,	21,650 ,,
1961	13,000 ,,	10,950 ,,

The miners who work a ten-month year from February to November number about a hundred. The company has a concession between latitudes 70° N. and 74° 30′ N. but despite strenuous prospecting the forecast life of the venture was only until 1962 or seven years.

Other small mining efforts have taken place in the past; among them graphite and marble—but these are now of no commercial importance.

In south-west Greenland, in the inner reaches of the fiords where the climate as we have seen is non-Arctic in character, a small agricultural industry exists today. A sheep station was established in 1915 at Julianehaab and the numbers have risen to between twenty and thirty thousand. At Brattahlid in 1953 a peasant community of 135 people sent 3,700 lambs to the cold storage station at Narssaq. Winter feeding is the problem and the local hay supplies during the last decade have covered only one-tenth of the requirements. Other crops also fail to ripen in the cool summer, but some barley has been grown and cut green as fodder for the hundred or more cows which are now in the agricultural region. Potatoes, kale, beets and even rhubarb have been successfully raised. Domestic reindeer were introduced in 1952 in the Godthaab district and their numbers have increased slowly but surely. Wild reindeer (caribou) are still to be found in western Greenland though their numbers are much reduced from former times.

In the last century sealing was the main occupation of the west Greenlander and seal skins and oil were sold to the government trading store in return for European trade goods. The prices of these latter were made deliberately artificial, 'luxuries' being overvalued and 'necessities' subsidized. There was also a trading tax whereby one-sixth of the purchase price of local produce went to a Public Fund from which was provided (in part only) medical services, charities and loans for boats and houses.

With the hydrographic changes on the west coast, beginning about 1915, which brought in warmer waters, the seals have migrated further north and the traditional concept of the Greenlander in his kayak harpooning seals has vanished from much of the coast. Fortunately it has been replaced by what is now the basic industry of south-west Greenland—fishing. The Atlantic cod has appeared in increasing numbers and in Davis Strait vessels of many nations are now fishing, in addition to the native Greenlanders. In 1915 the total production of fish from

Greenland was only about twenty tons. In the late 1950s this had risen in cod alone, to twenty-five thousand tons. In addition, cod-liver and shark-liver oil are also processed and there is considerable fishery of halibut on some of the shallow banks of the south-west coast. In 1948 large shrimp fields were found in the area of Disko Bay and also off Narssaq in the south. At both these localities shrimp canneries have been established and the production has risen from twenty tons in 1950 to approaching a thousand tons by the end of the decade. The fishing industry now accounts for some eight hundred motor-boats and eighty fishing depots on the south-west coast and with the requirements for canning, cold storage, salting and drying, has resulted in a great concentration of the population in the larger settlements and the abandonment of many smaller ones, spread widely as they used to be to take advantage of the seal hunting. In addition a port, Faeringerhavn, was built in 1927 for the Faeroe Island fishing fleet and ten years later this was opened to fishing fleets from other countries. In 1954 this was used by some 200 ships making 850 calls. Thus the sea, as before, provides the Greenland community with the bulk of its livelihood and Greenland is obviously vitally interested in an agreement on offshore fishing limits.

The policy of the Danish Government had been for many years one of 'paternalism', a gradual but very slow process of education and instruction in the arts of government. Literacy has long been established and the school system is now an excellent one. Over a hundred schools now exist in west Greenland with compulsory, free education from age 7 to fourteen. Many Greenlanders are now completing high school education and some going on to university in Denmark. During and since the Second World War, however, the process of self-government was hastened; not as in many parts of the world by an outbreak of nationalistic feeling, but by events of the war themselves which separated Greenland from the home country and forced self-government upon it. In 1953 the government trading monopoly ceased and private trading is now permitted. The other major factor was the establishment of foreign military bases in the country, another wartime necessity which has been continued since the war by the NATO organization. But Greenland has avoided the pitfalls of Alaska and northern

Canada where the military influx was allowed to swamp the ordinary native life and substitute too rapidly a wage-earning system for the traditional one. The American air bases have been strictly 'quarantined' and in the case of the largest, that of Thule in north Greenland, the native population has actually been moved away (in 1953) some hundred miles from the air base and a completely new settlement built for them at Qanak.

The growth of education and the improvement of health and sanitation particularly in the rapid progress towards elimination of tuberculosis has resulted in the population growing rapidly and concentrating where schools and fishing stations are established. The table, shown below, demonstrates this urbanization. In 1956 some 57 per cent. of the total population lived in the larger towns, Byer, and it will be seen that the population of the 'settlements' (the smallest outlying places), has declined. This is not true, however, of north and east Greenland where the traditional seal-hunting economy is more widely practised.

		West Greenland	East Greenland	North Greenland (Thule)	Total
Byer	1950	10,700	369	201	
(towns)	1956	15,328	626	143	
Udsteder	1950	7,160	—	85	
(villages)	1956	7,595	—	128	
Bopladser	1950	3,801	1,238	88	
(settlements)	1956	2,872	1,420	186	
Total	1927	14,765	814	284	15,863
	1950	21,661	1,607	374	23,642
	1956	25,795	2,046	457	28,298

The larger settlements (Byer) present an attractive appearance today with typically Scandinavian gaily painted wooden buildings scattered at differing levels usually over the rocky hills surrounding the harbour. Many of the towns now have a good piped water supply though only some of the houses are directly connected to the main, the remainder drawing from taps outside. The old turf hut is rapidly vanishing and only in north and east Greenland can be seen traditional Eskimo ways of life.

Godthaab, the capital, now has a population of over two thousand. Here is the chief high school of Greenland and the major hospital—the Queen Ingrid Sanatorium with over two hundred beds. A printing press has been publishing in the

Greenlandic tongue since 1861 and the Greenland Broad-casting System, centred here, has transmitters which can relay into almost every Greenland home. In the Godthaab district the introduced domestic reindeer herd has now grown to 1,700 in numbers.

Several other west coast towns have populations close to or above a thousand with the local industries employing a hundred or more people. These are:

Qutdligssat, where the coal mine under an English manager employs 140.

Jakobshavn, with halibut and shrimp canning.

Egedesminde.

Holsteinborg.

Christianshaab, shrimp canning employs 100, chiefly girls.

Frederikshaab, fish curing and packing.

Narssaq, shrimp and sheep packing.

Julianehaab, the 'southern' capital and second largest town.

Greenland since the Second World War has entered on a new and flourishing era. With (1956) a birth rate of 47·6 per thousand and a death rate of 13·4, its population is increasing rapidly and pressure on resources will soon be apparent. Some of the penalties of progress are seen in the present problems of drunkenness and venereal disease but on the whole Greenland has moved into a twentieth-century economy more smoothly than other Arctic lands.

FURTHER READING

Bogen om Grønland (Pocket Encyclopedia in Danish), Copenhagen, 1962.

Böcher, T. K. Holman and K. Jakobson, *Grønlands Flora*, Copenhagen, 1957.

Dunbar, M. J., 'Greenland, an Experiment in Human Ecology', *The Commerce Journal*, March, 1947, pp. 69-109.

Hobbs, W. H., *The Glacial Anticyclone*, New York, Macmillan, 1926.

Norlund, P., *Viking Settlers in Greenland*, Cambridge Univ. Press, 1936.

Chapter 15

THE HISTORY OF ANTARCTIC EXPLORATION

THE 'Last Continent' is a description that might well be given to Antarctica—the last to be discovered, the last word in climatic austerity. The human geographer, more interested in people than in places might well neglect a land where there is no permanent population, where the first woman appeared in 1935 and where no human child has yet been born. But we cannot neglect a region of one-tenth of the world's land area, however unfavourable the climate, representing as it does, an excellent geographical entity, the Ice Age in being, totally polar. Two features are present to satisfy the humanist—a dramatic story of exploration filled with episodes of human heroism and endeavour, and secondly an area in which the modern argument of nationalism and internationalism has a strong focus. In Antarctica the period of pure topographical discovery is still not ended but already it is being linked with detailed scientific exploration as is the case on other continents, particularly since the beginning of the International Geophysical Year in 1957.

Although unseen until less than a century and a half ago, it is a curious fact that everyone was always convinced that there was an Antarctic continent. The question was how big was this land? It was believed that all the earliest southern discoveries, such as Tierra del Fuego, Tasmania, even New Zealand, were projections of this supposed Terra Australis which occupies the whole southern portion of early world maps, or else were islands just off its shores. In the eighteenth century three voyages in particular did much to shatter the illusion of a possibly fertile vast southern continent and to begin its steady amputation. Bouvet de Lozier, in 1738–9, skirted the ice fields for a thousand miles and found only one island now named after him, but his observations of great tabular icebergs proved that a glacier-covered land must lie to the south. Another

French explorer, Kerguelen-Trémarec, 1772–3, explored far to the south in the Indian Ocean, finding again only the small group of islands which now bear his name. At the same time, 1772–5, came the second voyage of James Cook in the *Resolution*. He carried out a complete circumnavigation of the globe in quite high southern latitudes, crossing the Antarctic Circle itself three times and successfully proving that if a continent existed it all lay beyond the pack-ice belt and must be desolate and 'the world will derive no benefit from it'. This voyage and its report was enough to discourage further efforts by the colonial powers of the day, but it did not discourage commercial sealers and whalers who, in the search for animal oil, had begun to exhaust the northern lands. Southern island beaches were crowded with entirely fearless animals whose slaughter was simple. The sealing began in the last decade of the eighteenth century and by 1820 there were fifty American and British ships taking part in the industry. It was during this season that the actual continent, the tip of the Grahamland Peninsula, was sighted, whether by a British or an American ship makes remarkably little difference. In the same year an official Russian expedition, that of Bellingshausen, penetrated to even higher latitudes than had James Cook and discovered Peter I and Alexander I islands. For over 120 years the latter was thought to be part of the continent, whereas the Grahamland Peninsula was not. The next two decades saw the practical end of the sealing industry, the old story of man's all-too-rapid onslaught on a natural resource. As an example of the profits obtainable by this trade, one American vessel in a single voyage took forty-five thousand fur-seal skins which were sold in China for goods worth a quarter of a million dollars. Some further discoveries had been made by the traders. John Biscoe in 1831 had seen Enderby Land, a part of the continent, and Weddell had carried out his astonishing voyage to 74° 15′ S. in the Weddell Sea, since seldom found so open.

In the period 1838 to 1843 came a new and sudden re-crudescence of activity in the Antarctic. This took the form of no less than three national expeditions sent out by France, United States and Great Britain. The scientific era of exploration in the Antarctic had been born, inspired by the recent work on electro-magnetism by the German mathematician Gauss. All three of these expeditions were interested in locating the south magnetic-dip Pole and all in the course of this endeavour came on traces of the southern continent. The United States' expedition, commanded by Charles Wilkes, began the tradition of the enormous United States' naval expeditions of today, consisting, as it did, of six ships and 440 men. Wilkes, however was not made of the same stuff as Byrd and Cruzen and his equipment was lamentably poor. Wilkes and Dumont D'Urville the commander of the French expedition, both sighted land on almost the same day in 1840 in the sector where the magnetic pole was believed to be. D'Urville landed and collected rocks at Point Géologie, now occupied by the French Geophysical Year expedition, and named the country Adélie Land after his wife, who, in addition, gave her name to the most cheerful of Antarctica's inhabitants—the little Adélie penguin. Wilkes sailed westward to the Shackleton ice-shelf, making several sightings of land on the way, some of which were certain, others perhaps were only tabular icebergs and here he was forced to give up since his crew were in no fit state to continue the voyage.

James C. Ross, commander of the British expedition in the ships *Erebus* and *Terror*, started later than the others but achieved a higher latitude. He managed to penetrate the pack ice further east into the sea now named after him which he found surprisingly open. Sailing on he reached McMurdo Sound, the furthest south to which ships can possibly get in the Antarctic regions and then sailed along the ice barrier to the Bay of Whales. These became the two famous gateways to the south which were not to be opened again for fifty years.

This lack of enthusiasm, the refusal to follow up the important discoveries of these few years, is at first surprising. But the British were to be concerned with the Arctic, with Franklin and the North-West Passage search. The French were occupied with internal strife and the development of their African empire. For the Americans the reason is less clear. Certainly their sealing and whaling commercial interests were intensely maintained, concentrating, however, on the sub-Antarctic islands, and this trade itself took a severe blow during the American Civil War when shipping losses were tremendous. Men of the calibre of Peary and Byrd apparently just did not exist in this period of American history.

The next milestone in the Antarctic story is 1895. In that year the first landing on the Antarctic continent, apart from its Grahamland Peninsula, took place at Cape Adare. This was by Captain Bull of a Norwegian expedition sent out by the whaling master, Sven Foyn, who for the past two or three years had been·probing the whaling possibilities of the southern seas. Also, in 1895, came an important congress of the International Geographical Union at which a resolution was passed that the Antarctic represented the greatest piece of exploratory work yet to be accomplished. This was the era when great national geographical societies flourished, sponsored by wealthy private patrons who were ready to support financially a bold scheme of exploration in any part of the world. Six nations answered the call of this congress' resolution, and national expeditions were dispatched by Belgium, Germany, Sweden, France, Great Britain and even little Scotland. First in the field was the Belgian expedition of De Gerlache, whose son was to lead the Belgian I.G.Y. expedition of recent years. On board his ship were two other figures of whom much more was to be heard— Roald Amundsen and Frederick Cook. The *Belgica*, after explorations on the west coast of the Grahamland Peninsula, was beset in the pack ice and drifted for a year, the first vessel to winter south of the Antarctic Circle, experiencing seventy-one days of darkness (1898). Next year a British expedition led by the Norwegian Borchgrevink wintered at Cape Adare on the mainland. In 1901 three national expeditions set sail. The German expedition under Von Drygalski was caught in the Antarctic pack ice close to the mainland and forced to spend the winter, during which they sledded ashore to the region of Mount Gauss in longitude 90° E. The Swedish expedition, led by Otto Nordenskiöld with C. A. Larsen as skipper, also had its vessel, *Antarctic*, trapped for the winter in the ice of the Weddell Sea and this time it was crushed. Nordenskiöld, meanwhile, had landed with a wintering party provisioned for one year but was forced to spend a second separated from the crew of *Antarctic* who, twenty men strong, put in an emergency winter on Paulet Island. A third smaller group had also been landed and marooned by the loss of the ship but all three groups were successfully reunited and rescued by an Argentine vessel in January 1904. The British expedition which sailed in 1901 was commanded by R. F. Scott, wintering with its vessel in McMurdo Sound. They made the first extensive journey inland on the continent and carried out two complete years of important scientific work. Bruce, the leader of the Scottish expedition, did important oceanographical work in the Weddell Sea, where he discovered Coats Land, and, wintering on the South Orkney Islands, began the first permanent meteorological station which was taken over on his departure by the Argentine Government.

The stage had been set by these first tentative winterings, often forced, and the journeys of Scott and his party into the interior of the continent, for the great age of adventure that followed when the route to the South Pole itself was opened up. In this period, although mechanical vehicles were beginning to appear and were tried out on the polar ice, the explorers had to rely in the main on their muscles or those of animals. Aircraft and radio were missing so communications with the outside world were cut off and there was still a lack of understanding of the reasons for scurvy. This disease had hit Scott's first southern sledding party, particularly Lieutenant Shackleton, and on the return journey of 380 miles to their ship he had only just survived and was sent home before the second wintering. Yet Shackleton was back in 1907, this time leading his own privately financed party with the intention of pushing right through to the South Pole. He failed by only a little over a hundred miles, judiciously turning back at the last possible moment when the return journey could be accomplished. This expedition also saw the remarkable journey of Professor David together with the young Douglas Mawson to the location of the south magnetic Pole. As Shackleton was returning, J. B. Charcôt was carrying out his second wintering of the French National Antarctic Expedition, the first had been in 1904. During these two expeditions he had greatly increased our knowledge of the west side of the Grahamland Peninsula and discovered Charcôt Island.

Shackleton had pioneered a route towards the South Pole and within eighteen months of his return two other expeditions were seeking this final prize, Scott of the Royal Navy and Amundsen of Norway. Both were successful but at a tragic cost to the lives of all Scott's polar party. This expedition remains for all time the supreme example of fortitude when men were pitting their own muscular power against near-impossible distances and climate. The comparison between their travel methods has already been made in Chapter 8. It remains only to add that Amundsen's undoubtedly brilliant journey over a new route was almost exclusively a sporting feat. Scott's last expedition brought back immense scientific gains, the pathetic proof of which was the thirty pounds of geological specimens which his gallant band pulled until they died.

Before these two expeditions when the Pole was reached and when long-distance journeys were much in men's minds, another great problem had been considered and that was the journey between the two major indentations of the Antarctic continent—the Ross Sea, which was the base for Scott and Amundsen, and the Weddell Sea, whose limits had not yet been traced. The first to consider such a journey was the Scottish explorer Bruce but he was unable to raise funds. The same fate overtook Dr. Filchner of Germany, who, however, was sufficiently well backed to take an expedition to explore the limits of the Weddell Sea. After penetrating to what we now know to be its foot, Vahsel Bay, Filchner's landing party was swept out to sea again and a short time later his vessel *Deutschland* was trapped in the pack ice, spending a whole winter drifting northward parallel to the Grahamland Peninsula and luckily being released in November 1912. Almost immediately Shackleton began planning a similar venture which he named The British Imperial Trans-Antarctic Expedition, with a crossing party to be based on the Weddell Sea and a support party from McMurdo Sound to lay depots on to the polar plateau. Shackleton was even more unfortunate than Filchner since his vessel, *Endurance*, was caught in the Weddell Sea pack before a landing had even been made and this time, drifting closer to the Grahamland coast, was exposed to greater ice pressure and eventually crushed. Encamped now on the drifting ice, Shackleton's party slowly progressed towards the north and eventually when open water was reached, were able to reach Elephant Island in their boats. From here Shackleton with five companions made his famous open-boat voyage for help across the stormiest seas of the world to South Georgia, and even then only repeated attempts resulted, on the fourth try, in his party being relieved from their cramped and miserable quarters on Elephant Island.

Meanwhile on the opposite side of the continent Shackleton's supporting party were about their business, ignorant of the main party's disaster. Their base ship was carried out to sea with the ice in a winter's storm and the small ill-equipped shore party struggled manfully to fulfil their now futile obligations, losing Mackintosh the leader and two other men in the process.

One other story remains to be told of this early era in the Antarctic, the beginnings of the young southern nation Australia's interest in the polar world. Douglas Mawson had been with Shackleton's magnetic Pole party and in 1911 led the first Australian Antarctic Expedition. He wintered in Adélie Land at Cape Denison, choosing, it seems, the windiest place in the world, 'The Home of the Blizzard'. In one month the average wind speed was 60 m.p.h. yet despite this difficulty much scientific exploration was carried out. Mawson himself returned alone from the longest sled trip; one companion having been lost down a crevasse, the other dead from hunger and exhaustion. Mawson, Shackleton and Scott—their sagas epitomize this age of southern heroic endeavour; the forces that the continent could bring to bear were too heavy for men and animals alone to combat. The future must belong to the machine.

At the close of the First World War the approximate outline of the continent could be traced by joining the few successful penetrations. But we can see on the map how few these were and fewer still were the strikes inland.

In 1928 the American Geographical Society organized a symposium published as *Problems of Polar Research*. In this were contributions on the newest method of exploration, by aircraft, from Byrd, Wilkins and Ellsworth. These three men already had considerable aerial experience in the north and were now to transfer their activities to the Antarctic.

It was Wilkins who made the first flight over the southern continent in November 1928, attempting from Deception Island to find a suitable advanced base on the Weddell Sea from which to cross to the Ross Sea. In this he was unsuccessful, though he penetrated to about 70° S. He reported that the Grahamland Peninsula was cut by several straits up to twenty miles in width. This has been subsequently disproved and along with the exaggerated heights for mountains given by later aviators shows how easily major geographical mistakes can be made even by experienced polar men *from aircraft alone*.

In the same season, Byrd, equipped with three aircraft, reached his base, 'Little America', on the Bay of Whales on the first of his five major Antarctic forays. These were organized on a scale hitherto unattempted, both in numbers of men, lavishness of mechanical equipment and doggedly obtained finances. Byrd gave a new direction to polar exploration and aroused his country to a powerful degree of interest in the southern continent. He also, like Shackleton, had a genius for picking men and for ensuring their survival.

On his first expedition one of the aims was a south-polar flight and this was achieved in November 1929 in a tri-motored Ford piloted by Balchen. Only just did they clear the hump of the Queen Maud Range, which thirty years later was still to be a problem for poleward flying aircraft. Meanwhile, at the foot of the same mountains, Dr. L. Gould, Byrd's chief scientist, was carrying out geological work and extending knowledge further to the east than before on a 1,500-mile dog team journey (*see Plate 31*).

Byrd's next expedition, 1933-5, was also equipped with aircraft but was more noteworthy for the first large-scale use of tractors, for overland journeys. This was the time when Byrd, wintering alone, nearly died from carbon monoxide poisoning. Siple made an extended journey to the east into new territory and Poulter initiated the first seismic soundings of the Ross shelf ice.

It was into this new unclaimed territory to the east of Little America that the United States Government decided to mount a major expedition, again directed by Byrd, in 1939. Two parties operating from each end of the unclaimed sector were to explore and claim the whole area and the bases were meant to be permanent settlements. The United States' entry into the Second World War put an end to this expedition but not before more useful results had been obtained. This was in spite of the failure of the most ambitious land vehicle then conceived, the monster thirty-three-ton 'Snow Cruiser' which was to have been the chief travelling agency but could scarcely make more than one Antarctic mile.

Although Byrd's expeditions were the largest and perhaps the most important to the Antarctic in the inter-war years, others were at work. In 1933, together with Sir Hubert Wilkins and Bernt Balchen, Lincoln Ellsworth, who had flown over the North Pole with Amundsen, began several attempts to cross the Antarctic continent by air. After two unsuccessful seasons he tried again in 1935 (November). Taking off from the north-east tip of the Grahamland Peninsula in a single-engine Northrop aircraft Ellsworth and his pilot, Hollick Kenyon, deliberately made several landings on the plateau to wait for more favourable weather. Their last touch-down came when within twelve miles of Little America as their fuel was exhausted. While Ellsworth was making this bold crossing of the American corner of the continent, a British expedition led by Rymill was spending two winters on the west coast of the Grahamland Peninsula. Long sled journeys were made in different directions, and in particular they discovered King George VI Sound, proving that Alexander Island was in fact an island and not a part of the continent.

Meanwhile, other expeditions had been spending summers continuing to delineate the still vague coastline of the Indian Ocean sector of the continent. From 1929 to 1931, Sir Douglas Mawson's *Banzare* expedition landed at five points in what shortly after became the Australian-claimed sector, and throughout the thirties Norwegian expeditions under the enthusiastic whaling magnate Lars Christensen delineated much of Queen Maud Land and discovered the bare ground and ice free water area of the Vestfold Hills. This area of Queen Maud Land was the scene of a venture in 1938-9 of Hitler's Reich. The Schwabenland Expedition initiated new aerial photo-mapping techniques, but unfortunately most of the negatives were lost during the subsequent war. Despite this, however, the German work became generally known and had two results: first of all an official Norwegian claim to Queen Maud Land in January 1939, and secondly Professor Ahlmann's idea of an international expedition which was achieved finally in 1949.

Several times in this account to date the word 'national claim' has been mentioned. This aspect of the exploration of the continent began now to have more far-reaching effects. Great Britain had been the first to lay claim to Antarctic territory and to attempt to administer it. As early as 1908 letters patent had constituted the dependencies of the Falkland Islands and this claim and the disputes concerning it will be examined later. The New Zealand Government had followed in 1923 by laying claim to the territory between longitudes 160° E. and 150° W. France followed the next year by claiming a very narrow slice of the pie, from 140° to 145° E., named Terre Adélie. In 1933, Australia prodded by Mawson after his *Banzare* expedition, laid claim to a huge sector extending from 45° E. to the boundary of the New Zealand claim, excepting and therefore respecting, however, the French claim in this area. Norway, in 1939, continued claiming to the west of the Australian territory as far as 20° W., abutting, therefore, on the British Falkland Island dependencies claim. Only the territory between 150° W. and 80° W. was left unclaimed and in this area it was tacitly assumed that the Americans, having done most of the exploration in this very difficult-of-access region, had the prior claim. President Roosevelt did, in fact, instruct the official U.S. Antarctic Service in 1939 to make claims and these were duly carried out by the third Byrd expedition. Such was the situation up till the Second World War, but on 24 May 1940, when the fight in Europe was in full flood, Cordell Hull announced 'considerations of continental defence make it vital to keep for the twenty-one American republics a clearer title to that part of the Antarctic continent south of America than is claimed by any non-American country'. Thus, the American State Department, with its religious belief in Republicanism and against Colonialism opened the field wide for counter-claims by South American republics to Antarctic territory neighbouring to them. Argentina and Chile promptly made mutually overlapping claims in the territory of the Falkland Islands Dependencies. The situation is further complicated by the fact that Argentina has never accepted British sovereignty over the Falkland Islands themselves, claiming an inheritance from Spain which once had a settlement on these lands. Britain maintains that her nationals discovered all the sections of the Falkland Islands Dependencies. South Georgia and the South Sandwich Islands by Cook, Grahamland, the South Shetlands and the South Orkneys in the years 1819 to 1821 and Coats Land by Bruce in

1904. The latter, thinking of science more than politics upset matters by handing over his winter quarters on Laurie Island in the South Orkneys to Argentine meteorologists who have maintained a station there ever since. When in 1904 Larsen formed the Compagnia Argentina de Pesca in Buenos Aires and established a shore station on South Georgia he was granted a licence by the British Government. Seven other whaling companies were granted leases on South Georgia from 1908–11, the Hector Whaling Company on Deception Island in 1912 and the Tønsberg Whaling Company on Signy Island in 1920. Since 1909 Britain has maintained a resident magistrate (and since 1912 a Post Office) on South Georgia, and each summer from 1910 to 1930 a magistrate lived on Deception Island to control the whaling industry. By the latter date pelagic whaling with factory ships at sea had become the rule except for shore stations on South Georgia and the magistrate's office on Deception Island had become redundant. The British income from whaling licences had been used between 1925 and 1939 by the Discovery Committee in scientific investigations of the Dependencies, chiefly in carrying out important work on the biology of whales. The South American counter-claims, initiated when Britain was fully engaged in the war, might have had disastrous consequences but fortunately to date the incidents have been more amusing than warlike, consisting chiefly in obliterating each other's notices of sovereignty, in which occupation a great deal of paint has been used. In 1942 the Argentinians landed on Deception Island and planted a claim proclamation. In January 1943, the British cruiser *Carnarvon Castle* obliterated this painting, but a month later it had been repainted by the Argentinians. In January 1944, Britain established a permanent base on Deception Island but this did not stop the Argentinians building another base three years later a few hundred yards away. The situation became alarming in 1948 when warships including the cruiser *Nigeria* were sent to the region. But since that date annual agreements have been made not to send naval vessels to the area. By 1955 the rather unnecessary number of seventeen posts had been established between the three countries and the population of the Grahamland Peninsula had risen to something like 150. Britain, confident that her claim would be substantiated, has frequently proposed taking the case to the International Court but so far Argentina and Chile have refused.

At the end of the Second World War, Britain and the two South American nations were fully engaged in manning their posts in the disputed area and spending much money on paint. The United States Navy, however, now equipped with excellent modern ice-breakers and urged on·by Admiral Byrd, proceeded to mount a tremendous expedition with several groups of vessels and aircraft, attempting to map by aerial photographs the whole extent of the Antarctic coast-line. This was the famous 'High Jump' Expedition of 1946–7 in which thirteen ships and four thousand men took part. This vast flotilla was divided into three groups and much of the activity of the expedition was connected with the training of the United States Navy under polar conditions. Admiral Byrd was once more in overall command, with one of his former colleagues, Admiral Cruzen, in naval command. The eastern group of vessels was commanded by Admiral George Dufek, another man who had learnt his Polar work under Byrd. This group with a seaplane tender was allotted the task of mapping as much as possible of the coast of the American sector. A similar group under Captain Bond, the western group, worked mainly in the Australian sector of the Antarctic, its most important discovery being the ice free land termed the Bunger Oasis, named after the pilot of the aircraft who landed on one of the lakes. The central group pushed through exceptionally difficult pack ice to the Bay of Whales to establish a base at the site of old Little America. For the first time modern ice-breakers were available and without them undoubtedly the task force would never have reached its objective or been able to land. Even so, the delays of the difficult passage resulted in a curtailing of the flying programme from Little America IV, and their planes, DC-3s, were abandoned on the site after a few weeks. On the whole expedition more than a hundred flights were made, many of them photo-mapping flights but unfortunately due to cloudy weather, difficulties in navigation and above all the lack of any ground control, the flights, though extremely useful for reconnoitring much new territory, proved of slight use for correcting the existing maps.

In the same season a private United States expedition led by Finn Ronne left for the west coast of the Grahamland Peninsula to pick up the threads of the east base of Byrd's Third Expedition. Once again further penetrations were made in this area, including a magnificent sled trip along the Weddell Sea coast in co-operation with the British base at Ronne's location and supported by aircraft.

Meanwhile interest in the Antarctic was building up anew in other countries. Professor Ahlmann, impressed by the German photographs in Queen Maud Land, worked out a programme for an international expedition of British Commonwealth, Norwegian and Swedish members which established a base at Maudheim in 1949 and spent two successive winters at this site. An important all-round scientific programme, which stressed in particular glaciology and the measurement of ice thickness, was carried out by the mixed team who made a deep traverse inland from their ice-shelf base. While this expedition was spending its two winters on the coast of old Antarctica two other countries established semi-permanent bases in their claimed territory, France, in 1950, in Terre Adélie at the base called Port Martin, and Australia at the base known as Mawson, in 1952. Both these stations have been permanently occupied since their dates of establishment. At the French base, a short distance away, a most important Emperor penguin rookery was discovered, one of the fourteen now known.

The last half of the 1950 decade saw the greatest assault on the mysteries of the Antarctic of all times. This has been caused by the International Geophysical Year, high on the programme of which was the establishment of bases on the Antarctic continent to complete the world-wide coverage of simultaneous observation stations only possible, now, with modern transportation and living methods. The first and Second International Polar Years of 1882–3 and 1932–3 had been mainly for Arctic observations of magnetism, meteorology, and, in the second one, of auroral phenomena. But the science of geophysics had grown so rapidly since then that a wider field of subjects and the wider field of the whole earth were decided on, with particular concentration on three latitudinal regions, the Arctic, the Antarctic and the Tropics. Of the more than forty countries co-operating in the International Geophysical Year twelve of them decided to establish and maintain stations in the Antarctic and although the 'Year' began only on the first of July 1957, preparations and preliminary reconnaissance expeditions had started nearly two years earlier.

At the same time as the nations' preparations for Antarctic bases began, another long-thought-of project finally came to fruition. This was the crossing of the Antarctic continent on land, or rather on ice, from the Weddell Sea to the Ross Sea, planned by Bruce, attempted by Shackleton, and now to be completed by Sir Vivian Fuchs. Mechanical transport had now made possible this feat, which Shackleton could perhaps never have carried out successfully. But, with mechanical vehicles a new difficulty appears in Antarctic travel—that of the safe crossing of concealed crevasses—and the story of Fuchs' traverse and those of other major traverses which have taken place with vehicles during the I.G.Y. exploration period are full of stories and incidents of vehicles almost or quite disappearing into the major crevasses of the Antarctic ice sheet. Fuchs' journey, starting from the Weddell Sea was supported by a depot-laying expedition led by Sir Edmund Hillary, the New Zealand mountaineer, starting from the other side, in the same way as Shackleton had planned the depot-laying party of Macdonald. Fuchs' group, beginning with a small reconnaissance party, was on the ground for almost two years at Shackleton Base before the crossing actually began; and Hillary's for one year. The whole route, both sides of the Pole, was in fact over new territory since Hillary's supporting group moved up on to the Antarctic plateau via the Skelton Glacier, not far from McMurdo Sound and from then on was behind the great rampart of mountains which borders the Ross Sea. Fuchs' route was over completely unknown territory and he was perhaps fortunate to find only two small mountain ranges to be crossed. During the first preparatory winter when Fuchs' main party was ashore, a small group occupied a station in latitude 80° S., termed South Ice, and it was between here and the coast that the main crevasse difficulties were encountered. During the Antarctic summer of the actual traverse, 1957–8, Hillary's supporting parties using Ferguson tractors and aircraft to supply the actual 'dumps' pushed forward rapidly and Hillary was able to reach the Pole from which he returned by air, before Fuchs attained it from the other side. All the way across the continent Fuchs' party took seismic and glaciological measurements and this was the first major traverse which yielded information on the depth and stratification of the great Antarctic plateau (*see Plate 26*).

Meanwhile, the I.G.Y. groups were assembling at their stations mostly located on the continents' shore but with several fully manned inland stations. The largest programme of all was undertaken by the United States which had five stations as well as one shared with New Zealand at Cape Adare. Three of these were on the coast at Little America V, no longer in the same place as the previous four which had become inaccessible owing to the closing of the Bay of Whales, Weddell station, not far from Fuchs' base and Wilkes station on the other side of the continent. Two inland stations were set up—Byrd in Marie Byrd Land some six hundred miles from Little America and finally, most ambitious of all, the station named Amundsen-Scott at the geographic South Pole itself. The establishment of this station entirely by air at a height of nine thousand feet was a new landmark in Polar transportation. For the first time long-distance aircraft flew directly from New Zealand to an advanced base in McMurdo Sound and from there the equipment for a luxurious camp was ferried to the Pole itself in Dakota-type aircraft which had to use jet assistance to take off again even when unloaded. At this station, for the initial year's occupation the tonnage of stores landed by air was equivalent to what the old-fashioned Antarctic sea-going expeditions had taken in by ship. The commander of their base for its first winter was Paul Siple who had been with every one of the Byrd expeditions since 1928 and was now a senior scientist with the United States Services. The establishment of Byrd Station was equally a transportation feat. This time heavy tractors carried the equipment over territory a portion of which, anyway, was heavily crevassed and for which a 'Weasel'-carried crevasse detector was used. The major crevasses were then filled in with snow so that the tractor-train could safely pass. From this station several important traverses have been made—to the Horlick Mountains to the south, to the neighbourhood of the coast to the north—and to the Sentinel Mountains and the Weddell Sea to the east (see map p. 276, Antarctica I.G.Y.).

The next largest national contingent to establish in the Antarctic during the I.G.Y. was that of the Soviet Union. Its main base, named Mirniy, was built in the Australian sector in 1956 and during the same year two other stations were established, one 230 miles inland and another, Oasis, 220 miles to the east along the coast. Subsequently, further stations were established inland including one at latitude 88° S., longitude 55° E., the considered pole of inaccessability in the Antarctic continent at which the lowest temperatures recorded on the surface of the earth have been found: – 124° F. Connecting these various stations traverses have been made and once again a large section of the interior plateau Antarctica has been explored as far as ice thickness and character goes. During the winter of 1959–60 a Soviet tractor party visited the geographical South Pole on a lengthy traverse which exceeded two thousand miles. The wintering stations of other countries are shown on the accompanying map, and from most of them dog team or vehicle journeys and aircraft flights have been made, opening up new Antarctic territory. We can say, in fact, that during the second half of the 1950 decade a large portion of the Antarctic continent was viewed from the air and many traverses made across its surface. There are still blank spots on the map that have never been seen at all, but it is safe to say that the era of exploration in the south has now reached the stage that it was in the north in 1930, when although blank spaces were shown on the Arctic Ocean it was reasonably assumed that no land would be found in them. In the south our knowledge of the coast-line has become nearly complete and the map of it as definite as can be drawn in a country where the coast-line is constantly changing with the advance and breaking-off of ice shelves. Inland in those blank spaces that remain we believe that all that can be found out is the depth of the ice, as in the Arctic Ocean it is the depth of the water.

FURTHER READING

Kirwan, L. P., *The White Road*, London, 1959.

Roberts, B. B., 'Chronological List of Antarctic Expeditions', *Polar Record*, 9, pp. 97-134, 191-239.

Sullivan, W., *Quest for a Continent*, London, 1957.

Chapter 16

THE ANTARCTIC CONTINENT

HUNDREDS or even thousands of miles from the southern tip of the other continents is the Antarctic continental mass, as big as the United States and Australia put together and about as large as its antipode, the North Polar Sea. This is the ice continent. It is not only ice-capped, but is overflowing with ice into the surrounding waters in the form of glacier tongues afloat and ice shelves. There is, therefore, very little bare ground from which to re-create its geological history. From the purely topographical point of view the Antarctic creates very definite descriptive problems. What are its limits, for instance? Where do we draw the boundary for this land which is mainly snow and ice? What would it look like if the ice were removed? At present, counting its altitude to the summit of the ice carapace, it is the highest of the continents, but we are faced, as in Greenland, with the difficulty of representation of its true shape. Two sets of contours are needed, the upper (ice) surface and the lower (rock) surface. There is nothing very permanent about most of the seaward margin of the so-called land. The diagram (Fig. 66) shows some of the bounding limits as follows:

A. Land definitely above sea-level; but this boundary is unrecognizable except by sounding through the ice.

B. The edge of the land-based inland ice, sometimes but not always recognizable by strand cracks or by a sudden change in slope of the ice surface.

C. The edge of a floating ice-shelf, or of a glacier tongue afloat. But this, although fairly permanently maintained by supporting headlands or shoals is distinctly variable over periods of years in its position.

D. The edge of bay ice, quite definitely perennial in character and similar to the temporary winter land-fast ice in the Arctic.

E. The edge of the continental slope, generally accepted by geophysicists as the true continental edge, but here much deeper below mean sea-level, (400–500 metres), than is the case with most of the remainder of the continents.

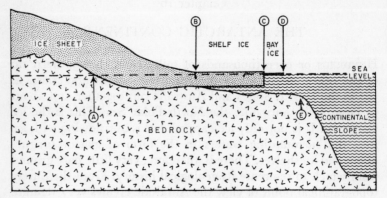

Fig. 66. Limits of Antarctic Continent.

Which of these limits are we to accept as the edge of the Antarctic continent? If it were to be A and were this well known (and at present it is only known in a very few localities) we would still not be sure if the Antarctic was one continent or two or even just several disjointed islands. But it must be remembered that if the enormous load of ice were to be removed from the land mass the latter would undoubtedly rise many hundreds or thousands of feet and the position of the seaward margin of the land mass would be radically changed from what it is revealed today by soundings through the ice.

From a structural point of view, however, there seems to be a fairly clear delimitation of the Antarctic into two major portions which, as was mentioned in the previous chapter, this work intends to call 'young' and 'old' Antarctica. Young Antarctica, that portion south of the Americas and of the south-eastern part of the Pacific, has affinities with the New World, containing folded mountain ranges akin to the Andes in rock and mineral composition. Old Antarctica, on the other hand, resembles in its basic geology and plateau-like appearance the Old World plateaus of Africa and Australia, opposite to which much of it lies. From what we know of the rocks of Old

28. Russian Icebreaker "Moskva" (*see p.* 158)

29. The Danish Arctic station at Godhavn, Greenland

30. Reconstruction of interior of Scott's hut (*see p.* 259 *and Plate* 32)

31. Admiral Byrd taking observations from aircraft (*see p.* 262)

Antarctica this appears to have been a stable region for a lengthy period of geological time. The basement rocks representing a Pre-Cambrian Shield are overlain by a more or less horizontal but very thick sedimentary series of Palaeozoic and sometimes of later age with considerable outpourings of fissure-type lavas. In the earliest investigated area from the classical expeditions based on McMurdo Sound, the basement rocks are seen to be granite and granite-gneiss with widespread crystalline limestones. The age of these lowest rocks appears to be Pre-Cambrian and they are succeeded by a very thick series of sedimentary rocks starting with a limestone (collected by Wilson from the Beardmore Glacier) containing definitely Cambrian fossils. Above this comes the very thick series which has been termed the Beacon sandstone, which though consisting basically of sandstone and arkose contains layers of coal and limestone as well. Fossil fish, of presumably Devonian times have been found in it and lower Mesozoic plant fossils towards its upper limit. It is within this group that very thick sills and dikes of diabase have been intruded and the whole series seems to have been laid down over a very lengthy period of geological stability in a continental or shallow water environment. In most of the other small areas of Old Antarctica's coast-line that have been investigated similar basement rocks have been found with only slightly metamorphosed rocks above, again intruded by thick sills of diabase.

In Young Antarctica we have a totally different geological appearance. Basic igneous rocks, particularly gabbros, of the Andean type are overlain by a thick series of sedimentary rocks, chiefly of Mesozoic age, though in the South Orkneys (forming part of the connecting Scotia Arc) fossils of Ordovician age have been found. Most of the Grahamland Peninsula consists of slates and sandstones of Jurassic and Cretaceous age, rich in fossil flora and highly folded and intruded by Andesite type lavas. To the north-east of the Grahamland Peninsula the youngest beds of Tertiary age appear. Vulcanism has been prominent right up to the present day and several dormant volcanoes are present in the South Shetland Islands including the crater harbour of Deception Island. Peter I Island is also volcanic. In the Ross Sea area a famous peak, Mount Erebus, the only volcano now active in the south, is connected by a

T

chain of other recent volcanoes extending out to Scott Island and the Balleny Islands and inland along the great mountain chain to the west of the Ross ice shelf. Across on the furthest side of Old Antarctica is the lonely recent volcano of Gaussberg.

The two major structural blocks of the Antarctic are separated by a very prominent horst which forms a tremendous block-faulted scarp along the western and southern sides of the Ross Sea and extends across, it is presumed, to the eastern crest of the Weddell Sea. Through the cross faults, which have now become valleys, pour down the great glaciers, such as the Beardmore, from Old Antarctica's plateau on to the Ross shelf ice. This embayment, with its counterpart the Weddell Sea, is believed to be a corresponding graben, but obscured by ice as this feature is, it is still difficult to prove, or to prove its continuity, in fact, between the two embayments. There now appears to be a blocking ridge along approximately 80° W. to 90° W. longitude. Young Antarctica seems to consist of the parallel foldings of the Grahamland Peninsula fanning out into a series of ranges extending over to Marie Byrd Land.

To date, the economic mineral discoveries made in the Antarctic have been extremely limited. The coal seams in the Beacon sandstone are of more scientific than economic interest, showing as they do that a sub-tropical climate once existed where these rocks were laid down. There is no reason to believe, however, that deposits of important minerals may not be discovered, particularly in the Grahamland Peninsula area where the formations are similar to many of the rich areas of the Andes; or that on the edge of Old Antarctica typical shield-rock mineral deposits again may occur. No evidence has been found that glaciation existed in the Antarctic prior to the Pleistocene age. Geologically, one can call it a normal continent until the age of ice, but since the Pleistocene began, the main mineral deposit has been ice.

It is with the ice of the Antarctic continent that we are primarily concerned in trying to describe the geographical facts of the area. Many of the earliest definitions of types of ice and theories as to its formation derived, in fact, from the classical investigations by Wright and Priestley from the second Antarctic expedition of Captain Scott. Their studies were the first to be carried out on a polar ice-cap and its surroundings, and it is only of recent years that we have realized the great differences between polar ice and the temperate ice of valley glaciers in well-known mountain areas. In the Antarctic, after all, we have over 90 per cent. of the world's ice cover and it is here that the major problems of glaciology must be solved. The Antarctic is, however, in some ways a special case in that the area of accumulation comprises almost all of the whole, and only in limited regions around the periphery is there any melting as we understand it from even the Greenland ice-cap. One of the main problems in Antarctic glaciology is in fact to measure this accumulation and since surface melting is so rare, to determine how it is dispersed from the continent's margin by other means of ablation, such as calving and melting by sea action.

The surface relief of the Antarctic continent is carved in ice. A few bare areas, like oases in the desert, do exist and will be described later, but overwhelmingly the shape of the continent's surface is the shape of the ice surface. This shape, as far as Old Antarctica is concerned is a giant dome, the highest part of which (so far discovered) is approximately thirteen thousand feet above sea-level. The dome slopes towards the coast-line in a shape which approximates that of a quarter ellipse steepening convexly as it approaches its edge; but on one side of the dome where the great Antarctic horst separates it from Young Antarctica the mountain range has a barrier effect and through it great valley glaciers pour down. Some of these are the largest valley glaciers of the world, such as the Beardmore up which Scott and Shackleton journeyed towards the Pole, the Axel Heiberg Glacier, Amundsen's route, and the Skelton Glacier pioneered by Hillary and then descended by Fuchs on his trans-Antarctic journey. But on the coastward margin of Old Antarctica the pattern is not entirely one of a simple convex slope towards the sea. Due to the configuration of the rock floor below, certain major 'ice streams' have now been described, down which the ice pours at a much more rapid rate than that of the less active areas in between. These are comparable with the major ice streams of Greenland whereas much of the coastal edge of the Antarctic ice sheet resembles a more tranquil edge of the Greenland sheet in Melville Bay. Some of these ice streams have been recognized

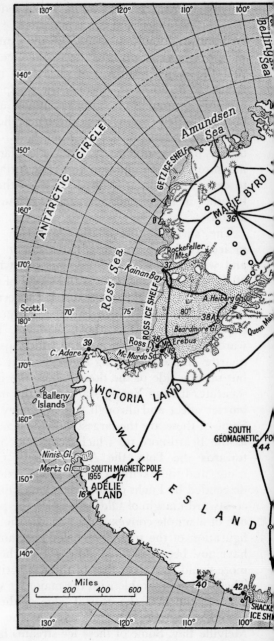

Fig. 67. Ma

Argentina
1. General Belgrano
2. Orcadas
3. Melchior
4. Decepcion
5. General San Martin
6. Almirante Brown
7. Esperanza
8. Teniente Camara

Australia
9. Mawson
10. Davis

Belgium
11. Roi Baudouin

Chile
12. Bernardo O'Higgins
13. Gonzalez Videla
14. Arturo Pratt
15. Pedro Aguirre Cerda

France
16. Dumont d'Urville
17. Charcot

Japan
18. Syowa

New Zealand
19. Scott-Base (see No. 39)

Norway
20. Norway Station

United Kingdom
21. Halley Bay
22. Shackleton
23. South Ice
24. Port Lockroy
25. Deception Island
26. Hope Bay
27. Argentine Islands
28. Admiralty Bay
29. Signy Island
30. Horseshoe Island
31. View Point (Duse Bay)
32. Detaille Island
33. Prospect Point

United States
34. Ellsworth
35. Amundsen-Scott
36. Byrd
37. Little America V
38. McMurdo Sound
38A. Beardmore (summer only)
39. Hallett (with New Zealand)
40. Wilkes

U.S.S.R.
41. Mirniy
42. Oazis
43. Pionerskaya
44. Vostok
44A. Vostok I
45. Komsomolskaya
46. Sovetskaya
46A. Lazarev (since March, 1959)
○   Airborne Traverse Stations
●   I.G.Y. Stations

Antarctica.

at the coast by their becoming glacier tongues afloat. Examples of these are the Denman and Scott ice tongues in longitude 100° E. and the Ninnis and Mertz ice tongues in longitude 147° E. The ice streams can be traced inland on to the main ice sheet as shallow depressions often showing by their heavily crevassed margins how their speed of movement is greater than that of their surroundings. Recently the Russian Antarctic parties have discovered one such depression 2,800 feet deep heading towards the Amery ice shelf. Another presumed ice stream which is yet to be proved should lie inland from Cape Denison, feeding the Ninnis and Mertz ice tongues and down which the incredibly powerful katabatic winds described by Mawson must funnel. But as yet no surface valley has been discovered here.

The rock floor below the ice sheet may give it its major surface shapes but the more obvious and immediate minor shapes are in fact created by the winds. On the summit of the Antarctic ice sheet *sastrugi* are developed to a state unknown elsewhere in the world. Lister, the glaciologist on the British trans-Antarctic expedition, mapped the sastrugi in fact, dividing them into groups: three feet in height, two feet, one foot, or less than one foot. From their direction the mean wind direction can be judged and this provides another small clue to the climate of the more inaccessible interior regions.

Lines of ice soundings showing the depth to the rock floor are beginning to appear now on the map of the Antarctic continent, as a result of the very extensive traverses made during and subsequent to the I.G.Y. The map (Fig. 67) shows some of these as reported. Many soundings show the subglacial floor as below sea-level but in Old Antarctica as a whole very few of these points would remain below sea-level if the ice load were to be removed. Essentially, therefore, we can consider Old Antarctica a uniform land mass, albeit with some depressions, covered with a dome of ice.

In Young Antarctica no such dome-shaped pattern exists—rather a sea of thick ice through which rise isolated peaks and ridges, the highest points on the folded mountain ranges of this portion of the continent. Many soundings here reveal the subglacial floor so far below sea-level that it would remain so even without the load of ice, and hence one must presume

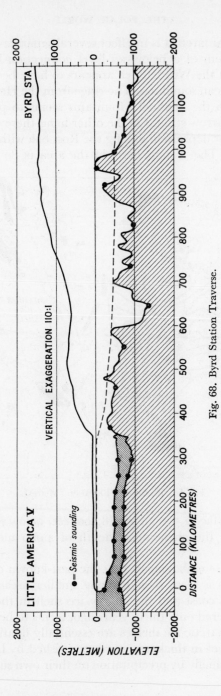

Fig. 68. Byrd Station Traverse.

that Young Antarctica is in effect several separate land masses.

The problem of a below-sea-level connection between the Ross Sea and the Weddell Sea appears to have been solved by recent American soundings. The ridge from the Horlick Mountains through the Sentinel Mountains seems to preclude any but a very narrow strait. On the other hand there now appears to be a major depression linking the Ross Sea with the Bellinghausen Sea. The trough here, in the area of 80° S. 105° W.

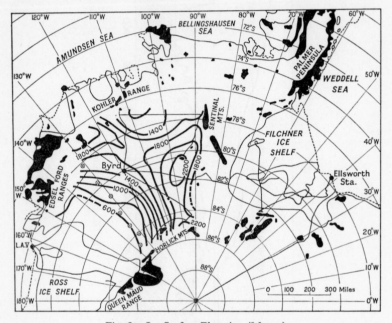

Fig. 69. Ice Surface Elevation (Metres).

has a rock surface 2,500 metres (8,000 feet) below sea-level now covered with the phenomenal depth of 4,000 metres (13,000 feet) of ice.

It is in these embayments that the best-known development of ice shelves is seen, though many smaller areas of ice shelf surround the coast and the Amery ice shelf in the Australian sector discovered only thirty years ago, seems to be the third in size. The Antarctic ice shelves are essentially floating ice up to a thousand feet in thickness, partly nourished by landward ice tongues but chiefly by precipitation on their own surfaces. They appear to need some anchoring points such as the headlands of deep bays or drowned offshore islands and seldom protrude far into deeper water. The Weddell and Ross shelves occur in deep embayments. King George Sound between Grahamland and Alexander Island is a narrow land-enclosed strait. The Shackleton ice shelf is in the lee of the Denman ice tongue with an island anchor, Masson Island. On the Queen Maud Land coast the ice shelf limit joins a series of peninsulas. At the land-

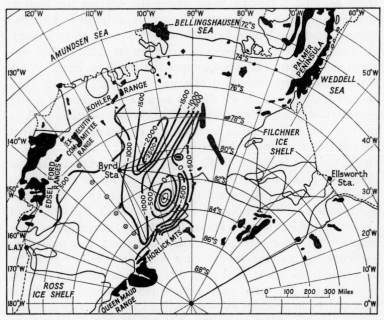

Fig. 70. Rock Surface Elevation (Metres).

ward of the ice shelves it is occasionally possible to recognize the boundary by hinge lines or small tide cracks on which there is slight movement. Here too, sounds can be heard as did Gould on the landward margin of the Ross shelf. He thought at first that the creaking sounds were due to his moving about in the morning and the evening. There tends to be little crevassing if the movement of the main mass of the inland ice and of the shelf is similar, but where ice streams reach the coast much crevassing occurs since the streams drag the ice shelf out faster than it can be replaced at the sides. The seaward margin of an ice shelf is in the main an ice cliff. On the Ross shelf this was given the name, The Great Ice Barrier, by Ross himself. If the shelf is of uniform thickness and is freely floating the height of the cliff gives an indication of the total thickness of the shelf, directly related to the specific gravity, which, since much of it is firn snow, tends to be a great deal less than 0·9. But as Swithinbank has pointed out, the edge may be up-tilted due to an underwater ram where wave action has been considerable, or there may be a sagging front where the edge of the shelf is strongly undercut. It is on these low parts of the shelf that convenient docks have been found for expedition vessels to unload. All the ice shelves are subject to a continuous outward and seaward movement. The average speed of the Ross ice shelf, for instance, is about one-third of a mile per year. Viewed from the air the edge of an ice shelf is seen to be formed of many tear-shaped cracks where eventually icebergs are going to float off into the ocean. These icebergs are of gigantic scale, often tens of miles in linear dimension and many hundreds of feet thick. On the Ross ice shelf, in the neighbourhood of Little America, many studies have been carried out in the various years when it has been occupied and in 1958–9 American glaciologists drilled practically through the shelf, 836 feet out of the estimated 850 feet thickness. They found, somewhat to their surprise, no trace of sea-ice in the drill core, thus providing evidence against the theory that some ice shelves grow by accretion from below. The Ross shelf at Little America consists of something like 1,200 years accumulated snow pressed by its own weight into plastic ever-spreading ice; the yearly addition being something like 20 centimetres (8 inches) of water equivalent. This continual addition to the shelves has buried the previous Little Americas; for instance Little America III, used in 1939–40, was found nineteen years later to be thirty feet below the then snow level. Although many ice shelves occupy areas of comparatively shallow water and must by their very nature be dependent on capes or shoals to prevent them breaking off into the southern ocean, they can cover certain areas of quite deep sea. The very detailed sounding which the Americans have carried out in lengthy traverses across the Ross shelf found at one spot a water depth as great as 4,400 feet. This, however, seems to have been an exceptional hole and the deep area covers an insignificant fraction of the area of the shelf as a whole.

Swithinbank has speculated on the changes that might result in some Antarctic ice shelves with greater or lesser amounts of glacierization. At the present in the case of deep embayments such as are occupied by the Ross, the Weddell, or the Amery shelf, considerable advances and retreats to new stable positions could be postulated, but on the open coast of Queen Maud Land (which he himself investigated) the only anchors for a shelf are off-shore shoals and since the edge of the continental shelf is not far off, no great advance seaward of the present ice shelf edge could take place even with greatly intensified glacierization. But a great increase in land ice volume would withdraw water from the sea itself and thus increase the chances of anchoring shoals.

The plastic character of ice shelves is shown by the conditions which occur when what should be an island (even though now completely ice-covered) appears within its area. Such is the case in the neighbourhood of the Bay of Whales where the various Little America stations were established. Here the Ross shelf ice divides around Roosevelt Island; one arm thereafter pushing on northwards, the other swinging around westwards and eventually impinging in a gigantic pincer movement on the north-flowing ice. Such a contact happened about 1954 closing the bay completely but the continuing process will probably split off one of the arms, re-creating the bay for a period of several decades before it closes once more.

The two great glaciological problems of the Antarctic have been: first, its volume, and secondly, its budget—how much is it accumulating and how much wasting. With regard to the first our knowledge has increased sharply over the last few years with the various long-distance traverse parties and their soundings and we now realize that a much greater average thickness (perhaps over two thousand metres) of ice exists than was previously thought possible. But with regard to the other great problem, whether the ice sheet is accumulating or wasting, the evidence introduced during the I.G.Y. has to date been conflicting. On the accumulation side of the picture we now have a fair amount of evidence. On the main coast of the continent net snow accumulation seems to average about 40 centimetres water equivalent per year,—e.g.

Mirniy　　　63 cm. but McMurdo Sound 16 cm.
Maudheim 30 cm.　　　Vahsel Bay　　　16 cm.

Inland accumulation falls off rapidly, the South Pole station reporting 6 centimetres and the British trans-Antarctic crossing party from pits 8–9 centimetres. Lister (the glaciologist with the latter party) and Loewe have estimated the average for the continent as a whole at 11 centimetres. And this on a total of thirteen million square kilometres.

It is with ablation (wastage) that we come into the realm of much greater speculation. Ablation in the Antarctic is composed of wind drift, evaporation, surface melting, calving of icebergs and undersurface melting of the ice front.

Wind drift was once considered a major factor but although Loewe has calculated that on blizzard days in Terre Adélie 240 tons of snow will pass over each metre of coast-line, he believes the average for the whole continental coast to be only one-thirtieth of this.

Evaporation and surface melting are both very slight— though at places such as the Old Antarctica coast between Mawson and Davis they are locally quite significant.

The last two processes, calving and sub-surface melting are the important ones and the most difficult to measure. These could in fact be combined into a single process did we know the volume of ice that flowed across the true but hidden coast.

Mellor has divided the Antarctic coast-line into three categories and has estimated their proportions of the total.

Ice shelf　　　7,500 km.
Sheet flow　　11,000 km. (the normal ice edge)
Stream flow　 1,500 km. (when ice streams debouch)

Measurements of the seaward velocities of ice shelf vary from between 300 to 500 centimetres per day and may average 400 centimetres. Sheet-flow measurements reveal a mean velocity of only about 4 cm./day whereas ice streams have been recorded as advancing from 30 to 300 centimetres daily and the average may be considered as 100 centimetres. It would appear from this that ice shelves contribute the great proportion of ice wastage by calving, but the thickness of ice streams and of the continental ice margin are still little known.

Also at present unknown is the rate of melting by sea-water below the ice shelves. At Maudheim the sea temperature was found to be 0·3° C. above the freezing-point of its particular salinity, so considerable melting could occur, but the quantitative estimates of its amounts are very variable.

All the estimates that have been made of the total Antarctic ablation come within only about 50 per cent. of the now reasonably known accumulation. Either the figures have a gross error of a factor 2 or the Antarctic ice-cap is increasing. Yet at present there is no indication that world sea-level is falling at a rate of one millimetre a year that the difference would require; rather a corresponding rise is taking place.

Obviously Antarctic glaciologists have much research still on their hands to settle this problem, which is of vital interest to the rest of the world, particularly the coastal world.

The Antarctic land ice has been discussed in some detail because it is the dominant 'landform'. But some bare ground does exist and it is here on the nunataks and 'oases' that local changes in the ice level can be observed. Apart from coastal and interior mountain nunataks there are three comparatively large bare ground areas so far discovered.

The earliest known of these oases are the 'dry valleys' of Victoria Land first described by Priestley and Debenham. Here are two large ice free valleys forty miles or so in length and five miles in width. The area is separated from McMurdo Sound by the Wilson Glacier which blocks the coastal end of the valleys.

In Wright Valley this ice dam is at an altitude of a thousand feet above sea-level and from here a river flows inland for twenty-five miles to Lake Vanda at four hundred feet. Beyond the lake the valley floor rises to two thousand feet in another ten miles and then rapidly to the interior ice plateau. The lake, 250 feet deep, has no outlet and at present evaporation must be balancing inflow. Here at 77° S. latitude a party which spent fifty days in the summer of 1958–9 found a mean temperature of 33° F., ten degrees higher than that recorded on the McMurdo sound coast forty miles away. On two days the shade temperature rose to 47° F. when 'föhn' effect winds were blowing from inland.

The bare rock and scree walls of the five-thousand-foot-deep valleys must experience much higher temperatures in direct sunlight and the biological examination of the region promises to give interesting results.

Bunger's Oasis discovered on expedition 'High Jump' in 1946-7 is about 250 square miles in extent. It is a comparatively flat area of ridges and shallow depressions, some of the latter filled with brackish lakes, whose level drops rapidly in summer time. For some reason the continental ice flows around this area which Shumskiy believes may have been ice free for ten thousand years. Now that it *is* ice free, it is self-perpetuating, radiation being absorbed by the bare ground in the amount of 80-85 per cent., instead of the 10-15 per cent. absorbed by the surrounding ice. And this heating superdries the already dry air so that to 'leeward' of the oasis a zone in which powerful ice surface melting takes place can be traced for thirty miles. Polygonal ground is well developed and there is no evidence of volcanicity which was first believed to be the cause of the ice free area.

Bunger's Oasis is located at 66° S. almost as low a latitude as the Antarctic continent proper can provide. Two degrees further south and six hundred miles to the east the region of the Vestfold Hills is another area of extensive bare ground and the most genial climate that this frigid continent provides. The coast-line in this section is the one area where the firn line is at an appreciable altitude above sea-level and considerable summer melting occurs.

Even on these slightly summer-warmed lands, however, the vegetation is very scanty. Outside the Grahamland Peninsula flowering plants have yet to be discovered—only algae, mosses and lichens have taken hold. Of the latter some four hundred species have been described and eight species were collected between latitudes 85° and 87°. Lichen growth can sometimes be considerable as witness a miniature 'heath fire' started by a discarded cigarette, described in a recent Russian report.

With so little vegetation it is not surprising that the land fauna is even more limited—only a few insects and rotifers have been discovered. Life belongs to the sea, the land being used for breeding places only and the most Antarctic creature of all, the emperor penguin, even scorns the limited bare ground areas, breeding on the ice itself.

The water around the Antarctic is so rich in phytoplankton that in places it is green in colour and the filter catch smells like freshly mown grass; on this feed the invertebrates which in turn colour the water red. It is this wealth of marine life that forms the food base for the truly Antarctic birds and mammals. Four seals belong to this category and in addition the elephant seal's range extends to the continent itself.

The commonest animal is the Weddell seal—a heavy slug-shaped grey seal up to nine feet in length. Living on fish and squids they are wintering seals which keep open breathing holes through the ice. Young Weddell seals, born in September–October, weigh about sixty pounds at birth and grow to six feet in length within a year, becoming adult in their third year.

Crabeater seals, smaller and lighter in colour, belong more to the pack ice belt. They feed almost entirely on 'krill' (not crabs) and are even more rapid-growing than the Weddell seal.

The Ross seal is extremely rare and occurs solitarily in the pack ice. Its food is chiefly fish and squids and it is probably a wanderer over extensive ocean areas. So is the leopard seal which lives chiefly on other seals and sea birds. Its twelve-foot-long tapering body is magnificently adapted to speed in the water and it has a formidable array of teeth. Its range extends from the margin of the continent to the Falkland Islands and Macquarie Island.

The birds of the Antarctic belong chiefly to the families of the petrels and penguins. The members of the former group that breed in the Antarctic proper are cape pigeons, Wilson petrel, Antarctic fulmar, Antarctic petrel, snow petrel, storm petrel and the Antarctic whale bird or dove petrel. Squids and krill form the bulk of their food but they are voracious scavengers and other birds' eggs and young are favoured meals when available.

It is the penguin that one thinks of as the truly Antarctic bird. Only a few species, however, breed on the continent, the king penguin and gentoo on the Grahamland Peninsula, the

Adélie penguin ubiquitously, and the emperor in occasional colonies, fourteen of which are now known.

The little Adélie winters on the pack ice and breeds in colonies, some of vast size, round the whole coast-line of the continent. Much has been written about this lovable bird and its habits and it has been filmed since the days of Scott's expedition.

The emperor is the creature most adapted to the polar environment. It has a strange breeding cycle, eggs being laid on the fast ice in midwinter and incubated on the parent's feet under a fold of feathered skin in temperatures of 40–60° below zero. The young are then tended until February; when at last fully fledged they are able to take to the water when their breeding place moves out to sea. During all this time one parent at least is starving for weeks at a time. The total emperor population is now estimated at 135,000. One colony discovered by helicopter in December 1958 on Coulman Island in the Ross Sea numbered about fifty thousand alone.

To date there is nothing that can be described as a permanent human population of the continent. Since 1944, however, there have always been men in residence and some of the settlements now give signs of being permanent. This chapter will conclude by describing some of these and their immediate surroundings, starting clockwise from the Weddell Sea area. Four expedition bases were set up here during the I.G.Y. and two were still functioning in 1960. The head of the Weddell Sea consists of an enormous area of shelf ice, the Filchner Shelf, some 450 miles in width extending from Bowman Peninsula in latitude 75° on the Grahamland Peninsula to Vahsel Bay in latitude 78° in the south-east corner. It was to the latter area that various expeditions have pressed from the time of Filchner in 1912. Here within a short distance of each other the bases of Fuchs (named Shackleton), of the Argentinians (named General Belgrano) and of the United States (named Ellsworth) were established. It was the intention to set up the latter station at the west end of the Filchner Shelf in the Bowman Peninsula area, but even with modern ice-breaker assistance this was found impossible. Only the eastern side of the bay gives at all reasonable navigation as the clockwise current pushes the pack ice of the Weddell Sea in ever increasing pressure towards its

32. McMurdo Sound, Ross Sea, Antarctica. *Left*, Scott's hut built in 1901; *centre and right*, winterized tents erected by U.S. "Expedition Deepfreeze", 1957

33. Mawson station, Australian sector of Antarctica (*see Fig. 67 and pp.* 289–290)

34. Antarctica vegetation –
Mastodia and *Caloplaca
elegans* on ice-smoothed
rocks, Goudier Islet

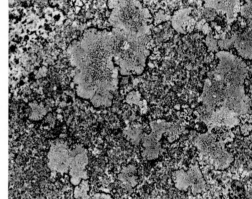

35. Antarctic vegetation – lichens
(two-fifths natural size)
(*see p.* 286)

36. Whale factory ship, showing stern ramp up which
whales are hauled
(*see pp.* 307–310)

western shore. These three bases were built on the shelf ice and although Ellsworth, now handed over to Argentina by the United States, is still in existence, all of them must be considered ephemeral. The edge of the shelf has broken back considerably since it was first discovered in 1912 and further breaks are likely to occur, sending these bases out to sea. During the first period of Fuchs' advanced party residence large quantities of stores were lost from the shelf edge by such a break. It was because of the difficulty of navigation to the foot of the bay that the British I.G.Y. station was established at Halley Bay on the eastern coast, named Coats Land, some two hundred miles north of Vahsel Bay. But this station, although still in occupation is on the shelf ice, albeit one and a half miles in from the existing edge. From this point for many miles to the eastward, in fact throughout most of Queen Maud Land, there are few points of real land on which permanent bases can be established. Maudheim was on the shelf ice, so too is the Norwegian I.G.Y. station on longitude 2° W., although this was built twenty miles back from the ice edge. The whole coast of Queen Maud Land is a series of shelves held together by projecting capes themselves thickly ice-covered and yielding vertical ice cliffs at their seaward edges. Inland the country rises rapidly and we have here one of the greatest mountain regions of Old Antarctica. These mountains rise to at least ten thousand feet in altitude and present with their steeply sloping faces a quite appreciable amount of bare ground, albeit of nunatak character. Much of this coast has proved extremely difficult of access through the pack ice belt. This was definitely the case with the establishment towards the east of Queen Maud Land of the Japanese I.G.Y. station known as Syowa. After strenuous efforts it was set up on Ongul Island in longitude 39° 40° E., but the first relief ship was unable to approach the station at all and the personnel had to be evacuated by air.

East from here comes the long Australian sector of Old Antarctica's coast-line and here a change comes over the character of the coast-line. Far more rocky points and islands are exposed by the inland ice which seems to be much more channelled into ice streams than was the case farther to the west. There has been therefore, the opportunity to establish bases on dry land, and such is the case with the oldest and

U

probably most permanent of the Australian bases named Mawson. This is at the head of a rocky horseshoe-shaped harbour, a perfect haven in fact were it not for the fact that the sea bottom is such smooth glaciated rock that it affords almost no holding for an anchor. First established in 1954, Mawson counted in 1960 some twenty-six buildings and has been continuously occupied during this period. No less than four emperor rookeries have been discovered during this time by far-ranging dog teams and other exploration parties from Mawson. Journeys have been made into the Prince Charles Mountains inland which project up to a thousand feet from a base of six thousand to seven thousand altitude ice. To the east of Mawson comes the large indentation known as the Amery ice shelf which is probably the third most important of such shelves on the continent and is contributed to by an immense ice stream flowing from somewhere deep in the continent behind. On the eastern side of this embayment in the Vestfold Hills area is Australia's other Antarctic station, Davis, a much smaller one. This is one of the largest ice free areas on the continent and its coast is composed chiefly of bouldery moraines. Because of these, great difficulty was found in moving stores up to the station, situated some eighty feet above sea-level.

Further east again is the very large base established by the Soviet Union in 1956, known as Mirniy, which is composed of some fifty buildings and where over a hundred men have wintered. From Mirniy itself the main continental ice slopes up in a smooth convex curve but both to east and to west of the base are two very large shelf-ice areas, one known as the West shelf ice and the other as the Shackleton. Both of these have shown great changes in their size and shape in the period from 1937 to 1957 when they were surveyed with reasonable accuracy. The Shackleton ice shelf to the east of Mirniy is itself divided in two by a great complex of ice streams, the chief of which is named the Denman. On the eastern side of this between it and the Shackleton ice shelf is situated the Bunger Oasis, now also the site of a Soviet station recently handed over to Poland. Various islands appear off this stretch of coast, Drygalski Island is some fifty miles out to sea from Mirniy, and the Shackleton shelf is itself held in place by several large islands. In the next bay to the east of the Shackleton ice shelf in longitude 110° E. was situated the base site (now no longer occupied) of the United States, known as Wilkes.

The coast-line of Old Antarctica continues to the east, roughly following the Antarctic Circle until Adélie Land, the thin strip of territory claimed by France, is reached, where it begins to trend into a slightly more southerly latitude. On the coast of Adélie Land the French have had a more or less permanent base for the past ten years but its site has been moved from the original Port Martin, which was destroyed by fire, to the Isle des Petrels where the French I.G.Y. station was set up. On the Isle des Petrels, close to Pointe Géologie, where the first rocks were collected from the Antarctic continent, the weather has proved to be slightly better than at Port Martin and better still than at Cape Denison, slightly further to the east, which was Mawson's base in 1911–14. But the whole coast-line of Adélie Land appears to be subjected to the most powerful winds of the whole continent. Although the French set up a temporary station some two hundred miles inland during the I.G.Y. they have not yet been able to prove satisfactorily the existence of the assumed depression in the inland ice which funnels these fearful winds. Eastwards of the French base comes a short sector of the continental coast-line which has seldom been seen or landed on. Then there is a sharp turn in the coast-line at the entrance of the Ross Sea at Cape Adare and here we reach much better-known territory. It was originally the intention of New Zealand and the United States to set up a joint station at Cape Adare but a more suitable site was eventually found seventy miles to the south. The site was already occupied and eight thousand penguins had to be forcibly ejected from the small spit of volcanic ash and sand on which the station was built.

The whole western coast of the Ross Sea is formed by the great mountain barrier of Victoria Land through which flow glaciers from the inland plateau, or where occasionally are situated the dry valleys described earlier. At the foot of the bay we reach the well-frequented McMurdo Sound where Ross Island is joined to the northern edge of the Ross ice shelf. This is the classic territory which has seen so many bases in the past and many again in the recent decade. Here was established at Pram Point, Scott Base, Hillary's end of the trans-Antarctic expedition, New Zealand's I.G.Y. base which is still in operation. This is on solid land on the southern corner of Ross Island, an impressive piece of land which rises to the twin peaks of Mount Erebus and Terror, the former a still highly active thirteen-thousand-foot volcano. Only a few miles away from Scott Base was the American air base used to supply the other three American I.G.Y. bases in the area. The actual airfield was established on the bay ice of McMurdo Sound and tended to be out of operation for at least two months of the year. Many efforts have been made to establish a more permanent airfield on some of the extensive ground that the shores of McMurdo Sound provide. The latest has been across on the western side of the sound at Marble Point where the first major airfield of the Antarctic will perhaps be developed. The eastern point of Ross Island, Cape Crozier, is famous as the site of the first emperor penguin rookery discovered and visited in midwinter by Dr. Wilson on Scott's last expedition. From here the immense area of the Ross shelf ice extends eastwards as far as Marie Byrd Land, broken only by perennial bays, such as Balloon Bight, from which Scott prospected the shelf ice surface from a captive balloon, the Bay of Whales, now temporarily extinct, and Kainan Bay on which Little America V was built for the I.G.Y. This most frequently occupied area is now once more abandoned. All the base sites in this area have been situated on the shelf ice which not only moves out to sea and breaks off but eventually buries any building under its steady accumulation of snow, so it is unlikely that any really permanent settlement will be established here. Further to the east comes the very inhospitable coast of the American sector extending from here as far as the Grahamland Peninsula. This has long been the most difficult coast to approach in the whole of the Antarctic and its very limits, the bays and capes, were unknown until a dozen years ago. It is composed of extensive ice shelves separated by highly mountainous peninsular lands and divided into two large though shallow indentations, the Amundsen and Bellingshausen seas. Off its coast, some hundreds of miles to the north lies the lonely island Peter I, discovered by Bellingshausen in 1819, and perhaps soon to be reoccupied as a weather station.

Although Wilkins' assertion that the Grahamland Peninsula was an island has now been disproved there is no doubt that geographically this peninsula is quite different from the remainder of the Antarctic. It extends to a much more northerly latitude than any other Antarctic land. Certainly on its western coast temperatures are more equable and its glacial metabolism is a great deal higher. On the western side at its root it is connected by areas of shelf ice to Alexander I island and to Charcot Island. Much of its coast even into quite northerly latitudes (64°), is also a shelf-ice area, the Larsen ice shelf; but the remainder of the coasts, although heavily glacier-covered, are free of shelf ice since here the firn line at last reaches an altitude somewhat above sea-level. The north-western coast is characterized by a great number of offshore islands of varying size, many of them much ice-covered and exhibiting a curious writing desk appearance since the ice-cap on each small island tends to slope strongly upwards to the south, the heaviest ice carapace being on the side of the island away from the sun. The backbone of the peninsula and indeed many of the offshore islands are highly mountainous with rocky peaks and cliff faces showing through the all-encompassing ice; but bare ground at low altitude is still at a premium. Many small areas of bare ground do exist, and on these a number of settlements have been established by the three nations who compete for the sovereignty of the peninsula. These posts have all been situated on the north-western coast down as far as latitude $68\frac{1}{2}°$ or on the many offshore islands with which here we include the South Shetland Islands, paralleling the northern tip of the peninsula. No less than seventeen of these stations were occupied during the I.G.Y. by Britain, Argentina and Chile. The British posts have been set up only partly as meteorological stations and partly as bases from which the topographical and geological exploration of the area as a whole can be carried out by dog team. There has, therefore, been a considerable shifting of bases and only certain of them can be considered at all permanent. The same is true of the South American bases. All of them have been established to a great extent in an attempt to prove sovereignty with the usual paraphernalia of Post Offices and postage stamps.

A large portion of the northern part of the peninsula from Adelaide Island northward has been accurately surveyed by the Falkland Islands Dependency Aerial Survey expeditions of 1955 onwards, but much yet remains to be known about the southern and wider part of the peninsula extending from latitude 68° S. From this latitude onwards access by sea on the west coast is impossible and this is true of almost the whole eastern Weddell Sea coast as far as the extreme tip of the peninsula where Nordenskiöld's first expedition wintered. One of the most permanent settlements is that on Deception Island. This is a breached volcanic crater in the South Shetland group where all three nations have established huts and occupancy dates off and on since the early part of this century. One can only hope the permanency of this station is not destroyed by natural means, for is is by no means certain that Deception Island is volcanically dead.

In this rapid geographical tour of the Antarctic continent we have stressed the settlements, some of them very ephemeral in character, which have been established. It is only around these as their occupancy lengthens that detailed geographical knowledge is gradually appearing and some of the curious problems of the continent are being solved. Between and around these isolated settlements we have yet only begun to sketch in the geographical features of this immense land.

There has been considerable speculation as to what human use Antarctica can be put. Now that long-range aircraft have been flying regularly from New Zealand to McMurdo Sound the possibility of trans-Antarctic flying, linking the large capitals of the southern hemisphere, is beginning to open up. At Marble Point on McMurdo Sound the Americans are now constructing a large airfield on land, which is essential if such communications do develop. As yet a suitable site for a similar land base airfield has not been discovered in the Australian sector but one here in this locality would do a lot to open up transpolar flying. It is important to maintain meteorological stations on the continent, but the strategic value of this land is doubtful although the Grahamland Peninsula could be important navally. As is the case with the Arctic, and even more so in this inhospitable environment, economic mineral deposits as yet undiscovered would have to be extremely rich to be worth the cost of their extraction, but there is little doubt that this continent does possess minerals, many of them as yet hidden under thousands of feet of ice. Discussions have been held on the value of the Antarctic as a giant refrigerator for storing surplus food from the granaries of the world. As Professor Debenham has pointed out, the storage of grain, the main perennial surplus of the world's food supplies, does not require low temperature. Fats on the other hand, do and it is just possible that a fat surplus storage might be reasonably established in the imperishable conditions which the Antarctic provides. The most lively future that one can see for the Antarctic is as a field for international scientific co-operation under the aegis of the United Nations. The I.G.Y. has already shown the way to this co-operation which over-rode a great many of the political suspicions established elsewhere in the world and the recent treaty concluded in Washington in late 1959 is a hopeful sign that this co-operation will be continued.

FURTHER READING

Lister, H., *Glaciology*, Vol. 5, Transantarctic Expedition, London, 1960.

Mellor, M., 'Mass Balance Studies in Antarctica', *J. Glaciology*, 3, (1959), p. 522.

Mercer, J. H., 'Glacier Variations in the Antarctic', Glac. notes, No. 11, Am. Geog. Soc., 1962.

Simpson, F. A. (editor), *The Antarctic Today*, New Zealand Ant. Soc., Wellington, 1952.

Swithinbank, C., *Glaciology*, Vol. 3, British Norvegian Swedish Antarctic Expedition, Oslo Norsk Polarinstitutt, 1957.

Chapter 17

METEOROLOGY AND CLIMATE OF THE ANTARCTIC

IT is only in the last few years that we are beginning to get a picture of the general circulation of the atmosphere in the Antarctic. Prior to this time we had some climatic statistics over one or two winters from the major polar expeditions and a few scattered meteorological stations in comparatively low latitudes. The first of these, continuously occupied, was that of Laurie Island from 1905 onwards, but Grytviken in South Georgia came into being only a year later. Only in the decade of the fifties have there been established on the continent meteorological stations which can be considered reasonably permanent and from which climatic statistics are beginning to emerge. This climate can be summed up in two brief words: cold and stormy. On the continent's surface have now been recorded the lowest temperatures of anywhere on earth and in the high latitudes surrounding the continent we have apparently some of the lowest mean sea-level pressures. This mean pressure distribution is on the whole symmetrical around this most symmetrical of our continents. Three main latitudinal belts can be distinguished:

(1) The high-pressure areas of the 30°s—in the Eastern Pacific, off the River Plate, in the Atlantic and Indian Oceans and over southern Australia.

(2) The low-pressure areas off the continental shore which form an almost continuous belt between latitudes 60° and 70° S.

(3) The high-pressure area over the continent itself in the region of latitude 80° S. (but care must be exercised over the meaning of 'mean sea-level pressure' where the land rises to nine thousand or ten thousand feet).

This average pressure pattern results in a sharp difference in the wind directions off the Antarctic coast. Immediately on the coast the tendency is for easterly winds, which prevail round practically the entire perimeter with the exception of the western side of the Grahamland Peninsula. Further north, between the low-pressure and high-pressure areas the winds are westerly. The areas of low mean pressure are determined by continual travelling cyclones around these latitudes. These are particularly frequent west and north-east of Grahamland, in longitudes 10° to 30° E., longitudes 70° to 100° E. and in the outer part of the Ross Sea. Over the continent the weak anticyclone produces generally out-flowing winds east to south-east near the coast. It seems seldom as highly developed as on northern hemisphere land masses and the effects of it are soon lost out over the ocean. Where very high pressures have been observed in the Antarctic they have usually been caused by 'blocking anticyclones' developed towards the south from the sub-tropical anticyclone belt in the winter. These when they occur are warm highs with the anticyclonic circulation extending up into the stratosphere. The anticyclone of the Antarctic with its outflowing katabatic winds is a real enough phenomenon but is by no means so invariable as W. H. Hobbs originally postulated. Depressions can and do cross the coast as well as much more frequently they cross the peninsula of Grahamland, and the wind circulation of these systems extends at least as high as the ice plateau giving gales at all altitudes and bringing precipitation. Recently it seems that evidence has been established for a major cyclone track from the Ross Sea through Marie Byrd Land to the Weddell Sea. Precipitation brought with these depressions is almost entirely snow which is difficult to measure except by its accumulation on the ground, yet rain has been recorded in all months of the year in Grahamland and, in fact, was recorded in mid-May at Wilkes Station on the Australian coast section, when the temperature rose above freezing for three days and even touched 40° F. Overcast skies with alto-stratus clouds have been frequently met with on the plateau during snowfalls. The frequency of low-pressure westerly winds and cyclonic situations seems to be higher in winter than in summer. Even at Little America there has been recorded a high percentage (30) of westerly winds over the twelve-month period, 1934–5.

Whereas cyclones and anticyclones can penetrate to the

continent there are long periods of very slack atmospheric circulation. Here the orographical control becomes important. Katabatic winds on the surface are funnelled down the slope and the dense cold air drains off the ice-cap. Undoubtedly the strongest developed high-pressure area is over central Old Antarctica. Here clear skies, light winds and strong outgoing radiation make this the coldest place on earth. In August 1958, the Russians at Sovietskaya Station recorded a surface air temperature of −124° F. (−86° C.). A few weeks earlier at the South Pole on 16 July 1958, the Americans had recorded −135° F. (−93° C.) from a meteorological balloon thirteen miles above the surface, the lowest temperature ever recorded in the earth's atmosphere. During anticyclonic conditions there are pronounced temperature inversions. On 17 September 1957 the surface temperature at the South Pole was −101° F. (−74° C.), at 10 metres it was −74° F. (−59° C.), and at 430 metres, −29° F. (−34° C.) falling again above this. These immensely low temperatures are, of course, the result of the presence in high latitude of high and entirely ice-covered land, but the Antarctic continent as a whole lies just south of the critical latitude at which summer heating could be of importance.

Climatic statistics in the Antarctic are still very sketchy. Roughly speaking there is a belt of stations which are near the Antarctic Circle, e.g. in the Grahamland Peninsula and on much of the coast of Old Antarctica, to Cape Adare. Here the warmest month is just plus or minus freezing-point and the coldest month slightly below zero F. (−20° C.), with a mean annual temperature +10° to +12° F. (−11° or −12° C.). At the base of the Ross Sea in the high 70°s of latitude it is, as might be expected, much colder. Little America has a warmest month of 23° F. (−5° C.) and a coldest of −36° F. (−38° C.); McMurdo Sound, 25° F. and −15° F. (−4° and −26° C.). On the plateau we have the means of determining mean annual temperature before climatic stations are long established, by borings in the ice. Here mean temperatures range from −30° to −60° and the summer temperature, that of the warmest month, is equivalent to midwinter temperatures in the Arctic.

Throughout most of the Antarctic region precipitation is almost entirely in the form of snow. This averages perhaps 30 to 40 centimetres rain equivalent on the coasts and a quarter of this figure on the plateau. Even at sea in summer south of latitude 55° most precipitation is in the form of snow adding to the volume of the pack ice and increasing the ice shelves.

Yet owing to the great cold the continent's air is essentially dry and some spectacular effects of preservation have been observed. The base huts of expeditions of fifty or more years show no sign of decay and at Hallett a one-foot-thick deposit of dried penguins has been accumulating over an estimated 1,200 years.

Dry, but windy. The Antarctic on the whole is a windier region than the Arctic; on the plateau sastrugi build up to four feet in height and nowhere in the world can match the Port Martin–Cape Denison coast where winds average forty knots for the year with 335 days of gale noted in 1951.

FURTHER READING

Antarctic Meteorology, Symposium at Melbourne, Pergamon Press Inc., New York, 1960.
Rooy, M. P. van, *Meterology of the Antarctic*, Pretoria, Weather Bureau, 1957.
U.S. Hydrographic Office, *Oceanographic Atlas of the Polar Seas*, Part 1, 1957.

Chapter 18

THE ANTARCTIC SEAS

WE must include the surrounding seas in a survey of the Antarctic for here is the basis of almost all life in this inhospitable region, and, to date, the only economic advantage that man has gained from its penetration. But these very seas have

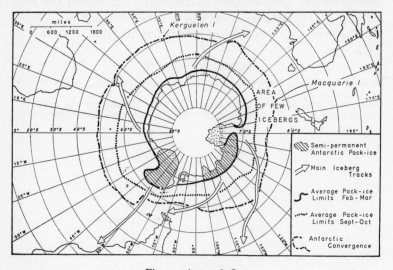

Fig. 71. Antarctic Ice.

proved a barrier to access. The unique fetch of the westerlies, infinite apart from the partial break provided by the Scotia Island Arc, results in the 'roaring forties and furious fifties', where the greatest waves in the world have been observed.

At latitude 50° S. the first icebergs will probably be seen and sometimes these, representing calvings from wide areas of shelf ice, are of island size with linear dimensions up to scores of miles. Each winter (or spring, rather) the pack ice belt is at a maximum (see Fig. 71) and even in the late Antarctic summer the withdrawal of the pack ice leaves many stretches of the coast encumbered and hard of access. Only to the western shore of the Ross Sea is a mean condition of ice free access to be expected. To the east of the Ross Sea and in the major part of the Weddell Sea lie near-permanent pack-ice areas equivalent to the permanent pack of the North Polar Sea. Yet this pack ice is not such a tough adversary as its northern counterpart, for two reasons. First it is of lesser density since much of its upper layers are of recent snow; secondly it is continually drifting with a northward component into regions of greater elbow room. This is more true in summer than in winter when there appears to be a tendency for the pack ice to bind closely around the continent.

In addition to the northward spread, the pack ice comes under the influence of the opposed prevailing wind-caused currents—the East Wind Drift south of 65° (and hence very close to much of the Old Antarctica shores) and the West Wind Drift in more northerly latitudes. In the Weddell Sea the ice drift is controlled by the clockwise current with a component against the Grahamland shore. Hence it is congested against the coast and becomes much rafted and heavier. It was in this area that the *Endurance* was crushed whereas, further east, the *Deutschland*, though similarly beset, was spared. From the eastern tip of the peninsula the ice plumes out to the east under the West Wind Drift influence, carrying a lobe of ice as far as 30° E. longitude in December and blocking the whole Weddell Sea approach west of 30° W. longitude even at its minimum extent in March.

In the eastern Pacific area off the coasts of Young Antarctica the ice edge at all seasons lies in a rather high latitude and varies little throughout the year. This seems to be a region of slack circulation and negligible currents so the ice is packed more tightly here than on the other sections of the open continental coast.

The ice-loaded surface layer of water corresponds to the cold surface layer of the North Polar Ocean. The physical oceanography of the Antarctic seas can be simplified in the diagram on page 302.

The surface temperature rises from south to north, not uniformly, but in two sharp steps at the Antarctic convergence

and the sub-tropical convergence. The Antarctic surface water
near the continent has a temperature in summer only a little
above the freezing-point for its salinity (less than 34%). At
the Antarctic convergence it varies from 0° to 3·5° C. The
thickness of the layer is least (70 metres) at the boundary
between the East and West Wind Drifts and thickens slightly
both north and south of this.

Below it comes a layer of warmer, highly saline water which
drifts southward to compensate for the northward moving surface layer. Finally comes a cold saline bottom layer, the major
origin of which seems to be the Weddell Sea. Only this lowest

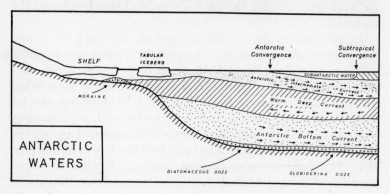

Fig. 72.

layer is interfered with by any rises in the ocean floor and this
negligibly, unlike the North Polar basin.

The Antarctic surface layer has a high concentration of CO_2
and other nutrient salts (phosphates and nitrates) and, as at
the Arctic ice margin, there is a spectacular development in
summer of phytoplankton and animal plankton forms. These
latter tend to be animals with siliceous rather than with carbon-
ate shells and so the bottom deposits of the Antarctic seas consist of diatomaceous muds together with many coarse rock
fragments transported by floating ice, and glacially derived
silts. Some areas of terrigenous muds surround the volcanic
island areas, and a well defined boundary is observable at the
convergence, when bottom deposits become rapidly more lime-
rich.

The most important small animal feeding on the proliferation of diatoms in the Antarctic water is the crustacean Euphausia known to the whalers as 'krill'. Four species of Euphausia occur, the one commonest south of the pack ice margin being *Euphausia superba*. This forms almost the sole food of the large fin whales but fish, crabeater seals and emperor penguins also devour it as do the squids which, in turn, form the food of sperm whales and elephant seals.

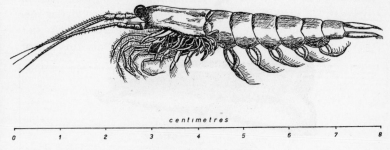

centimetres

0	1	2	3	4	5	6	7	8

Fig. 73. *Euphausia superba.*

On this minute but prolific life in the Antarctic seas has been built an important world industry—the only one, in fact, that exists in the deep seas—the pelagic whaling industry.

In the long and fluctuating history of this pursuit there have, in fact, been several distinct industries, dependent on the kind of whale sought and the growth of catching technique. To understand this it is necessary to examine briefly some of the characteristics of the order Cetacea (see Chapter 6).

The whale, being a warm-blooded, air-breathing mammal, requires to insulate itself against the cold waters in which it spends so much of its time by an even more tremendous layer of fat than other sea mammals. It is this fat (blubber), up to twenty tons per animal or one-fifth of its weight, that man has sought. Along with other animal and vegetable fats, it formed, until 1800 (coal gas) and 1869 (kerosene), one of the only products available for lighting. Of recent years it has again played an important part in the fats and oil trade, being used in margarine and soap. In addition, the 'whalebone' whales have up to a ton weight of 'whalebone' or baleen, long plates of a horny material suspended from the upper jaw. The inner edges of these plates are frayed and they act as a sieve to catch the crustacean whale food when the chunk of ocean that the whale's mouth has engulfed is expelled. The right whales had particularly long plates of baleen which, being springy, was in great

Humpback

Right

Sperm

Blue

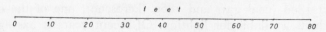

f e e t
0   10   20   30   40   50   60   70   80

Fig. 74. Main Types of Whale.

demand for making ribs of umbrellas, corsets, or stiffeners for collars.

The right whales, first hunted in mediaeval times by the

Basques, whose skills (and some linguistic terms, e.g. harpoon) were adopted after tuition by the Dutch and British and some American whalers in Arctic seas, are slow-moving and float when killed. They could therefore be approached by sailing vessel and even rowing boat and towed ashore or to a vessel's side when captured.

So could the sperm whale which lives chiefly in tropical waters and possesses, in addition to its normal blubber covering, a reservoir of special clear oil, spermaceti, in its vast head. Moby Dick was a sperm whale and this was the main quarry of the great New England fleet which flourished in the first half of the nineteenth century and employed up to seventy thousand men in 1850.

The members of the third group, the family Balaenopteridae, or fin whales, are infinitely speedier and sink when killed. Their pursuit was virtually impossible, therefore, until steam vessels could match their pace (up to sixteen knots) and the technique of rapid inflation of the carcass by use of air pumps was developed.

It is these fin whales that have formed the industry of Antarctic seas together with those sperm whales which left their main grounds and moved to cooler waters. There are four main species of the fin whales:

1. Humpback whales. These ungainly creatures, though faster than the right whales, are slow compared to the next three species, the rorquals. Their maximum length is about fifty feet but they have a very high oil yield for their weight. They are distinguished by knobbly projections around their snout and very long flippers with serrated leading edges.
2. Sei whales, the smallest of the rorquals, are similar in size to the humpbacks but much more streamlined in shape and with a lesser oil content.
3. Fin whales, now the commonest in Antarctic seas, attain lengths up to eighty feet and have differing colours on right and left sides of the jaw. As with all the rorquals, they have long grooves extending half-way back from the mouth on the body's underside.
4. The blue whale, the largest mammal of all times, grows up to a hundred feet in length and has a large oil yield. It is

W

normally a slaty blue in colour but often diatoms accumulate to such a degree on its belly that it is stained yellow, hence the alternative name 'sulphur bottom'. It has a much smaller dorsal fin than the fin whale.

These whales concentrate in certain areas of the Antarctic waters for summer feeding where their main food, the Euphausia

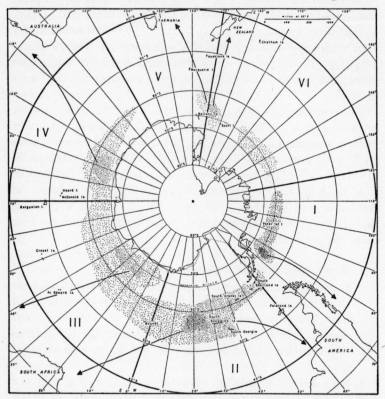

Fig. 75. Whale Concentrations, Migration Routes and International Whaling Sectors.

(krill) is thickest. During this period of gorging they put on fat rapidly (October to April). Then, like leviathans of industry, they spend the winter on a tropical cruise in search of relaxation. Eating nothing during this six-month mating and breeding season, they use up their fat reserves and start the next Antarctic summer lean again.

We have seen in earlier chapters how the right whale industry of Arctic seas rose and fell, over-hunting causing continual shifts in the areas of pursuit. The final diminution of stocks everywhere coincided with a drop in oil prices after the development of kerosene through the latter half of the nineteenth century. Another blow was the development of a substitute material for baleen in 1906 followed soon by the emancipation of the human female form from corsets.

But there remained the great stock of fin whales, too fast to be touched by the whaling methods of the times, until the invention by Sven Foyn in 1868, of his explosive-headed harpoon gun fitted to the bow of a small but speedy steam vessel. For thirty-five years Norway was the base of a revived whaling industry using and perfecting Foyn's methods and accounting for an average of five hundred whales a year. In the 1890s the world became aware that fin whale stocks in the Antarctic seas were prodigious compared with the lesser number accessible from Norwegian shores.

Then a curious combination of circumstances precipitated Antarctic whaling. In 1904 the Norwegian Government yielded to pressure from fishermen who claimed that whaling was disturbing the coastal fishing areas and forbade all whaling from Norwegian ports. At the same time Captain C. A. Larsen, a whaling captain who had commanded the vessel *Antarctic* of the Swedish National Expedition, was being fêted in Buenos Aires after his dramatic rescue. He suggested the formation of a company for exploiting the rich seas off South Georgia, and Argentinian capitalists subscribed on the spot to found Compania Argentina de Pesca with its base at Grytviken in South Georgia.

For the next twenty years southern whaling developed either from shore bases such as South Georgia or Kerguelen or from factory (processing) ships at anchor in some sheltered locality, one of the favoured ones being Deception Island in the South Shetlands. Truly pelagic whaling was introduced in 1924–5 again by Captain Larsen, with the first factory vessel designed with a slipway to process whales on the high seas. Meanwhile, the discovery of the hydrogenation process enabled whale oil to be purified and converted to a solid fat, making the product highly desirable to the soap trade (*see Plate 36*).

The subsequent history of the pelagic Antarctic whaling

industry has been a growth in size, numbers and efficiency of the factory ship with its attendant 'catchers' and the growing concern over whale stocks with regulation of the annual catch. The past history of whaling failures due to over-fishing is all too well known to the operators of the twentieth century, and there is a keen desire to continue in perpetuity an industry which employs over ten thousand men and is worth between £25 and £30 million a year.

For sound conservation measures for any wild animal stock it is necessary to know many factors—birth rate, maturing age, migration habits, among others. Much vital work on these lines has been done by the two nations most intimately concerned with the industry—Britain and Norway. The British research, undertaken by the Discovery Committee, has been a continuing programme since 1925, financed from the returns of whaling licences and export duties from South Georgia. Norway has inspired a large whale-marking programme as well as biological research on her factory ships and has concentrated particularly on statistical investigation.

From these researches it is now realized that the period of gestation of fin whales is about a year. Two years elapse between successive offspring of any female and births are usually single. In less than three years the whale is sexually mature by which time it has tripled its birth length. An empirical decision resulting from this knowledge is that the annual take of whales should be less than one seventh of the population. This is not true of the sperm whale in polar waters. Such animals are almost exclusively older males 'retired' from the herd (the sperm whale, unlike the fin whale, is polygamous). So there need be little restriction on the take of cold-water sperm whales, called Emperors by the old-time whalers, since these have no influence on future stocks.

Another discovery from the widespread research on whales is that there are five main areas of concentration (see map, Fig. 75) from each of which the whales migrate in fairly fixed paths with little mixing with the population of other areas. For conservation purposes, therefore, each area should be treated separately. The humpback whales, incidentally, show a tendency to migrate more closely along shore, hence are particularly vulnerable to the shore-based whaling stations from for instance, the coasts of South Africa and Australia.

As early as 1929 Norway began to impose regulations on her own fleet designed to conserve stocks. Then in 1931 was held an international convention at Geneva attended by the twenty-six chief whaling nations, which made it illegal to catch all right whales or calves or suckling cows of any species. All nations agreed to submit returns to a central office in Oslo (now Sandefjord) and to restrict the total catch to a certain number of 'Blue Whale Units'. This unit is based on the average oil yield from each species and after some adjustment now reads:

$$1 \text{ Blue Whale Unit} = 1 \text{ Blue Whale} = 2 \text{ Fin Whales} = 2\tfrac{1}{2}$$
$$\text{Humpback} = 6 \text{ Sei.}$$

Various subsequent international meetings were held and have been annual since the Washington meeting of 1946. The main regulations have been summarized below:

1937 Minimum size limits set for each species.
      Open season fixed at 8 December to 7 March.
      Shore stations to operate for six months only.
      No pelagic whaling north of latitude 40° S.
1938 Total protection of humpbacks.
      Pacific Sector (70° W. to 160° W., Zones I and VI) declared a sanctuary.
1944 16,000 Blue Whale Units limit set.
1949 1,250 Humpbacks permitted annually for two years.
1951 Opening date delayed to 2 January.
1956 Pacific sanctuary opened for three years.
1957 Season fixed at 7 January to 16 March.
1958 Season fixed at 7 January to 7 April.
      14,500 Blue Whale Units now limit.
      Humpbacks protected in Zone II.

One can note from the above selected regulations the concern for humpbacks, the success of allowing stocks in a 'sanctuary' to rise again, the steady diminution of the allowed total kill. Alterations in the date of the season show the desire for gaining a return of oil from fewer but larger whales since the animals put on fat rapidly once they start their southern dinner, and a whale in March may yield twice the oil it would have in December. The closing date is of less importance. Before this,

the agreed limit has usually been approached and with daily
returns wirelessed to Sandefjord the whole international industry
is abruptly halted by a voice from a little Norwegian coastal
town.

Despite these serious attempts to establish and retain a
steadily producing industry, whaling has had its ups and downs
and crises. A huge take in 1930–1 occurred at the onset of the
world economic depression and ·tumbling commodity prices.
Much of the oil remained unsold and next season Norway's
entire fleet stayed idle. The Second World War caused a
diminution to nearly nil returns, since many factory ships were
used as tankers and several Norwegian ships actually operating
were captured by armed German raiders. Others were sunk
and, in 1945, a slow start was made again with a different
national composition of the fleet as the table below shows. But it
is still overwhelmingly a Norse operation, Norwegians forming
a large proportion of other flag's crews and even working at
shore stations as widely flung as Newfoundland and French
West Africa during the off season for pelagic whaling. If a
woman wishes to see much of her husband she doesn't marry a
whaler.

Whaling Factory Ships in the Antarctic

Season	1938/9	1945/6	1946/7	1951/2	1957/8
Norway . . .	12	6	7	10	9
Great Britain . .	9	2	3	3	3
South Africa . .	—	1	1	1	—
Netherlands . .	—	—	1	1	1
U.S.S.R. . . .	—	—	1	1	1
Japan	6	—	2	3	6
Germany . . .	5	—	—	—	—
Panama . . .	1	—	—	1	—
United States . .	1	—	—	—	—
Total	34	9	15	20	20

Many advanced techniques have now been applied to the
industry. Factory ships have increased in size and efficiency in
processing and using more of the whale's carcass. The largest
vessel in 1958 was the Dutch *Willem Barendsz* of forty-four
thousand tons. Catchers, often a dozen to a factory, have
increased in size and speed. Asdic and helicopters are now used
to spot and follow whales. The Sven Foyn explosive harpoon
gun is still the basic weapon but other more humane and less

damaging methods have been tried and may supersede it. Electrocution is one of these, first used by German whalers.

But the most advanced technique is the international limitation agreement. Although this has had to withstand many strains and objections, it is still working and denying as it does the dictum 'There is no *profit* in the world's future only in its present', is an example to the world in which those interested in the polar regions can take great pride and hope.

FURTHER READING

Bertram, G. C. L., 'Depletion of Marine Vertebrate Populations', *Jour. Soc. Preservation of the fauna of the Empire*, Pt. LVIII, pp. 33-41.
Budker, P., *Whales and Whaling*, London, 1958.
Slijper, E. J., *Whales* (English translation), Hutchinson, London, 1962.

Chapter 19

THE SUB-ANTARCTIC ISLANDS

IN the southern ocean which was discussed in the previous chapter are a few islands and island groups which at least in their summer temperature values qualify as polar. They are lonely specks in the world's stormiest seas, sometimes havens for olden-times vessels, more often graves.

They are incomparable with any islands in the northern hemisphere since, latitude for latitude, there is a ten- to twenty-degree difference in their temperature régimes. Even Jan Mayen and Bear Island (Bjornøya) with their much lower winter temperatures are drier, sunnier and calmer. Jan Mayen is perhaps the closest analogy since most of the southern islands are of recent or active volcanic origin.

The main weather characteristics of the southern ocean, south of the Antarctic Convergence which we will take as the boundary to these sub-Antarctic isles, are a nearly continuous cloud cover and strong westerly winds. Astronomers viewing us from another planet would have as hard a job discovering these islands as did our voyagers. Precipitation tends to be moderately heavy, fifty to sixty inches, and with mean annual temperatures in the range of o to $+5°$ C. much of it falls as snow. Wherever the lands are high, therefore, there is extensive glaciation and on some of the islands glaciers descend to sea-level.

The unfavourable weather means that little use can be made of the islands for air bases, useful stepping stones though they might otherwise be. Even so, on Kerguelen attempts are being made to develop an airport. But they can serve as meteorological stations and these have been established in the last decades on most of them, greatly aiding the southern hemispheric coverage of weather data.

In the past, some of them have been used as shore bases for whaling but only South Georgia has become really developed

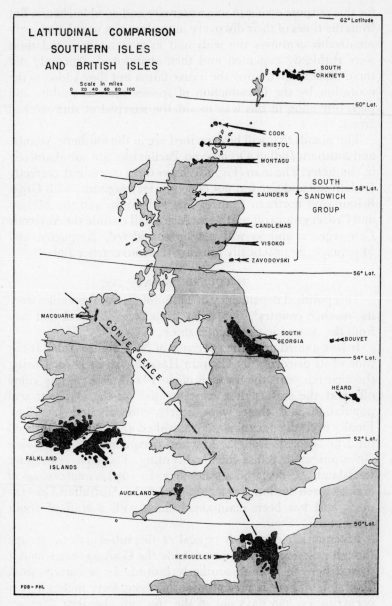

LATITUDINAL COMPARISON
SOUTHERN ISLES
AND BRITISH ISLES

Scale in miles
0 20 40 60 80 100

SOUTH
ORKNEYS

60° Lat.

COOK
BRISTOL
MONTAGU

58° Lat.

SAUNDERS

SOUTH
SANDWICH
GROUP

CANDLEMAS

VISOKOI

ZAVODOVSKI

56° Lat.

MACQUARIE

CONVERGENCE

SOUTH
GEORGIA

BOUVET

54° Lat.

HEARD

52° Lat.

FALKLAND
ISLANDS

AUCKLAND

50° Lat.

KERGUELEN

PDB-PHL

Fig. 76.

for this purpose owing to its greater size and good harbours. But from the times of their discovery in the late eighteenth and early nineteenth centuries the seals and even penguin populations were ruthlessly exploited and then abandoned. Not only did these expeditions destroy the native fauna but they added to the confusion by the introduction of species such as rabbits and pigs, intending in this way to aid the survival of shipwrecked crews.

The islands that will be described are in the southern Atlantic and southern Indian Oceans; no Pacific isles are sub-Antarctic in character. The map (Fig. 76) shows them compared, correctly for latitude and size but not of course for longitude, with Great Britain and northern France. The Falklands, and the Marion and Crozet groups off south-east Africa, fall outside the Antarctic Convergence and so will not be considered. Kerguelen and Macquarie lie practically athwart the convergence line.

MACQUARIE ISLAND

This political dependency of Tasmania is over 900 miles from its 'mother country', 600 miles from New Zealand and 900 from the Antarctic continental shore.

It was named after the governor of New South Wales at the time of its discovery by Captain Hasselburgh in 1810. During the next ten years the fur seals of the island were rapidly killed off, and the sealers then concentrated on the elephant seal population and these were nearly exterminated by 1834. Finally even the penguins were assaulted and boiled for their oil until in 1919 Sir Douglas Mawson persuaded the Tasmanian Government to refuse further licensing. Fourteen years later the island was declared a sanctuary. In 1948 a meteorological and research station was set up under the Australian Government and has been maintained since with a staff of about fifteen men.

Macquarie's climate is typical of the sub-Antarctic régime though it lies on average just outside the Convergence which is driven here to a more southerly latitude by a current from Tasmania. There is precipitation of about forty inches a year occurring on 330 days out of the 365 and cloudless skies are rare. Two-thirds of the winds are recorded from the westerly directions and the average wind speed is over twenty miles per hour. The temperature régime, as one would expect, shows extremely small daily and annual ranges. The warmest month's mean is 6·6° C. (44° F.) and the coldest 2·8° C. (37° F.). Thus, snowfall is light and lies only intermittently, and with no very high ground there is no glaciation at the present time.

The island is 21 miles long with a maximum breadth of 3 miles and an area of 46 square miles (120 square kilometres). It is a long narrow plateau with its main axis NNE.–SSW., 800 to 1,200 feet high in the north, 1,000 to 1,400 feet in the south.

On both coasts steep cliffs bound the plateau, leaving only a narrow beach terrace which is best developed on the northern part of the west coast. At the extreme north end a narrow beach isthmus joins North Head promontory, three-quarters of a mile in extent, with the remainder of the island and it is on this isthmus that the meteorological station has been built.

Glaciation was once heavy as evidenced by erratics, unsorted drift, terminal moraines and at least one U-shaped valley. The basic geology of the island is volcanic and igneous, with basalt flows, breccias and gabbro intrusions dating, it is believed, from Cretaceous to Tertiary times. The volcanic period in later Tertiary was characterized by upthrusts and faults which may have left a much larger island than now exists. Since there are suggestions of glaciation from the west it is in this direction that the island may have once extended, but it is difficult to credit the entire elimination of this land by the westerly rollers of a few thousand years.

The vegetation of Macquarie is uniquely sub-Antarctic, poor in species but quite extensive in coverage. More than half the island has a closed vegetation cover. No trees or shrubs are found but the dominant cover is of tussock grass, *Poa foliosa*, forming a dense mat up to four feet high. Macquarie Cabbage, *Stilbocarpa polaris*, is another typical plant of the tussock grasslands, and on higher ground are found the boulder-size cushions of *Azorella selago*. Thirty-eight species of vascular plants, forty-one mosses and forty-four lichens have been described to date. The most conspicuous member of the flora is the littoral giant kelp, *Durvillea antarctica*, which grows up to scores of feet in length and underlines again the richness of southern seas compared to the poverty of the land. No land fauna of any size was known before man introduced rabbits, rats, mice and cats which are now well established; the native animals belong to the sea.

The elephant seal has now recovered to numbers believed equivalent to those existing before their slaughter began. On the sheltered east coast up to fifty thousand seals breed annually during September and October. The fur seal has begun to breed again since 1955 and numbers up to two hundred have been counted in a day in the waters around the station.

Four species of penguins breed in spectacular colonies; the royal penguin rookery at Hurd Point contains about five hundred thousand adults, the king penguins at Lusitania Bay, once heavily slaughtered by the 'sealers' are now back to numbers of twenty thousand adults. Rockhopper and gentoo penguins nest in smaller groups around the coasts and the latter are year-round residents like the kings.

Four species of albatross are also native to the island and have recovered since the depredations of men and dogs ceased. But many other native birds like the burrow-breeding petrels have been seriously reduced by cats, rats and the unpleasant New Zealand native weka, a carnivorous flightless rail.

Since the establishment of the Australian weather station a series of huts have been constructed along the east coast and a subsidiary (auroral) station at the extreme southern tip of the island.

KERGUELEN ISLAND

Here in the middle of the Indian Ocean area we have, again just on the sub-Antarctic limit, the largest of the island groups 2,600 square miles in extent. It is thus about one-fifteenth the size of Iceland, much of which is comparable to this desolate lava-strewn and partly glacier-covered southern land.

It was discovered and landed on by Kerguelen-Trémarec in 1772 and visited by Cook in 1776. From 1790 onwards came the sealers, some British but mainly American, who exploited the beaches for the best part of a century. Ross in 1840 and the *Challenger* in 1874 began the detailed scientific investigations which have been carried on in the twentieth century mainly by the French. In 1924 the island group, together with St. Paul and Amsterdam islands further to the north, were annexed by France and attached to the administration of Madagascar. Since 1949 France has maintained a permanent scientific group on the island numbering up to a hundred men, beginning with a meteorological station and including now a small experimental farm.

As for Macquarie, there is here a typical southern ocean climate modified slightly by the much greater relief and extent of the land.

The established meteorological station is on the eastern, and hence lee, side of the island. Here the precipitation is of the order of forty inches but it must be considerably higher in the near-permanent cloud cover on the high exposed western coast where a large ice-cap exists.

The warmest and coldest month means are about $+8°$ and $+2°$ C. ($46°$ and $36°$ F.) with a more noticeable diurnal temperature range, particularly during summer. Since the beginning of the century a slight rise in the mean temperatures can be postulated though the records are too scanty for sure comparison.

Precipitation is chiefly in the form of rain coming mainly from a north-westerly air flow, but snow falls frequently in winter, seldom covering the low ground for more than a week. But on the plateau surface at an average height of 1,500 feet night frosts are the rule throughout the year.

The wind is the most felt meteorological phenomenon on Kerguelen. Though its annual mean force is little more than twenty miles per hour, gusts of more than five times this are frequent during the continual march of depressions along this latitude. Eighty per cent. of the winds are from the westerly directions and the rare fine spells of weather come with calms and easterly breezes as often in 'winter' as in 'summer'. But essentially Kerguelen has continuous 'autumn' weather.

The island is shaped somewhat like a miniature Newfoundland, deeply indented and fragmented on its northern coast with another deep bay, the Golfe de Morbihan, separating the large peninsulas, Courbet and Joffre. It is in this bay that the settlements have been made.

The major part of the land consists of a series of elevated plateaus deeply dissected by fiords and bays, covered with many lakes and showing all the signs of heavy past glaciation.

The bedrock is entirely volcanic, andesitic and basaltic flows with igneous intrusions and no sign of sediments or metamorphism. The age of these rocks is presumed to be early Tertiary and some of the fissure lava flows are three thousand feet in thickness. Fossil flora indicate a Miocene age for the period of greatest activity. This has now entirely ceased even on the slopes of Mount Ross, the six-thousand-foot heavily glaciated cone in the centre of the southern coast. Some steam vents, however, were reported to have been seen by early sealers and were last noted in 1914.

As the volcanic origin has given the land its plateau character, glaciation has resulted in the most recent physiographic traits. Glacial cirques, roches moutonées, and drumlins are widespread. Polygonal ground is much in evidence though permafrost no longer exists, and peat bogs and some lignite deposits are present.

Sub-Antarctic vegetation, quite treeless, covers much of the ground below 1,200 feet but even here are many bare or rocky areas. Tussock grass, *Poa cookii*, forms the main coastal dominant; inland great cushions of *Azorella selago* abound. Interspersed with these is the large crucifer, *Pringlea antiscorbutica*, or Kerguelen Cabbage, the most prominent purely native plant which flourishes on damp rocky sites. Other flowering plants are few in species count, but over two hundred mosses and lichens have been described. Once again the proliferation of local flora takes place in the sea, every coast and bay being filled with algae waving in the surf. A hundred species have been identified, a dozen unique to Kerguelen.

Fresh-water fishes and terrestrial vertebrates did not exist before man's arrival but rabbits and mice now abound and have done much to destroy the native vegetation. Trout have been introduced in recent years and appear to be flourishing. The sea mammals are recovering slowly from the slaughter of the nineteenth century and elephant seal herds now number in the hundreds of thousands. Fur seals are just beginning to reestablish themselves. Two species of penguins, royals and rockhoppers, have immense breeding colonies, and cormorants, skuas, petrels and albatrosses all breed freely. One Kerguelen native is the Eaton duck, *Anas acuta Eatoni*, which lives mainly in fresh-water lakes and bogs.

The early American sealers who often 'wintered' in the archipelago have left traces everywhere even in some of the more inaccessible parts of the island. A more permanent base was set up in 1908 at Port Jeanne d'Arc by an Anglo-Norwegian whaling firm which was later taken over by a South African company. Their activities ceased in 1926 and for a few years a French company directed by H. Bossière continued operations. Between 1920 and 1930 it is estimated that the 'take' was about forty-five thousand sea elephants a year together with a few whales.

Since the French Government established protective measures in 1931, attempts have been made to assess the economic potential of the islands. There is little of mineral value. A regular take could be made of elephant seal but only the oil from this animal has commercial value. One day, perhaps, the fur seal may recover sufficiently to form an industry as it does in the Pribilofs. Sheep culture has been attempted, the first efforts being made by Bossière as long ago as 1913, when a station, Port Couvreux, was established. But so far the local vegetation has not proved acceptable in quality and the competition from rabbits is severe. Reindeer have also been introduced in recent years. Kerguelen is perhaps just beyond the boundary of farming possibility, but unquestionably the scientific station can go a long way to be self-supporting by intensive horticulture.

HEARD ISLAND

Far removed in distance and climate from the two islands described so far is the other Indian Ocean group of Heard Island and its neighbours the small and as yet untrodden Macdonald Islands. Discovered by the whaling Captain Kemp in 1833, this is an icy land, but even so it did not deter the American sealers. Their first landing was made in 1855, soon after the island's second sighting by Captain Heard, and before long they were wintering there and filling their vessels with oil from the elephant seal. But by 1880 the resource was depleted and sealing abandoned. Desultory whaling attempts followed and scientific visits were made by *Challenger*, *Gauss* and by Mawson in 1929. In 1947 the Australian flag was hoisted and a meteorological station occupied from 1948 to 1955. The island is peculiarly suitable for forecasting outbursts of polar air which will shortly affect the Australian continent two thousand miles away. The annual mean temperature has proved to be a little above freezing (0·7° C.) with a variation from warmest to coldest month of only 5° C. (9° F.). The windspeed of sixteen miles per hour (annual average) is fairly low for these violent latitudes but there are fifty inches of precipitation, mostly snow, occurring on three hundred days, and the annual average sunshine is only six hundred hours.

Heard Island is hour-glass shaped, a small north-west peninsula (Laurens) connected by a narrow beach ridge to the main, nearly circular, body of the island. The latter is essentially one massive mountain, Big Ben, nine thousand feet in height, a crater-topped nearly extinct volcano down the slopes of which glaciers flow to sea-level. From a few vents smoke and steam still issue. As yet, despite frequent attempts, the peak has not been climbed, each expedition being driven back by difficult crevasses and by tremendous storms and snowfall.

Laurens peninsula, itself rising to a peak of two thousand feet, is underlain by early Tertiary limestone beds; these are covered by a thick series of agglomerates and above come the series of lava flows extending to recent times. The latter are exposed in cliff sections where ice does not reach the sea and are inferred from the inaccessible and ice-covered slopes of Big Ben itself. A large fault which has left escarpments visible under the ice cover must have occurred at a very recent date.

Atlas Cove, the site of the meteorological station, is on the north side of the beach connecting the two parts of the island. A three-mile-long sandspit extends from the east coast of the main island mass. It is in these two areas that a scanty vegetation exists and where the main faunal population lives. Here the ubiquitous *Azorella* flowers and on the lower ice free slopes *Poa cookii* forms tussocks, though in much less luxurious abundance than on Kerguelen Island. Mosses and lichens are more widespread than the remaining few vascular species. Once again the giant kelp dominates the many forms of marine algae offshore.

Now re-established, some fifty thousand elephant seals live on Heard Island, the greatest number on the eastern spit, but though the fur seal has been noted it does not appear to breed.

All the commoner Antarctic seals are recorded and the island appears to be a popular winter resort for the leopard seal; hundreds of this animal have been observed on the beaches, particularly in Corinthian Bay to the east of the station.

Macaroni, rockhopper and gentoo penguins are among the eighteen resident bird species recorded, which include petrels gulls, albatrosses and cormorants.

Like all the islands, Heard is of great scientific interest and it is to be hoped that the station there will be soon re-established.

BOUVET ISLAND

This lonely piece of land scarcely twenty square miles in extent lies 1,700 miles south-west of Cape Town. Although it is the home of sea elephants, penguins and other marine birds, it has so far defied man's attempt to obtain a foothold on it. For many years, in fact, after its discovery by Bouvet de Lozier in 1739, it was lost and although noted somewhere in the neighbourhood by various whalers it was not until 1898 that the German expedition on board *Valdivia* placed it accurately on the maps. The climate is severely influenced by the 'fetch' of the cold Weddell Sea Current which swings out to its most northerly point in the vicinity of Bouvet Island, resulting in an almost total glaciation of the land down to sea-level with a few rocky capes showing through. The altitude of the firn line and the general glaciation characteristics are reminiscent of Franz Josef Land in the Arctic, 25° of latitude closer to the Pole. Commonly wrapped in cloud, the island slopes gently up to a height of about three thousand feet with prominent cliffs on the north and west coasts, which are exposed to violent marine erosion. The *Norvegia* expedition in 1927 spent some time in the vicinity and returned in 1929, the date when the island was claimed by Norway. At the time provisions were landed and a hut was constructed but on the next visit to the island this had totally disappeared, presumably torn away by a violent westerly gale. The small rock outcrop on which this hut was planted consists of tuffs and basalt lavas which presumably underlie the remainder of the ice-covered land. The most accessible part of the island would be the ice sheet flowing more gently towards the east on the lee side of the island but so far attempts to obtain a lodgement here have also failed. Even in the International Geophysical Year plans for a meteorological station on the island were abandoned owing to the difficulty of landing and maintaining a party, but early in 1960 South Africa announced that a new attempt would be made to establish a weather station on Bouvet Island. Presumably the winds are no worse than those of Mawson's base in the Antarctic but it will be a hard life for any human being on this lonely speck of land.

SOUTH GEORGIA

The remaining sub-Antarctic islands below the Convergence form a great arc known as the Scotia Arc, stretching between the southern tip of South America and the Grahamland Peninsula of the Antarctic continent. By far the most prominent and important of these islands is South Georgia, the next largest, in fact, to Kerguelen among the islands we are considering—a hundred miles long in a north-west–south-east direction with an average breadth of twenty miles. The whole island is highly mountainous with peaks rising to 6,000, 7,000, or even 9,000 feet in altitude and the coasts are deeply indented by bays and fiords with very little flat land. The immense difficulty of travel inland, only possible by skilled mountaineers, together with the violent weather conditions resulted in a survey of the island being completed only in the decade of the 1950s, chiefly due to the expeditions led by V. D. Carse. The geology of the island is highly complex, consisting of a thick series of folded sedimentary rocks dating certainly from Palaeozoic and also from Mesozoic times. In the south-east of the island is a large igneous complex and in the south-west, and on Annenkov Island off the western shore, a series of spilitic lavas and fine-grained sediments. The main period of the folding of the sediments appears to be Post-Aptian.

South Georgia is situated near the limit of Antarctic drift ice coming from the Weddell Sea and its temperature is lowered by the cold current of the waters around its coast. The mean annual temperature is scarcely 2° C. and precipitation even on the comparatively sheltered north-east coast is of the order of fifty-five inches. Much of this falls as snow and the interior is highly glaciated, several glaciers reaching the sea and giving birth to small icebergs. With its typical sub-Antarctic climate and little area of ice free ground the vegetation is poor and only about a score of flowering plants have been described, nevertheless, there is considerable cover on the lower bare ground of tussock grass, *Poa Flabellata*. Rabbits and sheep which were introduced have not been able to survive the climate, but ponies and reindeer have been able to make use of the limited pasturage. The usual sub-Antarctic fauna has been exploited as with all the other islands but now under strict regulations the sea elephant herds are recovering since their near extinction in the 1880s.

South Georgia has a history of human settlement far exceeding that of the other sub-Antarctic isles. It was possibly discovered as far back as 1675 by the Spaniard de la Roche but the first landing and description of the island was made by Captain Cook, a hundred years later. From the early nineteenth century it has been the headquarters of sealing expeditions and during the present century of the whaling industry with several shore-based stations operating for at least six months in the year. Grytviken, the capital of South Georgia, and seat of the resident magistrate is the most important of these whaling stations, the town also comprising shops, a hospital, meteorological and radio stations and even a jail, the usual inhabitants of which have been visiting scientific expeditions. Other whaling stations located slightly farther north are at Leith and Stromness. Above Leith harbour on a prominent headland is the grave of Sir Ernest Shackleton who died there on his ship, the *Quest*, in 1922; a fitting monument in a lonely land to one of the greatest of Antarctic explorers.

THE SOUTH SANDWICH ISLANDS

Continuing down the chain of the Scotia Arc the next group, extending over two hundred miles in length, is the South Sandwich Group. This comprises eleven main islands plus some small rocky islets, all recent or even active volcanic cones, heavily ice-covered and difficult of access. Not more than half of them have been landed on, and no permanent base has ever been established here. The discovery was in part by Captain Cook in 1775, part by the Russian, Bellingshausen, in 1820, and part by other subsequent explorers. The largest of the islands, Montagu, fifty square miles in extent, rises to over four thousand feet. It appears to be quiescent but on at least five of the other islands sulphurous fumaroles can be seen, the most active being Zavodovski, Saunders and Candlemas. Bristol Island has been noted in actual eruption in 1935 and in 1956. No real geological work has been done on the islands but the lavas appear to be similar to those of Patagonia and to the Grahamland Peninsula. The islands are all heavily glaciated and the coasts are blocked with Weddell Sea pack ice for much of the year. On the rare beaches sea elephants are common and colonies of penguins and other Antarctic sea birds abound. Whales seem to be comparatively rare in the offshore waters. It should be noted that to the east of the whole group lies one of the world's deepest marine trenches, plunging to over eight thousand metres below the level of the ocean.

THE SOUTH ORKNEYS

Two degrees farther south and still three hundred miles from the tip of the Grahamland Peninsula lies the small group of islands known as the South Orkneys. These are much more polar in character than those islands we have been considering to date, but are reasonably free of ice and accessible for wintering bases and, in fact, we have here the longest lasting meteorological station in the whole South Polar region. The group consists of Coronation Island, by far the largest, and three smaller islands, Laurie, Signy and Powell. The latter is named after the sealing captain who discovered the islands in 1821. It was on Laurie Island that Bruce wintered in 1903–4 and his meteorological station taken over by the Argentinian Government has remained in action since this time. Now a British station of the British Antarctic Survey exists also on Signy Island. Geologically the group appears to be similar to South Georgia, with sedimentary rocks highly folded and contorted of Palaeozoic and Mesozoic age. In addition there are considerable complexes of schists and dolerite intrusions. Coronation rises to a height of five thousand feet and in this polar climate is heavily glaciated. The mean temperature, in fact, of the group is −5° C. and only in the warmest month does the temperature rise fractionally above the freezing-point. The polar condition of the climate is further evidenced by the much lower precipitation (of the annual order of fifteen inches only) which falls almost entirely in the form of snow. The vegetation, as might therefore be expected, is quite polar, consisting only of mosses and lichens and even less numerous species of these than are found on the mainland of the Grahamland Peninsula. Weddell seals and occasional crabeaters show also that the fauna here is becoming polar, but once again sea birds abound and we have reached the area of the Adélie Antarctic penguins. We are back, in fact, after this tour of the sub-Antarctic islands into the truly Antarctic region itself.

FURTHER READING

Aubert de la Rue, E., *Les Terres anstrales*, Paris, 1953, (Series 'Que sais-je', No. 603).
Deacon, G. E. R., 'The Antarctic Ocean', *Science Progress*, 1959, pp. 647-60.
Holdgate, M. W. and N. M. Wace, 'The Influence of Man on the Floras and Faunas of Southern Islands', *Polar Record*, 10 (1961), pp. 475-93.

INDEX

Abruzzi, Duke of, 36, 47
Adams, P., 238
Ahlmann, H., 233, 267
Air-masses, 50
Air transport, 160-165
Alaska, 201-210
  political, 175, 176
Amundsen, R., 29, 30, 38, 47, 148, 167, 258, 259
Andrée, S., 38
Angmagssalik, 31, 174
Antartic, climate, 296-299
  convergence, 302, 314
  fauna and flora, 286-288
  political, 264-265
  seas, 300-302
  treaty, 181
Arctic, areas, 10
  climate, 48-65
  limits, 9
Armstrong, T. E., 110, 168, 227, 228
Aubert de la Rue, E., 325

Back, G., 25
Baffin, W., 17, 30
  Bay, 104-105
Balchen, B., 262, 263
Baransky, N., 228
Barents Sea, 107
Barnes ice-cap, 193
Beaufort Sea, 37
Bellingshausen, 256, 323
Berg, L. S., 228
Bering, V., 22
  Sea, 107
Bernier, J. E., 12, 170
Bertram, G. C. L., 47, 148, 311
Bilello, M. A., 110
Bird, J. B., 192
Birket-Smith, K., 143, 145
Biscoe, J., 256
Bjornöya, 237
Blackader, R., 200
Blair, T. A., 5, 11
Bliss, L. C., 129
Böcher, T., 254
Borchgrevink, 258
Borisov, A., 65
Bossière, H., 319
Bouvet de Lozier, 255
Bouvet Island, 321

Brown, R. S. E., 88
Bruce, W., 259, 324
Budker, P., 311
Button, T., 17
Bylot, R., 17
Byrd, R. E., 47, 155, 261, 262, 266

Cagni, Capt., 37
Calvert, Cdr. J., 168
Canada (Arctic), 182-200
  geology, 182-183
  physiography, 183-193
  settlements, 194
Caribou, 121-122, 206
Chancellor, 14
Charcot, J. B., 259
Clavering, 31
Clothing, polar, 42
Coal mining, 235, 250
Cook, Capt. J., 256, 316, 323
Courtauld, A., 33, 45
Crary, A. P., 88
Croft, N. A. C., 47
Cruzen, Adm., 266
Cryolite, 249

David, Sir E., 167, 259
Davis, J., 17, 30
Deacon, G. E. R., 325
Debenham, F., 285
de Gerlache, 258
de Long, 36
de Quervain, A., 33
DEW Line, 179, 181
Dezhnev, 20
Discovery, 17
Discovery Committee, 308
Dogs, sled, 148-150
Dorsey, H. G., 65
Drygalski, von, 258
Dufek, Adm., 266
Dunbar, M. J., 9, 89, 110, 248, 254
D'Urville, Dumont, 257

Egede, H., 31, 173, 248
Ellsworth, L., 261, 263
Elton, C., 129
Eskers, 71
Eskimo, archaeology, 139-142
  culture, 132-139

Filchner, 260
Fiords, 71
Fishes, 124
Foxe, L., 19
Foyn, S., 307
Fram, 36, 91
Franklin, J., 25, 27, 34
Franz Joseph Land, 30, 36, 220
Frobisher, M., 16
  Bay, 196
Fuchs, V. E., 43, 45, 268

Georgia, South, 322-323
Giddings, L., 140
Godthaab, 30, 253
Gould, L. M., 262
Great Northern Expedition, 20-23
Greely, A. W., 35
Greenland, climate, 53
  exploration, 30-33
  general, 239-254
  political, 173, 177
Gruening, E., 210

Hall, C. F., 34
Hall, J., 31
Hanessian, J., 181
Hare, F. K., 11, 49
Hattersly-Smith, G., 69
Hayes, I., 34
Heard Island, 319
Hearne, S., 23
High-Jump Expedition, 46, 266
Hillary, E., 45, 152, 155, 268
Hobbs, W. H., 244, 254, 297
Holdgate, M., 325
Holm G., 31
Housing, polar, 41, 42
Hudson, H., 15, 17
  Bay, 17, 18, 19, 105-106
Hudson's Bay Co., 19, 23, 42, 194
Hustich, I., 7, 8, 11

Icebreakers, 157-158
Ice, islands, 68, 69
  patrol, 180
  sea, 94-99
  shelf, 68, 69, 70, 272
Igloos, 41, 134-135
Inlandsis, 242-246
Insurance, rates, 159-160

Jackson, 30, 36
James, T., 19
Jan Mayen Island, 237
Jenness, D., 141

Kane, E. K., 34
Kara Sea, 14

Kerguelen Island, 256, 316-319
Kirwan, L. P., 47, 270
Knight, J., 19
Koch, J., 33, 151
Koch, L., 110, 249
Köppen, W., 4, 5

Labrador, 29
La Fay, H., 181
Lantis, M., 145, 210
Larsen, C. A., 258, 265, 307
Lemmings, 120
Lenin, 157
Lister, H., 278, 284, 295
Loewe, F., 284
Lomen Bros., 208
Longyear, J., 235

Mackenzie, A., 24
Maclure, K., 166, 168
Macmillan, D., 170
Macquarie Island, 314-316
Magnetic Poles, 27, 167, 257, 259
Makarov, Adm., 157
Mathiassen, T., 140
Mathisen, T., 238
Mawson, Sir D., 156, 259, 261, 263, 319
M'Clintock, L., 28, 43, 47, 148
Mellor, M., 284, 295
Mercer, J., 295
Middendorf, 29
Mikkelsen, E., 32
Mirsky, J., 47
Morley, J. P., 168
Müller, F., 85, 88
Munck, J., 18
Murmansk, 108, 226, 227
Muscovy Co., 14, 16

Nansen, F., 30, 33, 36, 47, 100
Nares, G. F., 34
Nautilus, 158, 165
Navigation, polar, 165-167
Nicolson, N., 200
Nobile, U., 38, 45
Nome, 209
Nordenskiöld, A. E., 30, 32, 228, 233
Nordenskiöld, O., 5, 258
Norilsk, 222, 228
Norlund, P., 254
North Polar Sea, exploration, 33
Northeast Passage, 14-16, 29-30, 33, 224-226
Northwest Passage, 16-20, 25-29
Novaya Zemlya, 15, 30, 215

O'Dell, A. C., 238
Orkneys, South, 324
Ottar, 14

Papanin, I., 39, 41, 43, 47, 99, 146
Parry, W. E., 26, 34, 43, 44, 47
Patterned ground, 81
Peary, R., 31, 33, 35, 47, 174
Permafrost, 3, 65, 73-80
  engineering, 85-88
Pettersen, S., 65
Pingos, 84
Polunin, N., 129
Polynya, 102
Porsild, A. E., 84, 112, 129
Pressure, air, 51
Pribilof Islands, 125
Priestley, Sir R., 274, 285
Pytheas, 12, 89

Radisson, P., 19
Rae, J., 27, 28, 41, 47
Rasmussen, K., 29, 33, 143, 174
Rations, polar, 42, 43
Refraction, solar, 2
Reindeer herding, 131, 197, 207-209,
  221
Roberts, B. B., 270
Robin, G., 232, 278
Rodahl, K., 129
Ronne, F., 266
Rooy, M. van, 299
Ross, J., 25, 31
Ross, J. C., 26, 167, 257, 316
Rousseau, J., 129
Rudenko, S., 145
Rudmose-Brown, R., 238
Rymill, J., 263

Salekhard, 227
Scandinavians, in Greenland, 30, 147-
  148
Scheffer, V., 129
Scholander, P., 116
Scoresby, W., 31
Scott, R. F., 45, 148, 259
Scurvy, 43, 44
Seals, fur, 125, 206
  hair, 126
Sedov, 91
Severnaya Zemlya, 30, 217
Shackleton, E., 45, 148, 259, 260
Shumskiy, P., 286
Siberia, 20, 21, 214-228
  climate, 59-61
  political, 172, 177

Sibiriakov, 30, 226
Sikussag, 70
Simpson, T., 27
Siple, P., 61, 65, 269
Slijper, E., 311
Snow forms, 66
Snowmobiles, 153-156
Solifluction, 73
St. Roch, 29
Stefansson, V., 37, 47, 163, 173, 181
Sullivan, W., 270
Svalbard, 14, 15, 229-238
  political, 175, 176
Svarlien, O., 181
Sverdrup, H. U., 47, 93
Sverdrup, O., 35, 170
Swithinbank, C., 283, 295

Tanner, V., 6, 11
Taracouzio, T., 181
Tedrow, J., 88
Thomas, M. K., 65
Thornthwaite, C. W., 5, 11
Thule, 33
Tides, 108
Treeline, 7

Vahl, M., 4
Victor, P. E., 33, 47
Vilkitski, 30

Washburn, A. L., 81, 88
Watkins, G., 33, 42
Weddell, J., 256
Wegener, A., 33, 153
Weyprecht, 35
Whales, 303-311
'Whiteout', 64
Wiggins, I., 129
Wilkes, C., 257
Wilkins, Sir H., 38, 158, 261, 292
Willoughby, 14
Wilson, J. W., 112, 129
Windchill, 2, 4, 61-63, 112
Wordie, Sir J., 121
Wrangel Island, 173

Yermak, 157

Zubov, N., 98, 100, 110